SERVSAFE® 6th EDITION
COURSEBOOK

Updated with the
2013 FDA Food Code

ServSafe
National Restaurant Association

Coursebook, CBX6R (with exam answer sheet)	ISBN 978-1-58280-319-7
Coursebook, CBV6R (with online exam voucher)	ISBN 978-1-58280-318-0
Coursebook, CB6R (text only)	ISBN 978-1-58280-317-3

Printed in the USA

10 9 8 7 6 5 4 3 2 1

Introduction

A Message from the National Restaurant Association	iii
Staying Connected with the National Restaurant Association throughout Your Career	iv
Acknowledgements	vi
How to Use the *ServSafe Coursebook*	vii

Chapter 1   Keeping Food Safe

Foodborne Illnesses	1-2
How Foodborne Illnesses Occur	1-4
The Food Safety Responsibilities of a Manager	1-8

Chapter 2   Understanding the Microworld

Pathogens	2-2
Bacteria	2-4
Viruses	2-16
Parasites	2-20
Fungi	2-24
Biological Toxins	2-25

Chapter 3   Contamination, Food Allergens, and Foodborne Illness

Physical and Chemical Contaminants	3-2
The Deliberate Contamination of Food	3-4
Food Allergens	3-5

Chapter 4   The Safe Food Handler

Personal Hygiene and Contamination	4-2
A Good Personal Hygiene Program	4-4

Chapter 5   The Flow of Food: An Introduction

Cross-Contamination	5-2
Time-Temperature Control	5-3

Chapter 6   The Flow of Food: Purchasing and Receiving

Purchasing Considerations	6-2
Receiving Considerations	6-3
General Inspection Guidelines	6-5
Inspecting Specific Types of Food	6-8

Chapter 7   The Flow of Food: Storage

General Storage Guidelines	7-2
Storing Specific Food	7-6

Chapter 8   The Flow of Food: Preparation

Preparation	8-2
Cooking Food	8-8
Cooling and Reheating Food	8-12

Chapter 9 The Flow of Food: Service

Holding Food for Service   9-2

Serving Food Safely   9-4

Off-Site Service   9-7

Chapter 10 Food Safety Management Systems

Food Safety Management Systems   10-2

Active Managerial Control   10-3

Crisis Management   10-11

Chapter 11 Safe Facilities and Equipment

Designing a Safe Operation   11-2

Considerations for Other Areas of the Facility   11-7

Equipment Selection   11-10

Installing and Maintaining Kitchen Equipment   11-13

Utilities   11-14

Chapter 12 Cleaning and Sanitizing

Cleaning   12-2

Sanitizing   12-4

Dishwashing   12-8

Cleaning the Premises   12-11

Developing a Cleaning Program   12-15

Chapter 13 Integrated Pest Management

Integrated Pest Management (IPM) Programs   13-2

Identifying Pests   13-5

Working with a Pest Control Operator (PCO)   13-7

Treatment   13-8

Using and Storing Pesticides   13-9

Chapter 14 Food Safety Regulation and Standards

Government Agencies Responsible for Preventing
Foodborne Illness   14-2

The Inspection Process   14-4

Self-Inspections   14-8

Voluntary Controls within the Industry   14-8

Chapter 15 Staff Food Safety Training

Training Staff   15-2

Ways of Training   15-4

Glossary   G-1

Answer Key   AK-1

Index   I-1

A Message from The National Restaurant Association

Congratulations! By opening this book, you are joining millions of foodservice professionals in taking the first step in a commitment to food safety. ServSafe® training helps you understand all of the food safety risks faced by your operation. Once you're aware of these risks, you can find ways to reduce them. This will help you keep your operation, your staff, and your customers safe.

Created by Foodservice Industry Leaders   You can be confident knowing the ServSafe program was created by leaders in the foodservice industry. The topics you will learn in this book were determined by those who deal with the same food safety issues you face every day. From the basics of handwashing, to more complex topics such as foodborne pathogens, your industry peers have provided you with the building blocks to keep food safe throughout your operation.

Performed and Reinforced by You   Food safety doesn't stop once you've completed your training and certification. It is now your responsibility to take the knowledge you learned and share it with your staff. When you return to your operation, start by answering the following questions to assess your food handler training:

- Do you have food safety training programs for both new and current staff?
- Do you have assessment tools to identify staff's food safety knowledge?
- Do you keep records documenting that staff have completed training?

About Your Certification   To access your ServSafe Food Protection Manager Certification Exam results, register on ServSafe.com. You will need your class number, which your instructor will provide. Depending on how soon we receive your exam, results will be available approximately 10 business days after you take the exam. For security purposes, your exam results cannot be provided over the phone or sent through e-mail.

Your ServSafe Food Protection Manager Certification is valid for five years from your exam date. Local laws apply. Check with your local regulatory authority or company for specific recertification requirements.

If you have any questions about your certification or additional food handler training, please call (800) ServSafe (800.737.8723), or e-mail us at servicecenter@restaurant.org.

About the National Restaurant Association

The National Restaurant Association, founded in 1919, is the leading business association for the restaurant industry, which is comprised of 935,000 restaurant and foodservice outlets and a workforce of 12.8 million employees—making it the cornerstone of the economy, career opportunities, and community involvement. Along with the National Restaurant Association Educational Foundation, NRA Solutions and the Association work to represent, educate, and promote the rapidly growing industry. For more information, visit our Web site at restaurant.org.

Staying Connected with the National Restaurant Association throughout Your Career

The National Restaurant Association (NRA) has the resources and tools to support you throughout your education and career in the restaurant and foodservice industry. Through scholarships, educational programs, industry certifications, and member benefits, the NRA is your partner now and into the future.

Scholarships The NRA's philanthropic foundation, the National Restaurant Association Educational Foundation (NRAEF), offers scholarships to college students through its NRAEF Scholarship Program. These scholarships can help pave your way to an affordable higher education and may be applied to a culinary, restaurant management, or foodservice-related program at an accredited college or university. We encourage you to investigate the opportunities, which include access to special program scholarships for ProStart students who earn the National Certificate of Achievement, as well as ManageFirst Program® students. You may be awarded one NRAEF scholarship per calendar year—make sure you keep applying every year! The NRAEF partners with state restaurant associations to offer student scholarships. Check with your state to see if they offer additional scholarship opportunities. The NRAEF also offers professional development scholarships for educators. Visit nraef.org/scholarships for information.

College education As you research and apply to colleges and universities to continue your industry education, look for schools offering the NRA's **ManageFirst Program**. The ManageFirst Program and curriculum materials were developed with input from the restaurant and foodservice industry and academic partners. This management program teaches you practical skills needed to face real-world challenges in the industry, including interpersonal communication, ethics, accounting skills, and more. The program includes the ten topics listed below, plus ServSafe Food Safety Training and ServSafe Alcohol Training®:

- Controlling Foodservice Costs
- Hospitality and Restaurant Management
- Hospitality Human Resources Management and Supervision
- Customer Service
- Principles of Food and Beverage Management
- Purchasing
- Hospitality Accounting
- Bar and Beverage Management
- Nutrition
- Hospitality and Restaurant Marketing

You can also earn the ManageFirst Professional® (MFP™) credential by passing five required ManageFirst exams and completing 800 work hours in the industry. Having the MFP on your resume tells employers that you have the management skills needed to succeed in the industry. To learn more about ManageFirst or to locate ManageFirst schools, visit managefirst.restaurant.org.

Certification In the competitive restaurant field, industry certifications can help you stand out among a crowd of applicants.

- The NRA's **ServSafe** Food Protection Manager Certification is nationally recognized. Earning your certification tells the industry that you know food safety and the critical importance of its role—and enables you to share food safety knowledge with every other employee.

- Through ServSafe Food Safety, you'll master sanitation, the flow of food through an operation, sanitary facilities, and pest management. ServSafe is the training that is learned, remembered, shared, and used. And that makes it the strongest food safety training choice for you. For more information on ServSafe, visit ServSafe.com.

- The challenges surrounding alcohol service in restaurants have increased dramatically. To prepare you to address these challenges, the NRA offers ServSafe Alcohol. As you continue to work in the industry, responsible alcohol service is an issue that will touch your business, your customers, and your community. Armed with your ServSafe Alcohol Certificate, you can make an immediate impact on an establishment. Through the program, you'll learn essential responsible alcohol service information, including alcohol laws and responsibilities, evaluating intoxication levels, dealing with difficult situations, and checking identification. Please visit ServSafe.com/alcohol to learn more about ServSafe Alcohol.

National Restaurant Association membership As you move into the industry, seek out careers in restaurants that are **members of the NRA and your state restaurant association**. Encourage any operation you are part of to join the national and state organizations. During your student years, the NRA also offers student memberships that give you access to industry research and information that can be an invaluable resource. For more information, or to join as a student member, visit restaurant.org.

Management credentials After you've established yourself in the industry, strive for the industry's highest management certification—the NRA's **Foodservice Management Professional®** (FMP®). The FMP certification recognizes exceptional managers and supervisors who have achieved the highest level of knowledge, experience, and professionalism that is most valued by our industry. You become eligible to apply and sit for the FMP exam after you've worked as a supervisor in the industry for three years. Passing the FMP exam places you in select company; you will have joined the ranks of leading industry professionals. The FMP certification is also an impressive credential to add to your title and resume. For more information on the Foodservice Management Professional certification, visit managefirst.restaurant.org.

Make the NRA your partner throughout your education and career. Take advantage of the NRA's scholarship, training, certification, and membership benefits that will launch you into your career of choice. Together we will lead this industry into an even brighter future.

Acknowledgements

The development of the *ServSafe CourseBook* would not have been possible without the expertise of our many advisors and manuscript reviewers. Thank you to the following people and organizations for their time, effort, and dedication to creating this sixth edition.

Curt Archambault, Jack In The Box

Petra Balli, ARAMARK

Kelly Blakely, Valero

Robert Brown, Whole Foods

Nancy Caldarola, Concept Associates Inc.

Don Culver, Army and Air Force Exchange Service

Ana De La Torre, Santa Paula Oil Corp. dba To Go Stores

Claudia Diez, University of Minnesota

Jeff Drozdowski, Little Caesars

Shannon Flynn, Potbelly Sandwich Works

Kendra Kauppi, University of Minnesota

Linda Kender, Johnson & Wales University

Mahmood Khan, Virginia Tech

Geoff Luebkemann, Florida Restaurant and Lodging Association

Dave McNinch, Washoe County District Health Department

Mark Miklos, Waffle House

Eric Moore, ARAMARK

Michael Pozit, Integrated Food Service Consulting Corp.

Angela Sanchez, CKE Restaurants

Victoria Sánchez Martínez, New Mexico Restaurant Association

Mary L Sandford, Burger King Corporation

Edward Sherwin, Sherwin Food Safety

Allison Straley, WESCO, Inc.

Alan Tart, U.S. Food and Drug Administration

Cameron Underwood, Valero

Wanda Vinson, Long John Silver's

Justin Waldrep, RaceTrac

Brian Wickman, Compass Group North America

Boskovich Farms, Inc.

Centers for Disease Control and Prevention

Le Cordon Bleu College of Culinary Arts Chicago

How to Use the *ServSafe Coursebook*

The plan below will help you study and remember the food safety principles in this textbook.

Beginning of Each Chapter

Before you start reading each chapter, you can prepare by reviewing these sections.

Advanced Organizer   Chapter content is divided into sections. Each section begins with a graphic organizer at the top of the page. The graphic organizer identifies each section within that chapter. The graphic organizer uses a lighter green color to indicate where you are in the chapter structure.

The key topics for each section are also displayed. You will always know what to expect within a section.

Objectives   Located on the front page of each chapter, the objectives identify tasks you should be able to do after finishing the chapter. They are linked to the essential practices for keeping your operation safe.

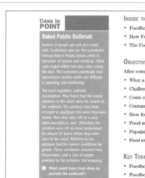

Case in Point   Each chapter begins with a food safety case study that relates to content in the chapter. They are designed to make you think about the food safety issues that will be presented in the chapter.

Throughout Each Chapter

Use the following learning tools to help you identify and learn key food safety principles as you read each chapter.

Key Terms   These terms are important for a thorough understanding of the chapter content. They are highlighted in blue text throughout the chapter, where either they are explicitly defined or their meanings are made clear within the content. Each key term is also defined in the Glossary.

Photos   Photos give you visual examples of key principles in the book. They are either in the margin next to a principle or in the text itself. Some of the photos show you what you should do, while others show you what you should not do. If the photo is a positive practice, it has a ✓ in the left corner. If the photo is a negative practice, it has a ✗ in the left corner, meaning that this practice should never be done.

Charts, illustrations, and tables   These visuals either present or organize content so that it is easier for you to learn. In some instances, they are used to reinforce key principles in the book.

Key point icons   These icons reinforce critical food safety principles, such as cross-contamination and correct cooling.

Technology   Interesting information on the latest trends in food safety technology.

Regulatory   This feature provides additional information about regulatory requirements related to food safety and the agencies that define the requirements.

Resources   The Resources feature highlights some of the agencies and organizations you should know about during your career.

Business   Interesting facts and information related to foodservice and food safety.

At the End of Each Chapter

Several activities have been provided at the end of each chapter to test your knowledge. These include:

Discussion Questions These questions are designed to make you think about some of the important food safety concepts presented in the chapter. Answers to the questions are provided in the Answer Key.

Case in Point Activities These food safety case studies ask you to identify the errors made by the food handlers in each story and the correct practices that should have been followed.

Study Questions These multiple-choice questions are directly based on the learning objectives. If you have difficulty answering them, you should review the content further. Answers are provided in the answer key.

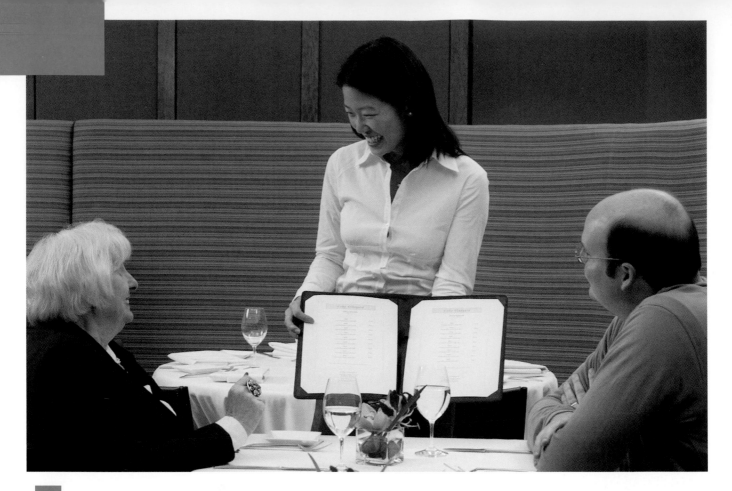

1 Keeping Food Safe

Foodborne Illnesses	How Foodborne Illnesses Occur	The Food Safety Responsibilities of a Manager
— Challenges to Food Safety — The Costs of Foodborne Illnesses	— Contaminants — How Food Becomes Unsafe — Food Most Likely to Become Unsafe: TCS Food — Populations at High Risk for Foodborne Illness — Key Practices for Ensuring Food Safety	— Marketing Food Safety

Case in POINT

Baked Potato Outbreak

Dozens of people got sick at a small café. Customers who ate the operation's famous Baked Potato Salad called to complain of nausea and vomiting. These calls began within two days after eating the dish. The customers eventually also experienced double vision and difficulty in speaking and swallowing.

The local regulatory authority investigated. They found that the baked potatoes in the salad were the source of the outbreak. The potatoes had been wrapped in aluminum foil when they were baked. Then they were left on a prep table overnight to cool. Ultimately, the potatoes were left at room temperature for almost 18 hours before they were used in the salad. Bacteria on the potatoes had the correct conditions for growth. These conditions included time, temperature, and a lack of oxygen provided by the potatoes' foil wrapping.

① **What could have been done to prevent the outbreak?**

For answers, please turn to the Answer Key.

INSIDE THIS CHAPTER

- Foodborne Illnesses
- How Foodborne Illnesses Occur
- The Food Safety Responsibilities of a Manager

OBJECTIVES

After completing this chapter, you should be able to identify the following:

- What a foodborne illness is and determine when one has occurred
- Challenges to food safety
- Costs of a foodborne illness
- Contaminants that can make food unsafe
- How food becomes unsafe
- Food most likely to become unsafe
- Populations at high-risk for foodborne illness
- Food safety responsibilities of the person in charge of a foodservice operation

KEY TERMS

- Foodborne illness
- Foodborne-illness outbreak
- Contamination
- Time-temperature abuse
- Cross-contamination
- TCS food
- Ready-to-eat food
- High-risk populations
- Immune system

Foodborne Illnesses	How Foodborne Illnesses Occur	The Food Safety Responsibilities of a Manager
— Challenges to Food Safety — The Costs of Foodborne Illnesses	— Contaminants — How Food Becomes Unsafe — Food Most Likely to Become Unsafe: TCS Food — Populations at High Risk for Foodborne Illness — Key Practices for Ensuring Food Safety	— Marketing Food Safety

FOODBORNE ILLNESSES

As a foodservice manager, you are responsible for your operation, your staff, and your customers. The best way to meet your obligations is to keep the food you serve safe. To start, you must know what foodborne illnesses are and whom they most affect. The more you learn about them, the more you will understand the need for strong food safety practices. The costs of a foodborne-illness outbreak can be devastating.

A foodborne illness is a disease transmitted to people by food. An illness is considered a foodborne-illness outbreak when two or more people have the same symptoms after eating the same food. However, this requires an investigation by a regulatory authority as well as confirmation by a laboratory. Millions of people contract a foodborne illness each year. Most cases go unreported and do not occur at restaurant or foodservice operations. Those that are reported and investigated help the industry learn about the causes of foodborne illnesses and what can be done to prevent them.

Challenges to Food Safety

You must work hard to maintain high standards of food safety throughout your operation. It is not always easy. Food safety faces many obstacles.

Time   Pressure to work quickly can make it hard to take the time to follow food safety practices.

Language and culture   Some staff may speak a language different from yours. This can create communication barriers. Cultural differences can influence how staff view food safety as well.

Literacy and education   Staff often have varying education levels. This can make teaching food safety to some of them more difficult.

Pathogens   Illness-causing pathogens are being found on food that was once considered safe. For example, nontyphoidal *Salmonella* is now appearing on produce more often than in the past.

Unapproved suppliers   Food might be received from suppliers that are not practicing food safety. This can cause a foodborne-illness outbreak.

High-risk populations   The number of customers at high risk for getting a foodborne illness is on the rise. One example is the growing elderly population.

Staff turnover   Training new staff in job tasks leaves less time for food safety training.

The ServSafe program will help you overcome challenges in managing a good food safety program.

The Costs of Foodborne Illnesses

Foodborne illnesses cost the United States billions of dollars each year. National Restaurant Association figures show that a foodborne-illness outbreak can cost an operation thousands of dollars.

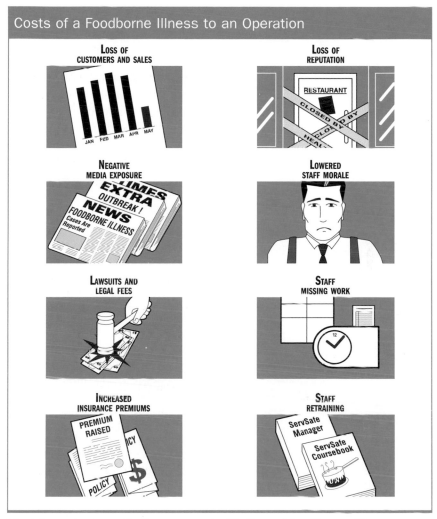

Costs of a Foodborne Illness to an Operation

LOSS OF CUSTOMERS AND SALES

LOSS OF REPUTATION

NEGATIVE MEDIA EXPOSURE

LOWERED STAFF MORALE

LAWSUITS AND LEGAL FEES

STAFF MISSING WORK

INCREASED INSURANCE PREMIUMS

STAFF RETRAINING

Most important are the human costs. Victims of foodborne illnesses may experience lost work, medical costs and long-term disability, and death.

Resources

National Food Safety Month

National Food Safety Month (NFSM) is an annual campaign held each September. Initially created in 1994, NFSM helps to raise awareness about the importance of food safety education. Each year, NFSM has a new theme and offers free training activities to reinforce food safety practices and procedures. These materials are based on ServSafe food safety training. Past themes have included allergen awareness, cross-contamination prevention, and lessons learned from health inspections. For more information, visit servsafe.com.

Foodborne Illnesses	How Foodborne Illnesses Occur	The Food Safety Responsibilities of a Manager
— Challenges to Food Safety — The Costs of Foodborne Illnesses	— Contaminants — How Food Becomes Unsafe — Food Most Likely to Become Unsafe: TCS Food — Populations at High Risk for Foodborne Illness — Key Practices for Ensuring Food Safety	— Marketing Food Safety

HOW FOODBORNE ILLNESSES OCCUR

Unsafe food is usually the result of contamination, which is the presence of harmful substances in food. To prevent foodborne illnesses, you must recognize the contaminants that can make food unsafe. These can come from pathogens, chemicals, or physical objects. They might also come from certain unsafe practices in your operation.

Contaminants

Contaminants are divided into three categories.

Biological   Pathogens are the greatest threat to food safety. They include certain viruses, parasites, fungi, and bacteria. Some plants, mushrooms, and seafood that carry harmful toxins are also included in this group.

Chemical   Foodservice chemicals can contaminate food if used incorrectly. The photo at left shows one example of how chemicals may contaminate food. Chemical contaminants can include cleaners, sanitizers, and polishes.

Physical   Foreign objects such as metal shavings, staples, and bandages can get into food. So can glass, dirt, and even bag ties. The photo at left shows this type of physical contaminant. Naturally occurring objects, such as fish bones in fillets, are another example.

Each contaminant listed above is a danger to food safety. But biological contaminants are responsible for most foodborne illness.

How Food Becomes Unsafe

If food handlers do not handle food correctly, it can become unsafe. These are the five most common food-handling mistakes, or risk factors, that can cause a foodborne illness:

1 Purchasing food from unsafe sources

2 Failing to cook food correctly

3 Holding food at incorrect temperatures

4 Using contaminated equipment

5 Practicing poor personal hygiene

Except for purchasing food from unsafe sources, each mistake listed above is related to four main factors. These include time-temperature abuse, cross-contamination, poor personal hygiene, and poor cleaning and sanitizing.

Time-temperature abuse   Food has been subjected to time-temperature abuse when it has stayed too long at temperatures that are good for the growth of pathogens. A foodborne illness can result if food is time-temperature abused. This can happen in many ways:

- Food is not held or stored at the correct temperature, as shown in the photo of potato salad at left.
- Food is not cooked or reheated enough to kill pathogens.
- Food is not cooled correctly.

Cross-contamination   Pathogens can be transferred from one surface or food to another. This is called cross-contamination. Cross-contamination can cause a foodborne illness in many ways:

- Contaminated ingredients are added to food that receives no further cooking.
- Ready-to-eat food touches contaminated surfaces.

- Contaminated food touches or drips fluids onto cooked or ready-to-eat food, as shown in the photo at left.
- A food handler touches contaminated food and then touches ready-to-eat food.
- Contaminated wiping cloths touch food-contact surfaces.

Poor personal hygiene   Food handlers can cause a foodborne illness if they do any of the following actions:

- Fail to wash their hands correctly after using the restroom.
- Cough or sneeze on food.

- Touch or scratch wounds and then touch food, as shown in the photo at left.
- Work while sick.

Poor cleaning and sanitizing   Pathogens can be spread to food if equipment has not been cleaned and sanitized correctly between uses. This can happen in the following ways:

- Equipment and utensils are not washed, rinsed, and sanitized between uses.
- Food-contact surfaces are wiped clean rather than being washed, rinsed, and sanitized.

- Wiping cloths are not stored in a sanitizer solution between uses, as shown in the photo at left.
- Sanitizing solutions are not at the required levels to sanitize objects.

Food Most Likely to Become Unsafe: TCS Food

Pathogens grow well in the food pictured below. It needs time and temperature control to limit this growth. For this reason, this food is called TCS food—food requiring time and temperature control for safety.

TCS Food

- Milk and dairy products

- Shell eggs (except those treated to eliminate nontyphoidal *Salmonella*)

- Meat: beef, pork, and lamb

- Poultry

- Fish

- Shellfish and crustaceans

- Baked potatoes

- Heat-treated plant food, such as cooked rice, beans, and vegetables

- Tofu or other soy protein
- Synthetic ingredients, such as textured soy protein in meat alternatives

- Sprouts and sprout seeds

- Sliced melons
- Cut tomatoes
- Cut leafy greens

- Untreated garlic-and-oil mixtures

Ready-to-Eat Food

Like TCS food, ready-to-eat food also needs careful handling to prevent contamination. Ready-to-eat food is exactly what it sounds like: food that can be eaten without further preparation, washing, or cooking. Examples include cooked food, washed fruit and vegetables (whole and cut), and deli meat. Bakery items and sugar, spices, and seasonings are other examples of ready-to-eat food.

Populations at High Risk for Foodborne Illness

Some groups of people have a higher risk of getting a foodborne illness than others. These high-risk populations include preschool-age children, elderly people, and people with compromised immune systems.

Preschool-age children   Very young children are at a higher risk for getting a foodborne illness because they have not yet built up strong immune systems.

Elderly people   As people age, changes occur in their organs. For example, stomach-acid production decreases as people get older. This allows more pathogens that previously may have been eaten to enter the intestines. A change in the stomach and intestinal tract also allows the body to store food for longer periods. This gives toxins more time to form.

People with compromised immune systems   This includes people with cancer or on chemotherapy, and people with HIV/AIDS. People who have had organ or bone-marrow transplants and those on certain medications are also immune-compromised.

Chemotherapy and certain medications weaken the immune system— the body's defense system against illness. People who have had organ or bone-marrow transplants have suppressed immune systems. That is because they take medication to prevent the body from destroying the new organ or bone marrow.

Key Practices for Ensuring Food Safety

Now that you know how food can become unsafe, you can focus on the following to keep it safe:

- Purchasing food from approved, reputable suppliers
- Controlling time and temperature
- Preventing cross-contamination
- Practicing personal hygiene
- Cleaning and sanitizing

Set up standard operating procedures (SOPs) that focus on these areas. The ServSafe program will show you how to design these procedures in later chapters.

1

Foodborne Illnesses	How Foodborne Illnesses Occur	The Food Safety Responsibilities of a Manager
— Challenges to Food Safety — The Costs of Foodborne Illnesses	— Contaminants — How Food Becomes Unsafe — Food Most Likely to Become Unsafe: TCS Food — Populations at High Risk for Foodborne Illness — Key Practices for Ensuring Food Safety	— Marketing Food Safety

THE FOOD SAFETY RESPONSIBILITIES OF A MANAGER

The Food and Drug Administration (FDA) recommends that regulatory authorities hold the person in charge of a foodservice operation responsible for ensuring the following standards are met:

- Food is not being prepared in a private home or in a room where people are living or sleeping.

- People other than food handlers are restricted from prep, storage, and dishwashing areas. If other people are allowed in these areas, steps are taken to protect food, utensils, and equipment from contamination.

- Maintenance and delivery workers are following food safety practices while in the operation.

- Staff handwashing is monitored in the operation.

- The inspection of deliveries is monitored to ensure that food is received from an approved source; at the correct temperature; and has not been contaminated.

- Food delivered after-hours is monitored to make sure it is received from an approved source; stored in the correct location; protected from contamination; and accurately presented.

- Food handlers are being monitored to make sure TCS food is cooked to required temperatures. Temperatures are being checked using calibrated thermometers, as shown in the photo at left.

- Food handlers are monitored to make sure TCS food is being cooled rapidly.

- Consumer advisories are posted notifying customers of the risk of ordering raw or partially cooked food.

- Cleaning and sanitizing procedures are monitored to make sure that sanitizer solutions are at the correct temperature and concentration and remain in contact with items for the correct amount of time.

- Customers are notified that they must use clean tableware when returning to a self-service area.

- Staff are handling ready-to-eat food with utensils or single-use gloves.

- Staff are trained in food safety, including allergy awareness.

- Staff, including conditional staff, are reporting illnesses and symptoms of illnesses that can be transmitted through food.

- Food safety procedures are written, implemented, and maintained where required by the regulatory authority.

Marketing Food Safety

Marketing your food safety efforts will show staff and customers alike that you take food safety seriously. Emphasize your support of food safety training and policies.

You can display your commitment in several other ways as well:

- Offer training courses and evaluate and update them as needed.

- Discuss food safety expectations. Document food-handling procedures and update them as needed.

- Consider awarding certificates for training and small rewards for good food safety records.

- Set an example by following all food safety rules yourself.

You should also show customers that staff know and follow food safety rules. Make sure your staff's hygiene and appearance reflect your food safety focus. Post food safety ideas and information in appropriate locations at your operation. Ensure that staff can answer simple food safety questions when asked.

Regulatory

Food Safety Modernization Act (FSMA)

Federal and state governments help to protect the public's health by ensuring the safety of the nation's food supply. For example, on January 4, 2011, President Obama signed the Food Safety Modernization Act (FSMA) into law. The goal of this act is to ensure the safety of the U.S. food supply by shifting the focus from *responding* to contamination to *preventing* contamination. The legislation has many aspects, ranging from food defense to import rules to inspection and hazard analysis improvements. This is the biggest food safety reform in 70 years. More information is available at fda.gov.

Summary

- A foodborne illness is a disease transmitted to people by food. An illness is considered an outbreak when two or more people have the same symptoms after eating the same food.

- Three types of contaminants threaten food safety. They are biological, chemical, and physical. Of these, pathogens pose the greatest danger.

- Food handlers who do not follow correct procedures can also threaten the safety of food. They can do this when they fail to cook food enough and when they hold it at incorrect temperatures. Food handlers can also cause an illness when they use contaminated equipment and when they practice poor personal hygiene.

- Food has been time-temperature abused when it has stayed too long at temperatures that are good for the growth of pathogens. Pathogens can be transferred from one surface or food to another. This is called cross-contamination. Pathogens can be spread to food if equipment has not been cleaned and sanitized correctly between uses.

- Pathogens grow well in TCS food. To prevent this growth, this food needs time and temperature control.

- Some groups are at a higher risk of getting sick from unsafe food. They include preschool-age children; the elderly; people with cancer or on chemotherapy; people with HIV/AIDS; transplant recipients; and people on certain medications.

- Important prevention measures for keeping food safe are controlling time and temperature; preventing cross-contamination; practicing good personal hygiene; purchasing from approved, reputable suppliers; and cleaning and sanitizing items correctly.

Apply Your Knowledge

Use these questions to review the concepts presented in this chapter.

Discussion Questions

1. What are the potential costs associated with foodborne-illness outbreaks?

2. Why are the elderly at a higher risk for getting foodborne illnesses?

3. What are the three major types of contaminants?

For answers, please turn to the Answer Key.

Undercooked Chicken Sends Children to the Hospital

A group of preschool children were on a field trip to the local pumpkin farm for their annual fall outing. Twenty-five children and two chaperones got sick after a stop at a local, family-owned restaurant.

Regulatory authorities determined that chicken used to make chicken sandwiches for the group was not fully cooked. It seemed that the cooks at the operation had a difficult time keeping up after the school bus arrived. As a result, the cooks rushed the cooking process and failed to check the internal temperature of the chicken. Most of the children became severely ill and had to be hospitalized. The two chaperones recovered quickly.

1. What caused the outbreak?

2. Why did so many children get sick?

For answers, please turn to the Answer Key.

With Power Comes Responsibility

The owner of a popular Italian restaurant needed a new manager. After careful consideration, the owner decided to promote Russell, a young cook who had worked for him for the last three years. Russell had showed great promise. He was attending culinary school and had taken and passed the food safety certification program with flying colors. He had a great work record and was rarely late for work.

In his new role as manager, Russell would be directly responsible for food safety in the operation. He knew how important this new role would be, and he took food safety very seriously.

1. What will the regulatory authority hold Russell accountable for in regard to food safety?

For answers, please turn to the Answer Key.

1

Circle the best answer to each question.

1. Why are preschool-age children at a higher risk for foodborne illnesses?

   A They have not built up strong immune systems.

   B They are more likely to spend time in a hospital.

   C They are more likely to suffer allergic reactions.

   D Their appetites have increased since birth.

2. Which is a TCS food?

   A Bread

   B Flour

   C Sprouts

   D Strawberries

3. The five common mistakes that can lead to foodborne illness are failing to cook food adequately, holding food at incorrect temperatures, using contaminated equipment, practicing poor personal hygiene, and

   A reheating leftover food.

   B serving ready-to-eat food.

   C using single-use, disposable gloves.

   D purchasing food from unsafe sources.

4. What is an important measure for preventing foodborne illness?

   A Serving locally grown food

   B Using new equipment

   C Measuring pathogens

   D Controlling time and temperature

5. Raw chicken breasts are left out at room temperature on a prep table. What is the main risk that could cause a foodborne illness?

   A Cross-contamination

   B Poor cleaning and sanitizing

   C Poor personal hygiene

   D Time-temperature abuse

6. A server cleans a dining table with a wiping cloth and then puts the wiping cloth in an apron pocket. What is the risk that could cause a foodborne illness?

   A Cross-contamination

   B Poor cleaning and sanitizing

   C Poor personal hygiene

   D Time-temperature abuse

For answers, please turn to the Answer Key.

Notes

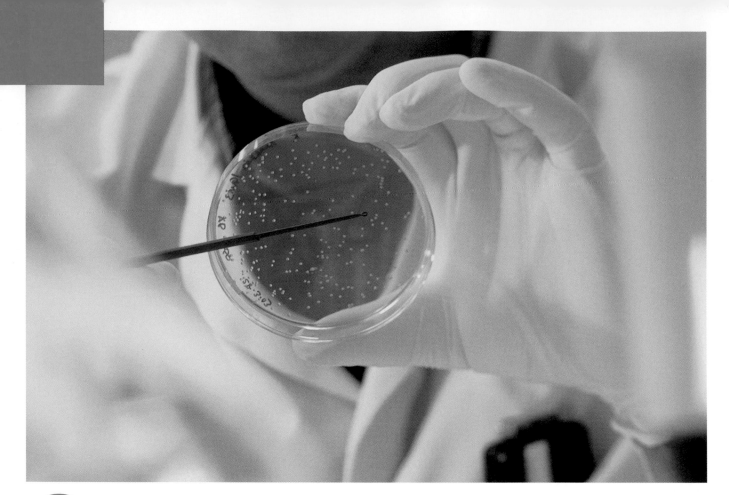

2 Understanding the Microworld

Pathogens	Bacteria	Viruses	Parasites	Fungi	Biological Toxins
– How Contamination Occurs – Symptoms of a Foodborne Illness – The Big Six	– General Information about Bacteria – What Bacteria Need to Grow – Bacterial Growth – Spores – Major Foodborne Bacteria	– General Information about Viruses – Major Foodborne Viruses	– Characteristics of Parasites – Major Foodborne Illnesses Caused by Parasites	– Mold – Yeast	– Seafood Toxins – Mushroom Toxins – Plant Toxins

Case in POINT

Shigella Outbreak

Sixteen guests and three catering hall staff got sick with *Shigella* spp. The guests were part of a large group of National Guard veterans at a reunion. They ate at a large and popular catering hall located in the southeastern United States.

Within one to three days after the catered event, reports began to come into the local regulatory authority. Those who had gotten sick reported very similar symptoms. Each had experienced stomach cramps, fever, and diarrhea. Three people went to the emergency room to seek treatment.

The specific food involved was never determined. But the regulatory authority confirmed that the outbreak was likely caused by the catering hall's lead cook. He was not feeling well the morning of the luncheon when he reported to work. He also had failed to wash his hands throughout his morning shift. The cook had prepped the food that was served at the luncheon.

1. What could have been done to prevent the outbreak?
2. What should the catering hall's owners and management team do to ensure that an outbreak like this does not occur in the future?

For answers, please turn to the Answer Key.

INSIDE THIS CHAPTER

- Pathogens
- Bacteria
- Viruses
- Parasites
- Fungi
- Biological Toxins

OBJECTIVES

After completing this chapter, you should be able to identify the following:

- Factors that affect the growth of foodborne bacteria (FAT TOM)
- Characteristics of TCS food
- Major foodborne pathogens and their sources; resulting illnesses and their symptoms
- Ways of preventing viral, bacterial, parasitic, and fungal contamination
- Naturally occurring toxins and ways of preventing illnesses from them

KEY TERMS

- Microorganisms
- Pathogens
- Toxins
- Bacteria
- FAT TOM
- Temperature danger zone
- Water activity (a_w)
- Spore
- Virus
- Parasite
- Fungi
- Mold
- Yeast

2

Pathogens	Bacteria	Viruses	Parasites	Fungi	Biological Toxins
— How Contamination Occurs — Symptoms of a Foodborne Illness — The Big Six	— General Information about Bacteria — What Bacteria Need to Grow — Bacterial Growth — Spores — Major Foodborne Bacteria	— General Information about Viruses — Major Foodborne Viruses	— Characteristics of Parasites — Major Foodborne Illnesses Caused by Parasites	— Mold — Yeast	— Seafood Toxins — Mushroom Toxins — Plant Toxins

Key Point

Pathogens are microorganisms that can make you sick.

PATHOGENS

Microorganisms are small, living organisms that can be seen only through a microscope. Many microorganisms are harmless, but some can cause illness. These are called pathogens. Some pathogens make you sick when you eat them. Others produce poisons—or toxins—that make you sick. An understanding of pathogens and the toxins that some produce is the first step in preventing foodborne illnesses.

The four types of pathogens that can contaminate food are viruses, bacteria, parasites, and fungi. Many viruses, bacteria, and parasites can cause an illness but cannot be seen, smelled, or tasted. On the other hand, some fungi, such as mold, can change the look, smell, or taste of food but may not make people sick.

How Contamination Occurs

Most pathogens get into food and onto food-contact surfaces because of the way that people handle them. For example, food handlers who do not wash their hands after using the restroom may contaminate food and surfaces with feces from their fingers. Once the food that the food handler touched is eaten, a foodborne illness may result. This is called the fecal-oral route of contamination.

Food handlers can also pass on pathogens when they are in contact with a person who is sick. Some pathogens are passed very easily in any of these ways:

- From person to person
- Through sneezing or vomiting onto food or food-contact surfaces
- From touching dirty food-contact surfaces and equipment and then touching food

Simple mistakes can result in contamination. For example, allowing ready-to-eat food to touch surfaces that have come in contact with raw meat, seafood, and poultry can lead to contamination. This is shown in the photo at left. Storing food or cleaning products incorrectly can also lead to contamination. So can the failure to spot signs of pests in the operation, because pests are a major source of disease.

Symptoms of a Foodborne Illness

Once pathogens get into food or onto food-contact surfaces, a foodborne illness can result. The symptoms of a foodborne illness vary, depending on which illness a person has. But most victims share some common symptoms:

- Diarrhea
- Vomiting
- Fever
- Nausea
- Abdominal cramps
- Jaundice (a yellowing of the skin and eyes)

Not every person who is sick with a foodborne illness will have all of these symptoms. Nor are the symptoms of foodborne illness limited to this list. Throughout this chapter, several foodborne illnesses will be presented. Symptoms specific to these illnesses are listed.

How quickly foodborne-illness symptoms appear in a person is known as the onset time of the illness. Onset times depend on the type of foodborne illness a person has. They can range from 30 minutes to as long as six weeks. How severe the illness is can also vary, from mild diarrhea to death.

The Big Six

According to the Food and Drug Administration (FDA), there are over 40 different kinds of bacteria, viruses, parasites, and molds that can occur in food and cause a foodborne illness. Of these, six have been singled out by the FDA. These have been dubbed the "Big Six" because they are highly contagious and can cause severe illness. They include:

- *Shigella* spp.
- *Salmonella* Typhi
- Nontyphoidal *Salmonella* (NTS)
- Shiga toxin-producing *Escherichia coli* (STEC), also known as *E. coli*
- Hepatitis A
- Norovirus

These pathogens are often found in very high numbers in an infected person's feces and can be transferred to food easily. A person does not have to eat much of the pathogen in order to get sick, and that illness is often severe. For this reason, food handlers diagnosed with illnesses from these pathogens cannot work in a foodservice operation while they are sick.

Pathogens	Bacteria	Viruses	Parasites	Fungi	Biological Toxins
— How Contamination Occurs — Symptoms of a Foodborne Illness — The Big Six	— General Information about Bacteria — What Bacteria Need to Grow — Bacterial Growth — Spores — Major Foodborne Bacteria	— General Information about Viruses — Major Foodborne Viruses	— Characteristics of Parasites — Major Foodborne Illnesses Caused by Parasites	— Mold — Yeast	— Seafood Toxins — Mushroom Toxins — Plant Toxins

BACTERIA

Bacteria are responsible for a large number of foodborne illnesses. Knowing what bacteria are and how they grow can help you control them.

General Information about Bacteria

Bacteria are single-celled, living microorganisms that can spoil food and cause foodborne illness. Bacteria share some basic characteristics.

Location   Bacteria can be found almost everywhere. They live in and on our bodies. Some types of bacteria keep us healthy, while others cause illness.

Detection   Bacteria cannot be seen, smelled, or tasted.

Growth   If conditions are correct, bacteria will grow in rapid numbers.

Toxin production   Some bacteria produce toxins in food as they grow and die. People who eat the toxins can get sick. Cooking may not destroy these toxins.

Prevention   The most important way to prevent bacteria from causing a foodborne illness is to control time and temperature.

What Bacteria Need to Grow

Bacteria need six conditions to grow. You can remember them by thinking of the words FAT TOM.

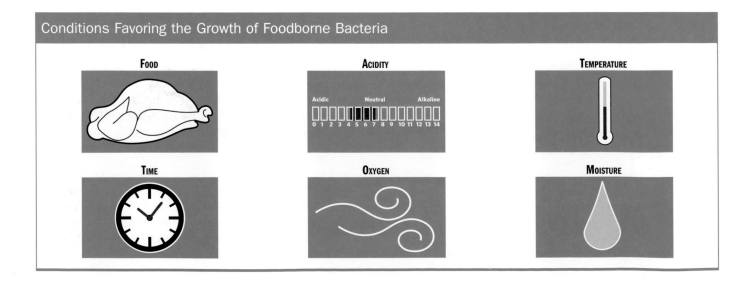

Conditions Favoring the Growth of Foodborne Bacteria

FOOD

ACIDITY

Acidic   Neutral   Alkaline
0 1 2 3 4 5 6 7 8 9 10 11 12 13 14

TEMPERATURE

TIME

OXYGEN

MOISTURE

Food

Most bacteria need nutrients such as carbohydrates or proteins to survive. TCS food supports the growth of bacteria better than other types of food. This includes meat, poultry, dairy products, and eggs.

Acidity

Bacteria grow best in food that contains little or no acid. pH is the measure of acidity. The pH scale ranges from 0 to 14.0. A value of 0 is highly acidic, while a value of 14.0 is highly alkaline. A pH of 7.0 is neutral. Bacteria grow best in food that is neutral to slightly acidic, a pH of 7.5 to 4.6. Here are some common types of food and their pH:

- Lemons and limes have a pH of 1.8–2.4.
- Tomatoes have a pH of 3.7–4.0.
- Mayonnaise has a pH of 3.8–4.0.

The following common types of food have a pH that is ideal for bacterial growth:

- Bread has a pH of 5.0–6.0.
- Raw chicken has a pH of 5.5–6.0.
- Cantaloupe has a pH of 6.1–6.5.
- Milk has a pH of 6.4–6.8.
- Cooked corn has a pH of 7.3–7.6.

Temperature

Bacteria grow rapidly between 41°F and 135°F (5°C and 57°C), as shown in the illustration at left. This range is known as the temperature danger zone. Bacteria grow even more rapidly from 70°F to 125°F (21°C to 52°C). Bacterial growth is limited when food is held above or below the temperature danger zone.

Time

Bacteria need time to grow. The more time bacteria spend in the temperature danger zone, the more opportunity they have to grow to unsafe levels.

Oxygen

Some bacteria need oxygen to grow. Others grow when oxygen is not there. Bacteria that grow without oxygen can occur in cooked rice, untreated garlic-and-oil mixtures, and temperature-abused baked potatoes.

Moisture

Bacteria grow well in food with high levels of moisture. The amount of moisture available in food for this growth is called water activity (a_w). The a_w scale ranges from 0.0 to 1.0. The higher the value, the more available moisture in the food. For example, water has a water activity of 1.0. Food with a water activity of 0.85 or higher is ideal for the growth of bacteria.

Temperature and Bacterial Growth

The Temperature Danger Zone

°F | °C

160 — 70
150 —
140 — 60
130 — 135°F
120 — 50 (57°C)
110 — 40
100 —
90 — 30
80 —
70 — 20
60 —
50 — 10
40 — 5 41°F
30 — 0 (5°C)
20 —
10 — -10
0 —
-20

You can help keep food safe by controlling FAT TOM. In your operation, however, you will most likely be able to control only time and temperature. To control time, limit how long TCS food spends in the temperature danger zone. To control temperature, keep TCS food out of the temperature danger zone.

Bacterial Growth

Bacterial growth can be broken into four progressive stages (phases): lag, log, stationary, and death. This growth is shown in the graph below.

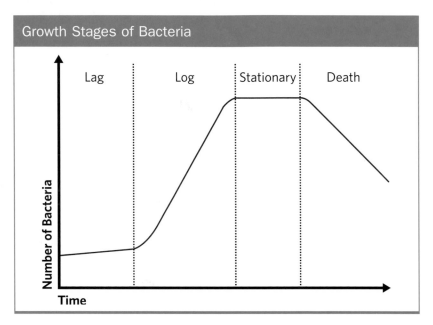

Growth Stages of Bacteria

Lag phase   Bacteria that are introduced to food go through an adjustment period called the lag phase. Their number is stable as they get ready to grow. To prevent food from becoming unsafe, prolong the lag phase by controlling the conditions for growth: temperature, time, oxygen, moisture, and pH. As mentioned earlier, you have the most control over time and temperature. For example, refrigerating food keeps bacteria in the lag phase.

Log phase   Bacteria reproduce by splitting in two. Under the correct conditions, they can double as often as every 20 minutes, as shown in the illustration at left. As a result, food will fast become unsafe.

Stationary phase   Bacteria can continue to grow until conditions become unfavorable. Eventually, they grow and die at the same rate.

Death phase   When dying bacteria outnumber growing bacteria, the population declines.

Bacterial Growth

Number of Cells		Time
○	1 cell	0 min.
○	2 cells	20 min.
○	4 cells	40 min.
○	8 cells	1 hr.
○	16 cells	1 hr. 20 min.
○	> 1 billion	10 hrs.

The time required for bacteria to enter a lag phase and grow in a log phase depends on FAT TOM conditions. The graph below shows how different temperatures affect the growth of *Salmonella* spp. *Salmonella* spp. grows more quickly at warmer temperatures (95°F [35°C]) than at colder ones (44°F and 50°F [7°C and 10°C]). At even colder temperatures (42°F [6°C]), it does not grow at all. But it does not die either, prolonging the lag phase. This is why refrigerating food correctly helps to keep it safe.

Growth of *Salmonella* spp. at Different Temperatures

Spores

To keep from dying when they lack nutrients, certain bacteria can change into a form called a spore. Spores are often found in dirt. They can contaminate food grown there, such as potatoes, other vegetables, and rice. They can also contaminate meat, poultry, fish, and other food exposed to dirt or dust.

Spores can resist heat and survive cooking temperatures. They can also change back into a form that grows. You can prevent this by storing food at the correct temperature. You also need to hold and cool food correctly.

Major Foodborne Bacteria

Several different types of bacteria can cause foodborne illness. These are listed on the next several pages. For each type of bacteria, you should understand the common source and food commonly linked with it. You should also be able to identify the most common symptoms associated with the illness caused by the bacteria. Finally, you should be able to determine the most important prevention measures.

The table on page 2-9 will help you recognize the similarities and differences among the different types of foodborne bacteria. It will help you remember the different types of bacteria as well.

Throughout this chapter you will see that pathogens have been grouped according to their most important prevention measure. This might include:

- Controlling time and temperature
- Preventing cross-contamination
- Practicing personal hygiene
- Purchasing from approved, reputable suppliers

Controlling Time and Temperature

These bacteria can be prevented through time and temperature control:

- *Bacillus cereus*   page 2-10
- *Listeria monocytogenes*   page 2-10
- Shiga toxin-producing *E. coli*   page 2-11
- *Campylobacter jejuni*   page 2-11
- *Clostridium perfringens*   page 2-12
- *Clostridium botulinum*   page 2-12

Preventing Cross-Contamination

These bacteria can be prevented by preventing cross-contamination:

- Nontyphoidal *Salmonella*   page 2-13
- *Salmonella* Typhi   page 2-13

Practicing Personal Hygiene

These bacteria can be prevented by practicing personal hygiene:

- *Shigella* spp.   page 2-14
- *Staphylococcus aureus*   page 2-14

Purchasing from Approved, Reputable Suppliers

These bacteria can be prevented by purchasing products from approved, reputable suppliers:

- *Vibrio vulnificus* and *Vibrio parahaemolyticus*   page 2-15

Major Foodborne Bacteria

Most Important Prevention Measure (positioned by bacteria):
- Controlling time and temperature — *Clostridium perfringens, Clostridium botulinum*
- Preventing cross-contamination — *Campylobacter jejuni, Nontyphoidal Salmonella*
- Practicing personal hygiene — *Salmonella Typhi, Shigella spp., Staphylococcus aureus*
- Purchasing from approved, reputable suppliers — *Vibrio vulnificus / Vibrio parahaemolyticus*

Bacteria Characteristics	Item	Bacillus cereus	Listeria monocytogenes	Shiga toxin-producing E. coli	Clostridium perfringens	Clostridium botulinum	Campylobacter jejuni	Nontyphoidal Salmonella	Salmonella Typhi	Shigella spp.	Staphylococcus aureus	Vibrio vulnificus / Vibrio parahaemolyticus
Commonly Linked Food	Poultry				•		•	•				
	Eggs							•				
	Meat	•	•	•	•		•					
	Fish											
	Shellfish											•
	Ready-to-eat food		•						•	•	•	
	Produce	•		•		•		•		•		
	Rice/grains	•										
	Milk/dairy products	•	•					•				
	Contaminated water						•		•	•		•
Most Common Illness Symptoms	Diarrhea	•		•	•		•	•		•	•	
	Abdominal pain/cramps			•	•		•	•	•	•	•	•
	Nausea	•				•					•	•
	Vomiting	•					•	•			•	
	Fever						•	•	•	•		
	Headache						•		•			
Prevention Measures	Handwashing								•	•	•	
	Cooking	•	•	•			•	•	•			•
	Holding	•			•	•					•	
	Cooling	•			•	•					•	
	Reheating				•	•					•	
	Approved suppliers			•								•
	Excluding food handlers			•				•	•	•		
	Preventing cross-contamination		•	•			•	•				

Most Important Prevention Measure: Controlling time and temperature

Bacteria	*Bacillus cereus* (ba-SIL-us SEER-ee-us)
Illness	*Bacillus cereus* gastroenteritis (ba-SIL-us SEER-ee-us GAS-tro-EN-ter-I-tiss)

Bacillus cereus is a spore-forming bacteria found in dirt. It can produce two different toxins when allowed to grow to high levels. The toxins cause different illnesses.

Food Commonly Linked with the Bacteria

Diarrhea illness

- Cooked vegetables
- Meat products
- Milk

Vomiting illness

- Cooked rice dishes, including fried rice and rice pudding

Most Common Symptoms

Diarrhea illness

- Watery diarrhea
- No vomiting

Vomiting illness

- Nausea
- Vomiting

Other Prevention Measures

- Cook food to minimum internal temperatures.
- Hold food at the correct temperatures.
- Cool food correctly.

Bacteria	*Listeria monocytogenes* (liss-TEER-ee-uh MON-o-SI-TAHJ-uh-neez)
Illness	Listeriosis (liss-TEER-ee-O-sis)

Listeria monocytogenes is found in dirt, water, and plants. Unlike other bacteria, it grows in cool, moist environments. The illness is uncommon in healthy people, but high-risk populations are especially vulnerable—particularly pregnant women.

Food Commonly Linked with the Bacteria

- Raw meat
- Unpasteurized dairy products
- Ready-to-eat food, such as deli meat, hot dogs, and soft cheeses

Most Common Symptoms

Pregnant women

- Miscarriage

Newborns

- Sepsis
- Pneumonia
- Meningitis

Other Prevention Measures

- Throw out any product that has passed its use-by or expiration date.
- Cook raw meat to minimum internal temperatures.
- Prevent cross-contamination between raw or undercooked food and ready-to-eat food.
- Avoid using unpasteurized dairy products.

Bacteria Shiga toxin-producing *Escherichia coli*
(ess-chur-EE-kee-UH KO-LI) (STEC), **also known as** *E. coli*, **including O157:H7, O26:H11, O111:H8, and O158:NM**

Illness   Hemorrhagic colitis (hem-or-RA jik ko-LI-tiss)

Shiga toxin-producing *E. coli* can be found in the intestines of cattle. It is also found in infected people. The bacteria can contaminate meat during slaughtering. Eating only a small amount of the bacteria can make a person sick. Once eaten, it produces toxins in the intestines, which cause the illness. The bacteria are often in a person's feces for weeks after symptoms have ended.

Food Commonly Linked with the Bacteria	Most Common Symptoms	Other Prevention Measures
• Ground beef (raw and undercooked) • Contaminated produce	• Diarrhea (eventually becomes bloody) • Abdominal cramps • Kidney failure (in severe cases)	• Cook food, especially ground beef, to minimum internal temperatures. • Purchase produce from approved, reputable suppliers. • Prevent cross-contamination between raw meat and ready-to-eat food. • Exclude food handlers with diarrhea who have been diagnosed with an illness caused by shiga toxin-producing *E. coli* from the operation.

Bacteria *Campylobacter jejuni* (Camp-ee-lo-BAK-ter Jay-JUNE-ee)
Illness   Campylobacteriosis (CAMP-ee-lo-BAK-teer-ee-O-sis)

Though *Campylobacter jejuni* is commonly associated with poultry, it has been known to contaminate water. Illness often occurs when poultry is incorrectly cooked and when raw poultry has been allowed to cross-contaminate other food and food-contact surfaces. The pathogen is best controlled through correct cooking and the prevention of cross-contamination.

Food Commonly Linked with the Bacteria	Most Common Symptoms	Other Prevention Measures
• Poultry • Water contaminated with the bacteria • Meats • Stews/gravies	• Diarrhea (may be watery or bloody) • Abdominal cramps • Fever • Vomiting • Headaches	• Cook food, particularly poultry, to required minimum internal temperatures. • Prevent cross-contamination between raw poultry and ready-to-eat food.

Bacteria *Clostridium perfringens* (klos-TRID-ee-um per-FRIN-jins)
Illness *Clostridium perfringens* gastroenteritis (klos-TRID-ee-um per-FRIN-jins GAS-tro-EN-ter-I-tiss)

Clostridium perfringens is found in dirt, where it forms spores that allow it to survive. It is also carried in the intestines of both animals and humans.

Clostridium perfringens does not grow at refrigeration temperatures. It does grow rapidly in food in the temperature danger zone. Commercially prepped food is not often involved in outbreaks. People who get sick usually do not have nausea, fever, or vomiting.

Food Commonly Linked with the Bacteria
- Meat
- Poultry
- Dishes made with meat and poultry, such as stews and gravies

Most Common Symptoms
- Diarrhea
- Severe abdominal pain

Other Prevention Measures
- Cool and reheat food correctly.
- Hold food at the correct temperatures.

Bacteria *Clostridium botulinum* (klos-TRID-ee-um BOT-chew-LINE-um)
Illness Botulism (BOT-chew-liz-um)

Clostridium botulinum forms spores that are often found in water and dirt. These spores can contaminate almost any food. The bacteria do not grow well in refrigerated or highly acidic food or in food with low moisture. However, *Clostridium botulinum* grows without oxygen and can produce a lethal toxin when food is time-temperature abused. Without medical treatment, death is likely.

Food Commonly Linked with the Bacteria
- Incorrectly canned food
- Reduced-oxygen packaged (ROP) food
- Temperature-abused vegetables, such as baked potatoes
- Untreated garlic-and-oil mixtures

Most Common Symptoms
Initially
- Nausea and vomiting
Later
- Weakness
- Double vision
- Difficulty in speaking and swallowing

Other Prevention Measures
- Hold, cool, and reheat food correctly.
- Inspect canned food for damage.

Most Important Prevention Measure: Preventing Cross-Contamination

Bacteria Nontyphoidal *Salmonella* (SAL-me-NEL-uh)
Illness Salmonellosis (SAL-men-uh-LO-sis)

Many farm animals carry nontyphoidal *Salmonella* naturally. Eating only a small amount of these bacteria can make a person sick. How severe symptoms are depends on the health of the person and the amount of bacteria eaten. The bacteria are often in a person's feces for weeks after symptoms have ended.

Food Commonly Linked with the Bacteria	Most Common Symptoms	Other Prevention Measures
• Poultry and eggs • Meat • Milk and dairy products • Produce, such as tomatoes, peppers, and cantaloupes	• Diarrhea • Abdominal cramps • Vomiting • Fever	• Cook poultry and eggs to minimum internal temperatures. • Prevent cross-contamination between poultry and ready-to-eat food. • Exclude food handlers who are vomiting or have diarrhea and have been diagnosed with an illness caused by nontyphoidal *Salmonella* from the operation.

Bacteria *Salmonella* Typhi (SAL-me-NEL-uh Ti-fee)
Illness Typhoid fever

Salmonella Typhi lives only in humans. People with typhoid fever carry the bacteria in their bloodstream and intestinal tract. Eating only a small amount of these bacteria can make a person sick. The severity of symptoms depends on the health of the person and the amount of bacteria eaten. The bacteria are often in a person's feces for weeks after symptoms have ended.

Food Commonly Linked with the Bacteria	Most Common Symptoms	Other Prevention Measures
• Ready-to-eat food • Beverages	• High fever • Weakness • Abdominal pain • Headache • Loss of appetite • Rash	• Exclude food handlers who have been diagnosed with an illness caused by *Salmonella* Typhi from the operation. • Wash hands. • Cook food to minimum internal temperatures.

Most Important Prevention Measure: Practicing Personal Hygiene

Bacteria	***Shigella* spp.** *(shi-GEL-uh)*
Illness	**Shigellosis** *(SHIG-uh-LO-sis)*

Shigella spp. is found in the feces of humans with the illness. Most illnesses occur when people eat or drink contaminated food or water. Flies can also transfer the bacteria from feces to food. Eating only a small amount of these bacteria can make a person sick. High levels of the bacteria are often in a person's feces for weeks after symptoms have ended.

Food Commonly Linked with the Bacteria

- Food that is easily contaminated by hands, such as salads containing TCS food (potato, tuna, shrimp, macaroni, and chicken)
- Food that has made contact with contaminated water, such as produce

Most Common Symptoms

- Bloody diarrhea
- Abdominal pain and cramps
- Fever (occasionally)

Other Prevention Measures

- Exclude food handlers who have diarrhea and have been diagnosed with an illness caused by *Shigella* spp. from the operation.
- Wash hands.
- Control flies inside and outside the operation.

Bacteria	***Staphylococcus aureus*** *(STAF-uh-lo-KOK-us OR-ee-us)*
Illness	**Staphylococcal gastroenteritis** *(STAF-ul-lo-KOK-al GAS-tro-EN-ter-I-tiss)*

Staphylococcus aureus can be found in humans—particularly in the hair, nose, and throat; and in infected cuts. It is often transferred to food when people carrying it touch these areas on their bodies and then handle food without washing their hands. If allowed to grow to large numbers in food, the bacteria can produce toxins that cause the illness when eaten. Cooking cannot destroy these toxins, so preventing bacterial growth is critical.

Food Commonly Linked with the Bacteria

Food that requires handling during prepping

- Salads containing TCS food (egg, tuna, chicken, and macaroni)
- Deli meat

Most Common Symptoms

- Nausea
- Vomiting and retching
- Abdominal cramps

Other Prevention Measures

- Wash hands, particularly after touching the hair, face, or body.
- Cover wounds on hands and arms.
- Hold, cool, and reheat food correctly.

Most Important Prevention Measure: Purchasing from Approved, Reputable Suppliers

Bacteria	***Vibrio vulnificus*** **and** ***Vibrio parahaemolyticus*** *(VIB-ree-o vul NIF-ih-kus and VIR-ree-o PAIR-uh-HEE-mo-lit-ih-kus)*
Illness	***Vibrio*** **gastroenteritis** *(VIB-ree-o GAS-tro-EN-ter-I-tiss)* ***Vibrio vulnificus*** **primary septicemia** *(VIB-ree-o vul-NIF-ih-kus SEP-ti-SEE-mee-uh)*

These bacteria are found in the waters where shellfish are harvested. They can grow very rapidly at temperatures in the middle of the temperature danger zone. People with chronic conditions (such as diabetes or cirrhosis) who get sick from these bacteria may get primary septicemia. This severe illness can lead to death.

Food Commonly Linked with the Bacteria	Most Common Symptoms	Other Prevention Measures
• Oysters from contaminated water	• Diarrhea • Abdominal cramps and nausea • Vomiting • Low-grade fever and chills	• Cook oysters to minimum internal temperatures.

Resources

Fight BAC!

Fight BAC! (short for "bacteria") is an initiative of the Partnership for Food Safety Education. Supported by dozens of organizations across the food industry, the Fight BAC! campaign focuses on supporting health educators and influencers through additional tools and connections to share food safety knowledge. Much of the material focuses on consumer food safety and encouraging children to understand how to keep food safe. Despite the different audience, the principles are based on many of the same principles used to build the ServSafe program. Many of the tools are free for download. Visit fightbac.org for more information.

Pathogens	Bacteria	Viruses	Parasites	Fungi	Biological Toxins
— How Contamination Occurs — Symptoms of a Foodborne Illness — The Big Six	— General Information about Bacteria — What Bacteria Need to Grow — Bacterial Growth — Spores — Major Foodborne Bacteria	— General Information about Viruses — Major Foodborne Viruses	— Characteristics of Parasites — Major Foodborne Illnesses Caused by Parasites	— Mold — Yeast	— Seafood Toxins — Mushroom Toxins — Plant Toxins

VIRUSES

As a manager, you should know what viruses are and about the illnesses they can cause. Most important, you should understand how to keep viruses from making your customers sick.

General Information about Viruses

The virus is the smallest of the microbial food contaminants. Viruses share some basic characteristics.

Location Viruses are carried by human beings and animals. They require a living host to grow. While viruses do not grow in food, they can be transferred through food and still remain infectious in food.

Sources People can get viruses from food, water, or any contaminated surface. Foodborne illnesses from viruses typically occur through fecal-oral routes. Norovirus is one of the leading causes of foodborne illness. It is often transmitted through airborne vomit particles.

Transfer Viruses can be transferred from person to person, from people to food, and from people to food-contact surfaces. When customers get sick from food contaminated with viruses, it is usually because their food was handled by an infected person. That person could be the operation's food handler, a staff member of the food manufacturer, or anyone else who has the virus. People carry viruses in their feces and can transfer them to their hands after using the restroom. For example, ready-to-eat food can become contaminated if hands are not washed correctly.

Prevention measure Viruses are not destroyed by normal cooking temperatures. That is why it is important to practice good personal hygiene when handling food and food-contact surfaces. The quick removal and cleanup of vomit is also important. Here are the best ways to prevent the spread of viruses in your operation:

- Prohibit food handlers who are vomiting or who have diarrhea or jaundice from working.

- Make sure food handlers wash their hands regularly and correctly, as shown in the photo at left.

- Avoid bare-hand contact with ready-to-eat food.

Key Point

Viruses can be transmitted from person to person, from people to food, and from people to food-contact surfaces.

Major Foodborne Viruses

Norovirus and hepatitis A are two viruses that are highly contagious and can cause severe illness. Food handlers diagnosed with these viruses must not work in a foodservice operation while they are sick. To have a good understanding of these viruses, you should become familiar with the following characteristics of each:

- Common source
- Food commonly linked with it
- Most common symptoms
- Most important prevention measures

The table on page 2-18 will help you recognize the similarities and differences between each virus. You will also see that the viruses are grouped according to their most important prevention measure—practicing personal hygiene. Other prevention measures are listed in the tables for the illnesses as well.

Practicing Personal Hygiene

Illnesses from the following viruses can be prevented by practicing personal hygiene:

- Hepatitis A   page 2-19
- Norovirus gastroenteritis   page 2-19

Regulatory

The CDC's Most Common Foodborne Illnesses

In its 2011 report on U.S. cases of foodborne illness, the Centers for Disease Control and Prevention (CDC) estimated that one of every six Americans (or approximately 48 million people) become sick with a foodborne illness each year. They also determined that, annually, approximately 128,000 people are hospitalized due to these illnesses and 3,000 people die from them.

In 2011, the top five pathogens for causing all illnesses were:

1. Norovirus
2. Nontyphoidal *Salmonella*
3. *Clostridium perfringens*
4. *Campylobacter* spp.
5. *Staphylococcus aureus*

Some other pathogens, including shiga toxin-producing *E. coli* and *Listeria monocytogenes*, contribute to the most hospitalizations and deaths each year.

According to the CDC, at least 31 pathogens that cause foodborne illness are known to public health officials. Many of them are tracked by public health systems in an attempt to limit disease and outbreaks. The staff-health reporting requirements mentioned in chapter 4 are an example of this type of tracking. You can learn more about foodborne-illness statistics at cdc.gov.

Major Foodborne Viruses

Most Important Prevention Measure		Controlling time and temperature		Preventing cross-contamination		Practicing personal hygiene		Purchasing from approved, reputable suppliers	
Virus						Hepatitis A	Norovirus		
Virus Characteristics	**Commonly Linked Food**	Poultry							
		Eggs							
		Meat							
		Fish							
		Shellfish				•	•		
		Ready-to-eat food				•	•		
		Produce							
		Rice/grains							
		Milk/dairy products							
		Contaminated water				•	•		
	Most Common Symptoms	Diarrhea					•		
		Abdominal pain/cramps				•	•		
		Nausea				•	•		
		Vomiting					•		
		Fever				•			
		Headache							
	Prevention Measures	Handwashing				•	•		
		Cooking							
		Holding							
		Cooling							
		Reheating							
		Approved suppliers				•	•		
		Excluding food handlers				•	•		
		Preventing cross-contamination							

Most Important Prevention Measure: Practicing Personal Hygiene

Virus	Hepatitis A *(HEP-a-TI-tiss)*
Illness	Hepatitis A

Hepatitis A is mainly found in the feces of people infected with it. The virus can contaminate water and many types of food. It is commonly linked with ready-to-eat food. However, it has also been linked with shellfish from contaminated water.

The virus is often transferred to food when infected food handlers touch food or equipment with fingers that have feces on them. Eating only a small amount of the virus can make a person sick. An infected person may not show symptoms for weeks but can be very infectious. Cooking does not destroy hepatitis A.

Food Commonly Linked with the Virus

- Ready-to-eat food
- Shellfish from contaminated water

Most Common Symptoms

- Fever (mild)
- General weakness
- Nausea
- Abdominal pain
- Jaundice (appears later)

Other Prevention Measures

- Exclude food handlers who have been diagnosed with hepatitis A from the operation.
- Exclude food handlers who have had jaundice for seven days or less from the operation.
- Wash hands.
- Avoid bare-hand contact with ready-to-eat food.
- Purchase shellfish from approved, reputable suppliers.

Virus	Norovirus *(NOR-o-VI-rus)*
Illness	Norovirus gastroenteritis

Like hepatitis A, Norovirus is commonly linked with ready-to-eat food. It has also been linked with contaminated water. Norovirus is often transferred to food when infected food handlers touch food or equipment with fingers that have feces on them.

Eating only a small amount of Norovirus can make a person sick. It is also very contagious. People become contagious within a few hours after eating it. The virus is often in a person's feces for days after symptoms have ended.

Food Commonly Linked with the Virus

- Ready-to-eat food
- Shellfish from contaminated water

Most Common Symptoms

- Vomiting
- Diarrhea
- Nausea
- Abdominal cramps

Other Prevention Measures

- Exclude food handlers who are vomiting or have diarrhea and have been diagnosed with Norovirus from the operation.
- Wash hands.
- Avoid bare-hand contact with ready-to-eat food.
- Purchase shellfish from approved, reputable suppliers.

Pathogens	Bacteria	Viruses	Parasites	Fungi	Biological Toxins
— How Contamination Occurs — Symptoms of a Foodborne Illness — The Big Six	— General Information about Bacteria — What Bacteria Need to Grow — Bacterial Growth — Spores — Major Foodborne Bacteria	— General Information about Viruses — Major Foodborne Viruses	— Characteristics of Parasites — Major Foodborne Illnesses Caused by Parasites	— Mold — Yeast	— Seafood Toxins — Mushroom Toxins — Plant Toxins

PARASITES

An illness from a parasite is not as common as one caused by a virus or bacteria. However, it is still important to understand these pathogens to prevent the foodborne illnesses they cause.

Characteristics of Parasites

Parasites share some basic characteristics.

Location   Parasites cannot grow in food. They require a host to live and reproduce.

Sources   Parasites are commonly associated with seafood, wild game, and food processed with contaminated water, such as produce.

Prevention measure   The most important way to prevent foodborne illnesses from parasites is to purchase food from approved, reputable suppliers. Cooking food to required minimum internal temperatures is also important. Also, make sure that fish that will be served raw or undercooked has been correctly frozen by the manufacturer.

Major Foodborne Illnesses Caused by Parasites

For each major foodborne illness caused by parasites, you should understand the following characteristics:

- Common source
- Food commonly linked with it
- Most common symptoms
- Most important prevention measures

The table on page 2-21 will help you recognize the similarities and differences among foodborne illnesses caused by parasites. It will help you remember each parasite as well.

Purchasing from Approved, Reputable Suppliers

These parasites can be prevented by purchasing products from approved, reputable suppliers:

- *Anisakis simplex*   page 2-22
- *Cryptosporidium parvum*   page 2-22
- *Giardia duodenalis*   page 2-23
- *Cyclospora cayetanensis*   page 2-23

Key Point

The most important way to prevent foodborne illnesses from parasites is to purchase food from approved, reputable suppliers.

Major Foodborne Parasites

			Most Important Prevention Measure: Controlling time and temperature	Preventing cross-contamination	Practicing personal hygiene	Purchasing from approved, reputable suppliers			
Parasite						*Anisakis simplex*	*Cryptosporidium parvum*	*Giardia duodenalis*	*Cyclospora cayetanensis*
Parasite Characteristics	Commonly Linked Food	Poultry							
		Eggs							
		Meat							
		Fish				●			
		Shellfish							
		Ready-to-eat food							
		Produce					●	●	●
		Rice/grains							
		Milk/dairy products							
		Contaminated water					●	●	●
	Most Common Symptoms	Diarrhea					●	●	●
		Abdominal pain/cramps					●	●	●
		Nausea					●	●	●
		Vomiting							
		Fever						●	●
		Headache							
	Prevention Measures	Handwashing					●	●	●
		Cooking				●			
		Holding							
		Cooling							
		Reheating							
		Approved suppliers				●	●	●	●
		Excluding food handlers					●	●	●
		Preventing cross-contamination							

Most Important Prevention Measure: Purchasing from Approved, Reputable Suppliers

Parasite *Anisakis simplex (ANN-ih-SAHK-iss SIM-plex)*

Illness **Anisakiasis** *(ANN-ih-SAH-KYE-ah-sis)*

People can get sick when they eat raw or undercooked fish containing this parasite.

Food Commonly Linked with the Parasite	**Most Common Symptoms**	**Other Prevention Measures**
• Raw and undercooked fish • Herring • Cod • Halibut • Mackerel • Pacific salmon	• Tingling in throat • Coughing up worms	• Cook fish to minimum internal temperatures. • If serving raw or undercooked fish, purchase sushi-grade fish that has been frozen to the correct time-temperature requirements.

Parasite *Cryptosporidium parvum (KRIP-TOH-spor-ID-ee-um PAR-vum)*

Illness **Cryptosporidiosis** *(KRIP-TOH-spor-id-ee-O-sis)*

Photo courtesy of Boskovich Farms, Inc.

Cryptosporidium parvum can be found in the feces of infected people. Food handlers can transfer it to food when they touch food with fingers that have feces on them. Day-care and medical communities have been frequent locations of person-to-person spread of this parasite. Symptoms will be more severe in people with weakened immune systems.

Food Commonly Linked with the Parasite	**Most Common Symptoms**	**Other Prevention Measures**
• Contaminated water • Produce	• Watery diarrhea • Abdominal cramps • Nausea • Weight loss	• Use correctly treated water. • Keep food handlers with diarrhea out of the operation. • Wash hands.

Parasite *Giardia duodenalis* (jee-ARE-dee-uh do-WAH-den-AL-is), **also known as** *G. lamblia* **or** *G. intestinalis*
Illness **Giardiasis** (JEE-are-DYE-uh-sis)

Photo courtesy of Boskovich Farms, Inc.

Giardia duodenalis can be found in the feces of infected people. Food handlers can transfer the parasite to food when they touch food with fingers that have feces on them.

Food Commonly Linked with the Parasite	Most Common Symptoms	Other Prevention Measures
• Incorrectly treated water • Produce	Initially • Fever Later • Diarrhea • Abdominal cramps • Nausea	• Use correctly treated water. • Keep food handlers with diarrhea out of the operation. • Wash hands.

Parasite *Cyclospora cayetanensis* (SI-klo-spor-uh KI-uh-te-NEN-sis)
Illness **Cyclosporiasis** (SI-klo-spor-I-uh-sis)

Cyclospora cayetanensis is a parasite that has been found in contaminated water and has been associated with produce irrigated or washed with contaminated water. It can also be found in the feces of infected people. Food handlers can transfer the parasite to food when they touch it with fingers containing feces. For this reason, food handlers with diarrhea must be excluded from the operation. It is also critical to purchase produce from approved, reputable suppliers.

Food Commonly Linked with the Parasite	Most Common Symptoms	Other Prevention Measures
• Incorrectly treated water • Produce such as berries, lettuce, or basil	• Nausea • Abdominal cramps • Mild fever • Diarrhea alternating with constipation • Loss of weight • Loss of appetite	• Purchase produce from approved, reputable suppliers. • Keep food handlers with diarrhea out of the operation. • Wash hands.

Pathogens	Bacteria	Viruses	Parasites	Fungi	Biological Toxins
— How Contamination Occurs — Symptoms of a Foodborne Illness — The Big Six	— General Information about Bacteria — What Bacteria Need to Grow — Bacterial Growth — Spores — Major Foodborne Bacteria	— General Information about Viruses — Major Foodborne Viruses	— Characteristics of Parasites — Major Foodborne Illnesses Caused by Parasites	— Mold — Yeast	— Seafood Toxins — Mushroom Toxins — Plant Toxins

FUNGI

So far, you have learned about pathogens that cause foodborne illnesses. Fungi are pathogens that only sometimes make people sick. Mostly, they spoil food. They are found in air, dirt, plants, water, and some food. Mold and yeast are examples.

Mold

Molds share some basic characteristics.

Effects   Molds spoil food and sometimes cause illness.

Toxins   Some molds produce toxins, such as aflatoxins.

Growth   Molds grow under almost any condition. They grow particularly well in acidic food with low water activity, such as jams, jellies, and cured, salty meat (e.g., ham, bacon, and salami).

Temperature   Cooler or freezer temperatures may slow the growth of molds, but they do not kill them.

Prevention measure   Some molds produce toxins that can cause allergic reactions, nervous system disorders, and kidney and liver damage. For example, aflatoxin, produced by the molds *Aspergillus flavus* and *Aspergillus parasticus*, can cause liver disease. Food such as corn and corn products, peanuts and peanut products, cottonseed, milk, and tree nuts (such as Brazil nuts, pecans, pistachio nuts, and walnuts) have been associated with aflatoxins.

Throw out all moldy food, unless the mold is a natural part of the product (e.g., cheese such as Brie, Camembert, and Gorgonzola). The FDA recommends cutting away moldy areas in hard cheese—at least one inch (2.5 centimeters) around them. You can also use this procedure on food, such as salami and firm fruit and vegetables.

Yeast

Yeasts share some basic characteristics.

Signs of spoilage   Yeasts can spoil food quickly. Signs of spoilage can include a smell or taste of alcohol. The yeast itself may look like a white or pink discoloration or slime, as show in the photo at left. It also may bubble.

Growth   Like molds, yeasts grow well in acidic food with little moisture, such as jellies, jams, syrup, honey, and fruit or fruit juice.

Prevention measure   Throw out any food that has been spoiled by yeast.

Pathogens	Bacteria	Viruses	Parasites	Fungi	Biological Toxins
— How Contamination Occurs — Symptoms of a Foodborne Illness — The Big Six	— General Information about Bacteria — What Bacteria Need to Grow — Bacterial Growth — Spores — Major Foodborne Bacteria	— General Information about Viruses — Major Foodborne Viruses	— Characteristics of Parasites — Major Foodborne Illnesses Caused by Parasites	— Mold — Yeast	— Seafood Toxins — Mushroom Toxins — Plant Toxins

BIOLOGICAL TOXINS

You learned earlier that most foodborne illnesses are caused by pathogens, a form of biological contamination. But you also must be aware of biological toxins or poisons that can make people sick.

Seafood, plant, and mushroom toxins can all cause illness. You should know what these toxins are and which illnesses they can cause. Most important, you should understand how to prevent them.

Seafood Toxins

Seafood toxins cannot be smelled or tasted. They also cannot be destroyed by freezing or cooking once they form in food. There are two groups of seafood toxins.

Fish toxins   Some fish toxins are a natural part of the fish. These are called systemic toxins. Puffer fish, moray eels, and freshwater minnows all produce them. Because of the extreme risk it poses, puffer fish should not be served unless the chef has been licensed to prep it.

Other toxins are made by pathogens on the fish. Some fish can also become contaminated when they eat smaller fish that have eaten a toxin.

Shellfish toxins   Shellfish, such as oysters, can be contaminated when they eat marine algae that have a toxin.

Major Seafood Toxins

For each major seafood toxin, you should understand the following characteristics:

- Common source
- Food commonly linked with it
- Most common symptoms
- Most important prevention measures

The table on page 2-26 will help you recognize the similarities and differences among seafood toxins. It will help you remember each seafood toxin as well.

Purchasing from Approved, Reputable Suppliers

These toxins can be prevented by purchasing products from approved, reputable suppliers:

- Histamine   page 2-27
- Ciguatoxin   page 2-27
- Saxitoxin   page 2-28
- Brevetoxin   page 2-28
- Domoic acid   page 2-29

Major Seafood Toxins

Most Important Prevention Measure			Controlling time and temperature	Preventing cross-contamination	Practicing personal hygiene	Purchasing from approved, reputable suppliers				
Seafood Toxin						Histamine	Ciguatoxin	Saxitoxin	Brevetoxin	Domoic acid
Seafood Toxin Characteristics	Commonly Linked Food	Fish				•	•			
		Shellfish						•	•	•
	Most Common Symptoms	Diarrhea				•		•	•	•
		Abdominal pain/cramps								•
		Nausea					•	•		
		Vomiting				•	•	•	•	•
		Fever								
		Headache				•				
		Neurological symptoms				•	•	•	•	•
	Prevention Measures	Handwashing								
		Cooking								
		Holding				•				
		Cooling								
		Reheating								
		Approved suppliers				•	•	•	•	•
		Excluding food handlers								
		Preventing cross-contamination								

Most Important Prevention Measure: Purchasing from Approved, Reputable Suppliers

Toxin	Histamine (HISS-ta-meen)
Illness	Scombroid poisoning (SKOM-broyd)

Histamine poisoning can occur when high levels of histamine in scombroid and other species of fish are eaten. When the fish are time-temperature abused, bacteria on the fish make the toxin. It cannot be destroyed by freezing, cooking, smoking, or curing.

Food Commonly Linked with the Toxin

- Tuna
- Bonito
- Mackerel
- Mahimahi

Most Common Symptoms

Initially

- Reddening of the face and neck
- Sweating
- Headache
- Burning or tingling sensation in the mouth or throat

Possibly later

- Diarrhea
- Vomiting

Other Prevention Measures

- Prevent time-temperature abuse during storage and prepping.

Toxin	Ciguatoxin (SIG-wa-TOX-in)
Illness	Ciguatera fish poisoning (SIG-wa-TAIR-uh)

Ciguatoxin is found in some marine algae. The toxin builds up in certain fish when they eat smaller fish that have eaten the toxic algae. Ciguatoxin cannot be detected by smell or taste. It is not eliminated by cooking or freezing the fish. Symptoms may last months or years depending on how severe the illness is.

Food Commonly Linked with the Toxin

Predatory tropical reef fish from the Pacific Ocean, the western part of the Indian Ocean, and the Caribbean Sea.

- Barracuda
- Grouper
- Jacks
- Snapper

Most Common Symptoms

- Reversal of hot and cold sensations
- Nausea
- Vomiting
- Tingling in fingers, lips, or toes
- Joint and muscle pain

Other Prevention Measures

- Purchase predatory tropical reef fish from approved, reputable suppliers.

Toxin   Saxitoxin *(SAX-ih-TOX-in)*
Illness   Paralytic shellfish poisoning (PSP) *(PAIR-ah-LIT-ik)*

Some types of shellfish can become contaminated as they filter toxic algae from the water. People can get sick with paralytic shellfish poisoning (PSP) when they eat these shellfish. Saxitoxin cannot be smelled or tasted. It is not destroyed by cooking or freezing. Death from paralysis may result if high levels of the toxin are eaten.

Food Commonly Linked with the Toxin

Shellfish found in colder waters, such as those of the Pacific and New England coasts.

- Clams
- Mussels
- Oysters
- Scallops

Most Common Symptoms

- Numbness
- Tingling of the mouth, face, arms, and legs
- Dizziness
- Nausea
- Vomiting
- Diarrhea

Other Prevention Measures

- Purchase shellfish from approved, reputable suppliers.

Toxin   Brevetoxin *(BREV-ih-TOX-in)*
Illness   Neurotoxic shellfish poisoning (NSP) *(NUR-o-TOX-ik)*

Some types of shellfish can become contaminated as they filter toxic algae from the water. People can get sick with neurotoxic shellfish poisoning (NSP) when they eat these shellfish. Brevetoxin cannot be smelled or tasted. It is not destroyed by cooking or freezing.

Food Commonly Linked with the Toxin

Shellfish found in the warmer waters of the west coast of Florida, the Gulf of Mexico, and the Caribbean Sea.

- Clams
- Mussels
- Oysters

Most Common Symptoms

- Tingling and numbness of the lips, tongue, and throat
- Dizziness
- Reversal of hot and cold sensations
- Vomiting
- Diarrhea

Other Prevention Measures

- Purchase shellfish from approved, reputable suppliers.

Toxin	Domoic acid *(duh-MO-ik)*
Illness	Amnesic shellfish poisoning (ASP) *(am-NEE-zik)*

 Some types of shellfish can become contaminated as they filter toxic algae from the water. People can get sick with amnesic shellfish poisoning (ASP) when they eat these shellfish. The severity of symptoms depends on the amount of toxin eaten and the health of the person. Domoic acid cannot be smelled or tasted. It is not destroyed by cooking or freezing.

Food Commonly Linked with the Toxin

Shellfish found in the coastal waters of the Pacific Northwest and the east coast of Canada.

- Clams
- Mussels
- Oysters
- Scallops

Most Common Symptoms

Initially

- Vomiting
- Diarrhea
- Abdominal pain

Possibly later

- Confusion
- Memory loss
- Disorientation
- Seizure
- Coma

Other Prevention Measures

- Purchase shellfish from approved, reputable suppliers.

Mushroom Toxins

Foodborne illnesses linked with mushrooms are almost always caused by eating toxic wild mushrooms collected by amateur hunters. Most cases happen because toxic mushrooms are mistaken for edible ones. The symptoms of illness depend on the type of toxic mushrooms eaten.

Mushroom toxins are not destroyed by cooking or freezing. Use only mushrooms and mushroom products purchased from approved, reputable suppliers, as shown in the photo at left.

Plant Toxins

Plant toxins are another form of biological contamination. Illnesses from plant toxins usually happen because an operation has purchased plants from an unapproved source. Some illnesses, however, are caused by plants that have not been cooked correctly. The following are examples of items that have made people sick:

- Toxic plants, such as fool's parsley or wild turnips, mistaken for the edible version
- Honey from bees allowed to harvest nectar from toxic plants
- Undercooked kidney beans

Purchase plants and items made with plants only from approved, reputable suppliers. Then cook and hold dishes made from these items correctly.

SUMMARY

- Microorganisms are small, living organisms that can be seen only through a microscope. While many are harmless, some can make people sick. These are called pathogens. Understanding pathogens and the toxins (poisons) that some produce is the first step to preventing foodborne illnesses.

- Bacteria need certain conditions to grow. They include food, acidity, temperature, time, oxygen, and moisture (FAT TOM). Food items with the correct FAT TOM conditions favor greater bacterial growth. They are also often involved in foodborne-illness outbreaks.

- Bacteria can usually be controlled by keeping food out of the temperature danger zone. Some bacteria can change into spores to preserve themselves when lacking nutrients. Others can produce toxins in food that can make people sick.

- Viruses are the leading cause of foodborne illness. They cannot grow in food, but they can survive refrigeration and freezer temperatures. Good personal hygiene helps prevent the spread of viruses.

- Parasites need to be in the meat of another animal to survive. They can contaminate both food and water—particularly water used to irrigate produce. Purchasing products from approved, reputable suppliers helps prevent foodborne illnesses caused by parasites.

- Fungi, such as molds and yeasts, mostly spoil food. However, some molds can produce harmful toxins. Food containing mold should always be discarded unless the mold is a natural part of the product. Yeasts can spoil food quickly. Food spoiled by yeast should also be thrown out.

- Biological toxins such as seafood toxins, plant toxins, and mushroom toxins can make people sick.

- Fish toxins can be a natural part of the fish. Other toxins are made by pathogens on the fish. Some also occur when fish eat smaller fish containing the toxin. Shellfish, such as oysters, can likewise become contaminated when they eat marine algae that have a toxin.

- Foodborne illnesses linked with mushrooms are almost always caused by eating toxic wild mushrooms collected by amateur hunters. Purchasing products from approved, reputable suppliers helps prevent these types of foodborne illnesses.

Apply Your Knowledge

Use these questions to review the concepts presented in this chapter.

DISCUSSION QUESTIONS

1. What are the six conditions that support the growth of bacteria?

2. What two FAT TOM conditions are easiest for an operation to control?

3. How can an outbreak of Norovirus be prevented?

4. What measures should be taken to prevent a seafood-specific foodborne illness?

5. What six pathogens have been dubbed the "Big Six"? Why have they been singled out by the FDA?

For answers, please turn to the Answer Key.

Apply Your Knowledge

Rice Makes Children Sick

CASE IN POINT

A day-care center decided to prepare stir-fried rice to serve for lunch the next day. The rice was cooked to the correct temperature at 1:00 p.m. It was then covered and placed on a countertop, where it was allowed to cool at room temperature. At 6:00 p.m., the cook placed the rice in the cooler. At 9:00 a.m. the following day, the rice was combined with the other ingredients for stir-fried rice and cooked to 165°F (74°C) for at least 15 seconds. The cook covered the rice and left it on the stove until noon when she reheated it. Within an hour of eating the rice, several of the children complained that they were nauseous and began to vomit.

1. What pathogen caused the illness and why?

For answers, please turn to the Answer Key.

Study Questions

Circle the best answer to each question.

1. What are the most common symptoms of a foodborne illness?

   A   Diarrhea, vomiting, fever, nausea, abdominal cramps, and dizziness

   B   Diarrhea, vomiting, fever, nausea, abdominal cramps, and headache

   C   Diarrhea, vomiting, fever, nausea, abdominal cramps, and jaundice

   D   Diarrhea, vomiting, fever, nausea, abdominal cramps, and tiredness

2. What is the most important way to prevent a foodborne illness from bacteria?

   A   Control time and temperature.

   B   Prevent cross-contamination.

   C   Practice good personal hygiene.

   D   Practice correct cleaning and sanitizing.

3. Shiga toxin-producing *E. coli* is commonly linked with what type of food?

   A   Potato salad

   B   Thick stews

   C   Dairy products

   D   Raw ground beef

4. What is the most important way to prevent a foodborne illness from viruses?

   A   Control time and temperature.

   B   Prevent cross-contamination.

   C   Practice good personal hygiene.

   D   Practice correct cleaning and sanitizing.

5. A customer called an operation and told the manager about getting sick after eating there. The customer complained of vomiting and diarrhea a few hours after eating the raw oysters. What pathogen probably caused the illness?

   A   Norovirus

   B   *Shigella* spp.

   C   *Salmonella* Typhi

   D   Shiga toxin-producing *E. coli*

6. Parasites are commonly linked with what type of food?

   A   Rice

   B   Poultry

   C   Seafood

   D   Canned food

7 A customer had a reversal of hot and cold sensations after eating seafood. What most likely caused the illness?

A Toxin

B Virus

C Bacteria

D Parasite

8 Which pathogens are found in high numbers in an infected person's feces, are highly infectious, and can cause severe illness?

A Histamine, aflatoxin, brevetoxin, ciguatoxin, saxitoxin, and domoic acid

B Hepatitis A, Norovirus, *Salmonella* Typhi, nontyphoidal *Salmonella*, *Shigella* spp., and shiga toxin-producing *E. coli*

C *Anisakis simplex*, *Cryptosporidium parvum*, *Giardia duodenalis*, *Vibrio vulnificus*, and *Clostridium botulinum*

D *Bacillus cereus*, *Listeria monocytogenes*, *Staphylococcus aureus*, *Clostridium perfringens*, *Campylobacter jejuni*, and *Vibrio parahaemolyticus*

9 Which FAT TOM condition will a foodservice operation be most able to control?

A Acidity

B Time

C Oxygen

D Moisture

10 Which pathogen can be controlled by washing hands and controlling flies inside and outside the operation?

A Hepatitis A

B *Shigella* spp.

C *Clostridium botulinum*

D *Vibrio parahaemolyticus*

For answers, please turn to the Answer Key.

3 Contamination, Food Allergens, and Foodborne Illness

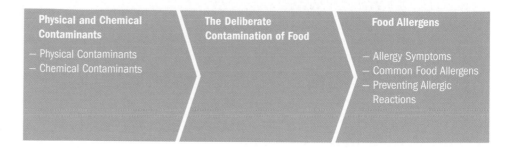

Physical and Chemical Contaminants
— Physical Contaminants
— Chemical Contaminants

The Deliberate Contamination of Food

Food Allergens
— Allergy Symptoms
— Common Food Allergens
— Preventing Allergic Reactions

INSIDE THIS CHAPTER

- Physical and Chemical Contaminants
- The Deliberate Contamination of Food
- Food Allergens

OBJECTIVES

After completing this chapter, you should be able to identify the following:

- Physical and chemical contaminants and methods of prevention
- Points in the operation where food is at risk from deliberate contamination
- The most common food allergens and their associated symptoms
- Methods of preventing allergic reactions

KEY TERMS

- Food defense
- Food allergen
- Cross-contact

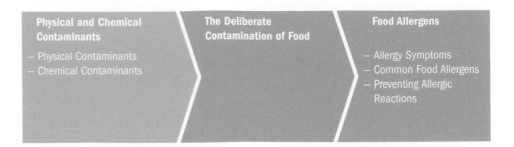

Physical and Chemical Contaminants
— Physical Contaminants
— Chemical Contaminants

The Deliberate Contamination of Food

Food Allergens
— Allergy Symptoms
— Common Food Allergens
— Preventing Allergic Reactions

PHYSICAL AND CHEMICAL CONTAMINANTS

Although biological contaminants are the leading cause of foodborne illness, physical and chemical contaminants also pose a risk to food safety.

Physical Contaminants

Food can become contaminated when objects get into it. It can also happen when natural objects are left in food, such as bones in a fish fillet.

Sources   Some common objects that can get into food include:

- Metal shavings from cans, as shown in the photo at left
- Wood
- Fingernails
- Staples
- Bandages
- Glass
- Jewelry
- Dirt

Naturally occurring objects, such as fruit pits and bones, can also be contaminants.

Symptoms   Bleeding and pain may be the most outward symptoms. Mild to fatal injuries are possible. This could include:

- Cuts
- Dental damage
- Choking

Prevention   Purchase food from approved, reputable suppliers to prevent physical contamination. Closely inspect the food you receive. Take steps to make sure no physical contaminants can get into it. This includes making sure that food handlers practice good personal hygiene.

Chemical Contaminants

Many people have gotten sick after consuming food and beverages contaminated with foodservice chemicals. To keep food safe, follow these guidelines.

Sources   Chemicals can contaminate food if they are used or stored the wrong way. The following chemicals can be risks:

- Cleaners
- Sanitizers
- Polishes
- Machine lubricants
- Pesticides
- Deodorizers
- First-aid products
- Health and beauty products, such as hand lotions and hairsprays

Certain types of kitchenware and equipment can be risks for chemical contamination. These include items made from pewter, copper, zinc, and some types of painted pottery. An example is shown at left. These materials are not food grade and can contaminate food. This is especially true when acidic food, such as tomato sauce, is held in them.

Symptoms   Symptoms vary depending on the chemical consumed. Most illnesses occur within minutes. Vomiting and diarrhea are typical. If an illness is suspected, call the emergency number in your area and the Poison Control number. Consult the chemical's Material Safety Data Sheet (MSDS), which contains important safety information about the chemical.

Prevention   The chemicals you use must be approved for use in a foodservice operation. They must also be necessary for the maintenance of the facility. Here are some ways to protect food and food-contact surfaces from contamination by chemicals:

- Purchase chemicals from approved, reputable suppliers.
- Store chemicals away from prep areas, food-storage areas, and service areas. Chemicals must be separated from food and food-contact surfaces by spacing and partitioning. Chemicals must never be stored above food or food-contact surfaces.
- Use chemicals for their intended use and follow manufacturer's directions.
- Only handle food with equipment and utensils approved for foodservice use.

- Make sure the manufacturer's labels on original chemical containers are readable, as shown in the photo at left.
- Keep MSDS current, and make sure they are accessible to staff at all times.
- Follow the manufacturer's directions and local regulatory requirements when throwing out chemicals.

3

Physical and Chemical Contaminants	The Deliberate Contamination of Food	Food Allergens
— Physical Contaminants — Chemical Contaminants		— Allergy Symptoms — Common Food Allergens — Preventing Allergic Reactions

Technology

Biometric Employee IDs

Successful food defense relies on vigilance from all employees in a unit. One emerging technology—biometric scanning—could eliminate the need for physical employee ID cards (which can be lost or stolen) and help to prevent unauthorized people from entering secure areas of a business. Placed at the entries of secured areas, fingerprint identification systems allow employees to enter only after their fingerprint has been read and accepted by the scanner. Across a number of industries, time clocks have also recently begun to use fingerprint scanning to record hours worked. Machines that scan hand veins have also gained in popularity.

It is important to note that not all states currently approve biometric systems for use in these ways, largely due to privacy and data protection concerns for the employees. Manufacturers continue to work to improve the security of the technology.

THE DELIBERATE CONTAMINATION OF FOOD

Certain people could try to tamper with your food. This includes terrorists or activists, current or former staff, vendors, or competitors. They may use biological, chemical, or physical contaminants. They may even use radioactive materials. Attacks might occur anywhere in the food supply chain. But they are usually focused on a specific food item, process, or business.

The best way to protect food is to make it very difficult to tamper with. A food defense program should address the points in your operation where food is at risk. The Food and Drug Administration (FDA) has created a tool that can be used to develop a food defense program. It is based on the acronym A.L.E.R.T. It can be used to help you identify the points in your operation where food is at risk.

Assure   Make sure that products you receive are from safe sources:
- Supervise product deliveries.
- Use approved suppliers who practice food defense.
- Request that delivery vehicles are locked or sealed.

Look   Monitor the security of products in the facility:
- Limit access to prep and storage areas. Locking storage areas is one way to do this.
- Create a system for handling damaged products.
- Store chemicals in a secure location.
- Train staff to spot food defense threats.

Employees   Know who is in your facility:
- Limit access to prep and storage areas.
- Identify all visitors and verify credentials.
- Conduct background checks on staff.

Reports   Keep information related to food defense accessible:
- Receiving logs
- Office files and documents
- Staff files
- Random food defense self-inspections

Threat   Identify what you will do and who you will contact if there is suspicious activity or a threat at your operation:
- Hold any product you suspect to be contaminated.
- Contact your regulatory authority immediately.
- Maintain an emergency contact list.

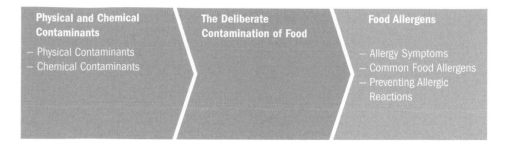

Physical and Chemical Contaminants	The Deliberate Contamination of Food	Food Allergens
— Physical Contaminants — Chemical Contaminants		— Allergy Symptoms — Common Food Allergens — Preventing Allergic Reactions

FOOD ALLERGENS

A food allergen is a protein in a food or ingredient that some people are sensitive to. These proteins occur naturally. When enough of an allergen is eaten, the immune system mistakenly considers it harmful and attacks the food protein. This can result in an allergic reaction. There are specific signs that a customer is having an allergic reaction. To protect your customers, you should be able to recognize these signs and know what to do. You also should know the types of food that most often cause allergic reactions to help prevent them from happening.

Allergy Symptoms

Depending on the person, an allergic reaction can happen just after the food is eaten or several hours later. This reaction could include some or all of these symptoms:

- Nausea

- Wheezing or shortness of breath

- Hives or itchy rashes, as shown in the photo at left

- Swelling of various parts of the body, including the face, eyes, hands, or feet

- Vomiting and/or diarrhea

- Abdominal pain

Initially symptoms may be mild, but they can become serious quickly. In severe cases, anaphylaxis—a severe allergic reaction that can lead to death—may result. If a customer is having an allergic reaction to food, call the emergency number in your area and inform them of the allergic reaction.

Common Food Allergens

You and your staff must be aware of the most common food allergens and the menu items that contain them.

While more than 160 food items can cause allergic reactions, just eight of these account for 90 percent of all reactions in the United States. These eight food items are known as the Big Eight.

- Milk

- Eggs

- Fish, such as bass, flounder, and cod

- Crustacean shellfish, such as crab, lobster, and shrimp

- Wheat

- Soy

- Peanuts

- Tree nuts, such as walnuts, and pecans

Preventing Allergic Reactions

Fifteen million Americans have a food allergy, and allergic reactions result in 200,000 emergency room visits every year. Both service staff and kitchen staff need to do their parts to avoid serving food containing allergens to these customers. These policies would also apply to addressing food sensitivities that a customer might mention, such as a gluten intolerance.

Service Staff

Your staff should be able to tell customers about menu items that contain potential allergens. At minimum, have one person available per shift to answer customers' questions about menu items. When customers say they have a food allergy, your staff should take it seriously. When working with a customer to place an allergen special order, they must be able to do the following.

Describing dishes Tell customers how the item is prepared. Sauces, marinades, and garnishes often contain allergens. For example, peanut butter is sometimes used as a thickener in sauces or marinades. This information is critical to a customer with a peanut allergy.

Identifying ingredients Tell customers if the food they are allergic to is in the menu item. Identify any "secret" ingredients. For example, your operation may have a house specialty that includes an allergen.

Suggesting items Suggest menu items that do not contain the food that the customer is allergic to.

Identify the allergen special order Clearly mark or otherwise indicate the order for the guest with the identified food allergy. This is done to inform the kitchen staff of the guest's food allergy.

Delivering food Confirm the allergen special order with the kitchen staff when picking up the food. Make sure no garnishes or other items containing the allergen touch the plate. Food should be hand-delivered to guests with allergies. Delivering food separately from the other food delivered to a table, as shown in the photo at left, will help prevent contact with food allergens.

Kitchen Staff

Staff must make sure that allergens are not transferred from food containing an allergen to the food served to the customer. This is called cross-contact. Here are a few examples of how it can happen:

- Cooking different types of food in the same fryer oil can cause cross-contact. In the photo at left, shrimp allergens could be transferred to the chicken being fried in the same oil.

- Letting food touch on surfaces, equipment, or utensils that have touched allergens can cause cross-contact. For example, putting chocolate chip cookies on the same parchment paper that was used for peanut butter cookies can transfer some of the peanut allergen.

Food Labels

Food labels on the products that you purchase are an important tool to identify allergens in the operation. Federal law requires manufactured products containing one or more of the Big Eight allergens to clearly identify them on the ingredient label. The allergen may be included in the common name of the food, such as "buttermilk", or it may be shown in parentheses after the ingredient. Often, allergens will be shown in a contains statement.

How to Avoid Cross-Contact

Staff can avoid cross-contact by following these procedures:

- Check recipes and ingredient labels to confirm that the allergen is not present.

- Wash, rinse, and sanitize cookware, utensils, and equipment before prepping food, as shown at left. This includes food-prep surfaces. Some operations use a separate set of cooking utensils just for allergen special orders.

- Make sure the allergen does not touch anything for customers with food allergies, including food, beverages, utensils, equipment, and gloves.

- Wash your hands and change gloves before prepping food.

- Use separate fryers and cooking oils when frying food for customers with food allergies.

- Label food packaged on-site for retail sale. Name all major allergens on the label and follow any additional labeling requirements.

SUMMARY

- Physical contamination can occur when foreign objects get into food. It can also take place when natural objects are left in food, such as the bones in a fish fillet.

- To prevent contamination, closely inspect the food you receive. Take steps to make sure food will not become physically contaminated during its flow through your operation.

- Chemical contaminants can come from many common substances within an operation. To prevent contamination, use only utensils and equipment that are made for handling food. Also store chemicals away from food, utensils, and equipment used for food. Follow the chemical manufacturers' directions for use as well.

- Take steps to prevent the deliberate contamination of food. The key is to make food very difficult to tamper with at your operation. A food defense program should address where food can be at risk.

- Managers and staff should be aware of the most common food allergens, which include milk, eggs, fish, crustacean shellfish, wheat, soy, peanuts, and tree nuts.

- Service staff should be able to tell customers about menu items that contain potential allergens. Kitchen staff need to make sure that allergens are not transferred from food containing an allergen to food being served to a customer.

 Resources

FDA

The Food and Drug Administration (FDA) is a government agency within the Department of Health and Human Services. The FDA is responsible for protecting and promoting public health through the regulation and supervision of human and veterinary drugs, vaccines, medical devices, cosmetics, dietary supplements, tobacco products, and food. The Center for Food Safety and Applied Nutrition is the part of the FDA that is responsible for a large amount of the analysis and recommendations made by the FDA regarding safe food.

While the FDA headquarters are in Maryland, the agency has over 200 field offices and 13 laboratories throughout the United States. In 2008, the FDA extended its scope of activities to offices in foreign countries, including China, India, and the United Kingdom, among others.

Learn more about the FDA through videos and FAQS on their site, fda.gov. You can find recalls and alerts, as well as approvals and clearances of certain products. Problems with food can also be reported.

Apply Your Knowledge

Use these questions to review the concepts presented in this chapter.

DISCUSSION QUESTIONS

1. What arc some ways to keep chemicals from contaminating food?

2. What are some ways to prevent the deliberate contamination of food?

3. What measures can be taken to help ensure the safety of customers with food allergies?

For answers, please turn to the Answer Key.

Apply Your Knowledge

The 1984 Rajneeshee Bioterror Attack

CASE IN POINT

In the fall of 1984, the single largest bioterrorist attack in the United States occurred in Oregon. It was carried out by members of a cult who had hoped to influence the turnout of a local election. They sprinkled *Salmonella* Typhimurium on salad bars at 10 local restaurants. As a result, over 750 people got sick, with 45 being hospitalized. The victims suffered from symptoms including fever, chills, diarrhea, nausea, and vomiting. Most had abdominal pain, diarrhea, and bloody stools. Fortunately, there were no fatalities. Those responsible for the attacks spread a liquid containing the pathogen over the food on the salad bars. They also poured the liquid into the salad dressing.

1. What could have been done to prevent what happened?

For answers, please turn to the Answer Key.

Study Questions

Circle the best answer to each question.

1. A food handler stored a sanitizer spray bottle on a shelf above the prep table that had just been sanitized. Throughout the day, the food handler used the sanitizer on the prep table, storing it in the same spot. What should the food handler have done differently?

   A   Stored the sanitizer bottle away from the prep area

   B   Stored the sanitizer bottle on the floor between uses

   C   Stored the sanitizer bottle on the prep table between uses

   D   Stored the sanitizer bottle with food supplies below the prep table

2. Eggs and peanuts are dangerous for people with which condition?

   A   FAT TOM

   B   Food allergies

   C   Chemical sensitivity

   D   Poor personal hygiene

3. Wheezing and shortness of breath are symptoms of what?

   A   Hepatitis A

   B   *Bacillus cereus*

   C   Allergic reaction

   D   Hemorrhagic colitis

4. What should food handlers do to prevent food allergens from being transferred to food?

   A   Clean and sanitize utensils before use.

   B   Buy from approved, reputable suppliers.

   C   Store cold food at 41°F (5°C) or lower.

   D   Label chemical containers correctly.

5. To prevent the deliberate contamination of food, a manager should know who is in the facility, monitor the security of products, keep information related to food security on file, and know

   A   when to register with the EPA.

   B   how to fill out an incident report.

   C   where to find MSDS in the operation.

   D   who to contact about suspicious activity.

For answers, please turn to the Answer Key.

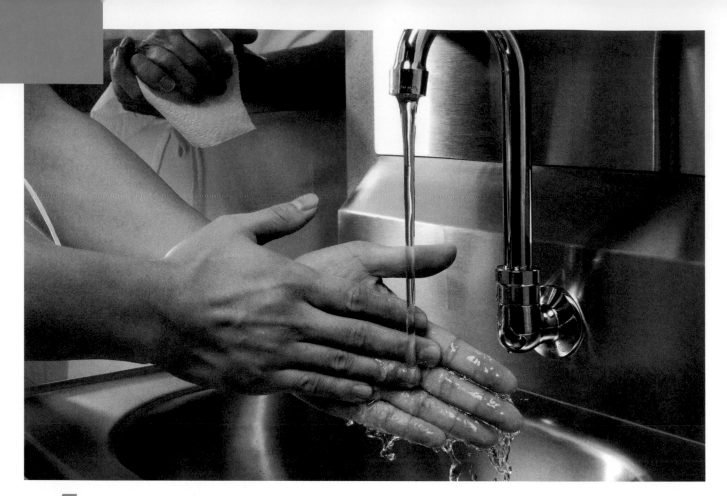

4 The Safe Food Handler

Personal Hygiene and Contamination	A Good Personal Hygiene Program
— How Food Handlers Can Contaminate Food — Diseases Not Transmitted through Food	— Handwashing — Hand Care — Single-Use Gloves — Other Good Personal Hygiene Practices — Reporting Health Issues

Case in POINT

Hepatitis A Scare

Hepatitis A vaccinations were offered to thousands of customers who had visited a local casual-dining operation in the Gulf Coast region of the United States. The vaccinations were made available by the local regulatory authority after a food handler at the operation tested positive for hepatitis A, exposing the customers to the virus. The identified food handler was responsible for preparing and setting up items on the salad bar. The food handler was excluded from work until approved to return by a physician and the regulatory authority. The local regulatory authority also worked with the operation's owners and management team to ensure they had all of the correct processes in place to protect customers and staff.

❶ What could have been done to prevent this situation from occurring in the first place?

For answers, please turn to the Answer Key.

INSIDE THIS CHAPTER

- Personal Hygiene and Contamination
- A Good Personal Hygiene Program

OBJECTIVES

After completing this chapter, you should be able to identify the following:

- How food handlers can contaminate food
- Correct handwashing procedure
- When and where hands should be washed
- Hand antiseptics and when to use them
- Hand-maintenance requirements including fingernail length, false fingernails, and nail polish
- Correct way to cover infected wounds
- The importance of avoiding bare-hand contact with ready-to-eat food
- How to use single-use gloves and when to change them
- Requirements for staff work attire
- Jewelry that poses a hazard to food safety
- Policies regarding eating, drinking, and smoking as they relate to food safety
- Criteria for excluding staff from the operation or restricting them from working with or around food
- Illnesses that need to be reported to the regulatory authority

KEY TERMS

- Carriers
- Hand antiseptics
- Finger cots
- Hair restraint

Personal Hygiene and Contamination	A Good Personal Hygiene Program
— How Food Handlers Can Contaminate Food — Diseases Not Transmitted through Food	— Handwashing — Hand Care — Single-Use Gloves — Other Good Personal Hygiene Practices — Reporting Health Issues

PERSONAL HYGIENE AND CONTAMINATION

Food handlers can contaminate food and cause customers to get sick at every step in the flow of food through the operation. Good personal hygiene is a critical protective measure against foodborne illness.

As a manager, you can minimize the risk of foodborne illness by carrying out the following responsibilities:

- Establishing specific personal hygiene policies
- Training food handlers on those policies and retraining them regularly
- Modeling correct behavior for food handlers at all times, as shown in the photo at left
- Supervising food safety practices at all times
- Revising policies according to changes in law and food safety science

It is important for staff to not only have the correct knowledge, skills, and attitudes toward personal hygiene; but also to know how they can contaminate food if they are not careful.

How Food Handlers Can Contaminate Food

You have learned that staff can make people sick by transferring pathogens to food they touch. These pathogens often come from the food handlers themselves. Food handlers can contaminate food when they have any of the following:

- A foodborne illness
- Symptoms, such as diarrhea, vomiting, or jaundice (a yellowing of the eyes or skin)
- Wounds that contain a pathogen
- Sneezing or coughing
- Contact with a person who is sick
- Unwashed hands after touching a contaminant

With some illnesses, a person may infect others before showing symptoms. For example, a person could spread hepatitis A for weeks before having any symptoms. With other illnesses, such as Norovirus, a person may infect others for days after symptoms are gone.

Key Point

With some illnesses, a person may infect others before showing any symptoms.

Some people also carry pathogens and infect others without getting sick themselves. These people are called carriers. The bacteria *Staphylococcus aureus* is carried in the nose of 30 to 50 percent of healthy adults. About 20 to 35 percent of healthy adults carry it on their skin as well. Food handlers transfer this bacteria to food when they touch the infected areas of their bodies and then touch food. This could happen in the photo at left.

The following scenarios show other ways in which staff can contaminate food:

- A deli food handler diagnosed with salmonellosis failed to inform his manager that he was sick. He was later determined to be the cause of an outbreak involving more than 200 customers through 12 different items.

- A food handler with diarrhea did not wash his hands after using the restroom. He made close to 5,000 people sick when he mixed a vat of buttercream frosting with his bare hands and arms.

Simple acts, such as running fingers through the hair, wiping or touching the nose, rubbing an ear, scratching the scalp, or touching a pimple or an infected wound can contaminate food. For this reason, food handlers need to monitor what they do with their hands.

Diseases Not Transmitted through Food

In recent years, the public has expressed growing concern over communicable diseases spread through intimate contact or by direct exchange of bodily fluids. Diseases such as Acquired Immune Deficiency Syndrome (AIDS), hepatitis B and C, and tuberculosis are not spread through food.

As a manager, you should be aware of the following laws concerning staff who have tested positive for the Human Immunodeficiency Virus (HIV) or who have tuberculosis or hepatitis B or C:

- The Americans with Disabilities Act (ADA) provides civil-rights protection to those who are HIV positive or who have hepatitis B. This prohibits employers from firing people or transferring them out of food-handling duties simply because they have these diseases.

- Employers should maintain the confidentiality of any staff who have an illness that is not foodborne.

Key Point

Diseases such as AIDS, hepatitis B and C, and tuberculosis are not spread through food.

Technology

Hand Sanitizers

Automatic hand-sanitizer dispensers detect the presence of hands, measure the same amount of sanitizer dispensed each time, and spray downward. The direction of the spray is important, because sanitizers that spray outward could disperse through the air, landing on food-contact surfaces and contaminating them.

Studies have shown that sanitizers can reduce the potential for cross-contamination by killing most disease-causing pathogens in 15 seconds. These sanitizers typically contain at least 60 percent alcohol, which has been identified by groups such as the Centers for Disease Control and Prevention as the minimum amount needed to kill many pathogens. Some non-alcohol sanitizers are also gaining in popularity.

The hand sanitizer market has seen tremendous growth in sales in recent years, due in part to large-scale health scares such as H1N1 flu. A 2011 report by Global Industry Analysts, Inc., states that the U.S. market for hand sanitizers will exceed $400 million by 2015.

Remember: hand sanitizers should be used only *after* washing hands correctly; they don't replace handwashing!

Personal Hygiene and Contamination	A Good Personal Hygiene Program
— How Food Handlers Can Contaminate Food — Diseases Not Transmitted through Food	— Handwashing — Hand Care — Single-Use Gloves — Other Good Personal Hygiene Practices — Reporting Health Issues

A GOOD PERSONAL HYGIENE PROGRAM

Good personal hygiene is key to the prevention of foodborne illness. Customers expect it as well. When staff have the correct knowledge and attitudes about personal hygiene, the operation is closer to keeping food safe.

A personal hygiene program should include these hygiene policies:

- Following hygienic hand practices:
  - Handwashing
  - Hand care
  - Glove use
  - Preventing bare-hand contact with ready-to-eat food
- Maintaining personal cleanliness
- Wearing clean and appropriate clothing, restraining hair, and removing jewelry
- Avoiding certain habits and actions
- Maintaining good health
- Covering wounds
- Reporting health issues

Train your staff on these policies and then enforce them.

Handwashing

Every day our hands touch surfaces covered with pathogens that we cannot see. Remember, even healthy people can spread pathogens. For this reason, handwashing is the most important part of personal hygiene. It may seem basic and routine. However, many food handlers fail to wash their hands correctly and as often as needed. You must train your food handlers to wash their hands, and then you must monitor them.

Where to Wash Hands

Hands need to be washed in a sink designated for handwashing. Do not wash hands in sinks for food prep, dishwashing, or utility services.

How to Wash Hands

To wash hands or prosthetic devices correctly, follow the steps below. The whole process should take at least 20 seconds.

1 Wet hands and arms.

Use running water as hot as you can comfortably stand. It should be at least 100°F (38°C).

2 Apply soap.

Apply enough to build up a good lather.

3 Scrub hands and arms vigorously.

Scrub them for 10 to 15 seconds. Clean under fingernails and between fingers.

4 Rinse hands and arms thoroughly.

Use running warm water.

5 Dry hands and arms.

Use a single-use paper towel or a hand dryer. Consider using a paper towel to turn off the faucet and to open the door when leaving the restroom.

When to Wash Hands

Food handlers must wash their hands before they start work. They must also do it after the following activities:

- Using the restroom. Food handlers carrying pathogens, such as Norovirus, can transfer them to food if they do not wash their hands after using the restroom.
- Handling raw meat, poultry, and seafood (before and after).
- Touching the hair, face, or body.
- Sneezing, coughing, or using a tissue.
- Eating, drinking, smoking, or chewing gum or tobacco.
- Handling chemicals that might affect food safety.
- Taking out garbage.
- Clearing tables or busing dirty dishes.
- Touching clothing or aprons.
- Handling money.
- Leaving and returning to the kitchen/prep area.
- Handling service animals or aquatic animals.
- Touching anything else that may contaminate hands, such as dirty equipment, work surfaces, or wiping cloths. The food handler in the photo at left should wash his hands after using the wiping cloth to wipe the prep counter.

Hand Antiseptics

Hand antiseptics are liquids or gels that help lower the number of pathogens on skin. If used, they must comply with the Code of Federal Regulations (CFR) and Food and Drug Administration (FDA) standards. Hand antiseptics must only be used after handwashing and not in place of it. Once an antiseptic is applied, food handlers should not touch food or equipment until the substance has dried.

Hand Care

In addition to washing, hands need other care to prevent the spread of pathogens. Make sure food handlers follow these guidelines.

Fingernail length   Keep fingernails short and clean, as shown in the photo at left. Long fingernails may be hard to keep clean and can rip gloves. They can also chip and become physical contaminants.

Fingernails should be trimmed and filed. This will allow nails to be cleaned easily. Ragged nails can be hard to keep clean. They may also hold pathogens and break off—becoming physical contaminants.

False fingernails   Do not wear false fingernails. They can be hard to keep clean. They can also break off into food. Some regulatory authorities allow false nails if single-use gloves are worn. Check your local requirements.

Nail polish   Do not wear nail polish. It can disguise dirt under nails. It may also flake off into food. Some regulatory authorities allow nail polish if single-use gloves are worn. Check your local requirements.

Infected wounds or cuts   Infected wounds, cuts, or boils contain pus. They must be covered to prevent pathogens from contaminating food and food-contact surfaces. How a wound is covered depends on where it is located:

- Cover wounds on the hand or wrist with an impermeable cover. "Impermeable" means that liquid cannot pass through the cover. Examples include bandages and finger cots—protective coverings. Next, place a single-use glove over the cover. The food handler in the photo at left is covering an infected wound correctly.

- Cover wounds on the arm with an impermeable cover, such as a bandage. The wound must be completely covered.

- Cover wounds on other parts of the body with a dry, durable, tight-fitting bandage.

Bare-Hand Contact with Ready-to-Eat Food

Food can become contaminated when it has been handled with bare hands. This is especially true when hands have not been washed correctly or have infected cuts or wounds. For this reason, do not handle ready-to-eat food with bare hands. This is especially important if you primarily serve a high-risk population.

There are times when it may be acceptable to handle ready-to-eat food with bare hands. This is true in the following situations:

- The food will be added as an ingredient to a dish that does not contain raw meat, seafood, or poultry, but will be cooked to at least 145°F (63°C). For example, adding cheese to pizza dough.

- The food will be added as an ingredient to a dish containing raw meat, seafood, or poultry, and the dish will be cooked to the required minimum internal temperature of the raw item(s). For example, adding vegetables to a beef stew.

Some regulatory authorities allow bare-hand contact with ready-to-eat food. If your jurisdiction allows this, you should have specific policies in place about staff health. You must also train staff in handwashing and personal hygiene practices. Check your local regulatory requirements.

Single-Use Gloves

Single-use gloves can help keep food safe by creating a barrier between hands and food. They should be used when handling ready-to-eat food. Gloves do not need to be worn when washing produce. They also do not need to be worn when handling ready-to-eat ingredients for a dish that will be cooked to the correct internal temperature.

Buying Gloves

Follow these guidelines when purchasing single-use gloves.

Approved gloves   Purchase only gloves approved for foodservice. This includes gloves bearing the NSF Mark (to be discussed in Chapter 11).

Disposable gloves   Buy only single-use gloves for handling food. Do not wash and reuse them.

Different types   Supply different gloves for different tasks. Long gloves, for example, should be used for hand-mixing salads. Colored gloves can also be used to help prevent cross-contamination.

Multiple sizes   Provide gloves of varying sizes. Gloves that are too big will not stay on. Those that are too small will tear or rip easily. The photo at left shows a correct fit.

Latex alternatives   Some food handlers and customers may be sensitive to latex. Consider providing gloves made from other materials.

How to Use Gloves

If you are not careful when using gloves, the food you handle can become unsafe. Follow these guidelines:

- Wash your hands before putting on gloves when starting a new task. You do not need to rewash your hands each time you change gloves as long as you are performing the same task, and your hands have not become contaminated.
- Choose the correct glove size.
- Hold gloves by the edge when putting them on. Avoid touching the glove as much as possible.
- Once you have put them on, check the gloves for rips or tears.
- Do not blow into gloves.
- Do not roll gloves to make them easier to put on.

When to Change Gloves

Food handlers must change gloves at these times:

- As soon as the gloves become dirty or torn
- Before beginning a different task
- After an interruption, such as taking a phone call
- After handling raw meat, seafood, or poultry and before handling ready-to-eat food

Gloves can give food handlers a false sense of security, especially if they are not changed as often as they should be. Reinforce correct glove use with all food handlers.

Other Good Personal Hygiene Practices

Personal hygiene can be a touchy subject for some. But because it is so important to food safety, managers should address the subject with every food handler.

Personal Cleanliness

Pathogens can be found on hair and skin. They have a greater risk of being transferred to food and food equipment if food handlers do not shower or bathe before work. Make sure all staff members do this.

Correct Work Attire

Food handlers in dirty clothes may give a bad impression of your operation. More important, dirty clothing may carry pathogens that can make people sick. These pathogens can be transferred from the clothing to the hands and to the food being prepped. Set up a dress code and make sure staff follow it. The code should include the following guidelines.

Hair restraints   Wear a clean hat or other hair restraint when in a prep area, as shown in the photo at left. A hair restraint will keep hair away from food and keep the food handler from touching it. Do not wear hair accessories that could become physical contaminants. Hair accessories should be limited to items that keep hands out of hair and hair out of food. False eyelashes can likewise become physical contaminants and should not be worn. Food handlers with facial hair should also wear a beard restraint.

Clean clothing   Wear clean clothing daily. If possible, change into work clothes at work. Store street clothing and personal belongings in designated areas. Dirty clothing that is stored in the operation must be kept away from food and prep areas. You can do this by placing it in nonabsorbent containers or washable laundry bags. This includes dirty aprons, chef coats, and other uniforms.

Aprons   Remove aprons when leaving prep areas. For example, aprons should be removed and stored before taking out garbage or using the restroom. Never wipe your hands on your apron.

Jewelry   Remove jewelry from hands and arms before prepping food or when working around prep areas. The food handler in the photo at left is removing her watch before prepping food. Do not wear any of the following:

- Rings, except for a plain band
- Bracelets, including medical bracelets
- Watches

Your company may also require you to remove other jewelry. This may include earrings, necklaces, and facial jewelry. These items can fall off and become a physical contaminant. Ornate jewelry can also be difficult to clean and can hold pathogens. Servers may wear jewelry if allowed by company policy. Check with your regulatory authority regarding jewelry requirements.

These requirements should be included in written policies that are both monitored and enforced. Newly hired staff who have not started working yet should also be made aware of these policies.

Eating, Drinking, Smoking, and Chewing Gum or Tobacco

Small droplets of saliva can contain thousands of pathogens. Eating, drinking, smoking, or chewing gum or tobacco can transfer saliva to hands or directly to food being handled.

Do not eat, drink, smoke, or chew gum or tobacco when doing any of the following:

- Prepping or serving food
- Working in prep areas
- Working in areas used to clean utensils and equipment

Only eat, drink, smoke, and chew gum or tobacco in designated areas.

Some regulatory authorities allow food handlers to drink from a covered container while in these areas. Check your local regulatory requirements to be sure.

If food must be tasted during prepping, it should be placed in a separate dish and tasted with a clean utensil. The food handler in the photo at left is tasting food correctly using single-use items. The dish and utensil should then be removed from the prep area or discarded.

Reporting Health Issues

Require staff to let you know when they are sick. This includes newly hired staff who have not started working yet. Your regulatory authority may ask for proof that you have done this. You can provide it in the following ways:

- Presenting signed statements in which staff have agreed to report illness
- Providing documentation showing staff have completed training, which includes information on the importance of reporting illness
- Posting signs or providing pocket cards that remind staff to notify managers when they are sick

Staff must report any health problems to you before coming to work. They should also let you know right away if they have gotten sick while working, as the food handler in the photo at left is doing.

When food handlers are sick, you may need to restrict them from working with or around food. You might also need to exclude them from working in the operation. Use the chart on the next page to help you decide how to handle staff illnesses. Note that for most illnesses, however, you should work with your local regulatory authority to determine how to respond.

Handling Staff Illnesses

If	Then
The food handler has a sore throat with a fever.	Restrict the food handler from working with or around food. Exclude the food handler from the operation if you primarily serve a high-risk population. The food handler can return to the operation and/or work with or around food when he or she has a written release from a medical practitioner.
The food handler has at least one of these symptoms from an infectious condition: • Vomiting • Diarrhea • Jaundice (yellow skin or eyes)	Exclude the food handler from the operation. **Vomiting and diarrhea** Food handlers must meet one of these requirements before they can return to work: • Have had no symptoms for at least 24 hours • Have a written release from a medical practitioner **Jaundice** Food handlers with jaundice must be reported to the regulatory authority. Food handlers who have had jaundice for seven days or less must be excluded from the operation. Food handlers must have a written release from a medical practitioner and approval from the regulatory authority before returning to work.
The food handler is vomiting or has diarrhea and has been diagnosed with an illness caused by one of these pathogens: • Norovirus • *Shigella* spp. • Nontyphoidal *Salmonella* • Shiga toxin-producing *E. coli*	Exclude the food handler from the operation.
The food handler has been diagnosed with an illness caused by one of these pathogens: • Hepatitis A • *Salmonella* Typhi	Exclude the food handler from the operation. Some food handlers diagnosed with an illness may not experience symptoms, or their symptoms may have ended. Work with the medical practitioner and the local regulatory authority to determine whether these food handlers must be excluded from the operation or restricted from working with or around food. They will also determine when the employee can safely return to the operation and/or carry out their regular food handling duties.

This chart is only a guide. Work with your local regulatory authority to determine the best course of action.

SUMMARY

- Good personal hygiene is critical to prevent contamination and foodborne illness. A successful personal hygiene program depends on trained, knowledgeable food handlers.

- Food handlers can contaminate food when they have been diagnosed with a foodborne illness. It is also possible when they are vomiting or have diarrhea, have wounds containing a pathogen, or touch anything contaminated and then do not wash their hands. Even simple acts such as running fingers through the hair can contaminate food.

- Correct handwashing should always be practiced. This is especially important before starting work; after using the restroom; after sneezing, coughing, smoking, eating, or drinking; and before and after handling raw meat, poultry, and seafood.

- Fingernails should be kept short and clean. False fingernails and nail polish should not be worn. Infected wounds on hands or wrists should be covered with an impermeable cover and a single-use glove.

- Single-use gloves can create a barrier between hands and food. However, hands always need to be washed before putting on gloves when starting a new task. Hands do not need to be rewashed each time gloves are changed as long as food handlers are performing the same task and hands have not become contaminated. Gloves used to handle food are for single use.

- Food handlers should shower or bathe before going to work. Food handlers also must put on clean clothing and a hair restraint before handling food or working in prep areas.

- Food handlers must remove jewelry from hands and arms. Servers may wear jewelry if allowed by company policy. Aprons should always be removed and stored when the staff member leaves prep areas.

- Food handlers should never eat, smoke, or chew gum or tobacco in food prep or service areas, or in areas designated for cleaning.

- Require staff to report health problems to management. Managers must restrict food handlers who have a sore throat with fever from working with or around food. They must exclude food handlers who are vomiting or have diarrhea and have been diagnosed with a foodborne illness caused by certain pathogens, such as nontyphoidal *Salmonella*. Food handlers diagnosed with an illness from *Salmonella* Typhi or hepatitis A must always be excluded from the operation.

Apply Your Knowledge

Use these questions to review the concepts presented in this chapter.

DISCUSSION QUESTIONS

1. What are some basic work-attire requirements for staff?

2. What personal behaviors can contaminate food?

3. What is the correct procedure for covering infected wounds on hands or arms?

4. What procedures must food handlers follow when using gloves?

5. What staff health problems pose a possible threat to food safety? What are the appropriate actions that should be taken?

For answers, please turn to the Answer Key.

Apply Your Knowledge

More Than They Bargained For

CASE IN POINT

At an operation on the East Coast, the salad bar was a popular attraction. A food handler assigned to prep items for the salad bar noticed she had an infected cut on her finger. She bandaged the cut and went to work. While she was tossing the salad, the bandage fell off of her finger and into the lettuce. A short time later, a customer notified the manager that she had found a used bandage in her salad. The manager made the necessary apologies and quickly comped her meal. Fortunately, the customer was very understanding, and the rest of the evening proceeded without incident.

1. What should have been done to prevent this situation?

For answers, please turn to the Answer Key.

4

Randall's Day

CASE IN POINT

Randall is a food handler at a deli. It is 7:47 a.m., and he has just woken up. He is scheduled to be at work and ready to go by 8:00 a.m. When he gets out of bed, his stomach feels queasy. He blames that on the beer he had the night before. Fortunately, Randall lives only five minutes from work. Despite this, he doesn't have enough time to take a shower. He grabs the same uniform he wore the day before when prepping chicken. He also puts on his watch and several rings.

Randall does not have luck on his side today. On the way to the deli, his oil light comes on. He is forced to pull off the road and add oil to his car. When he gets to work, he realizes that he has left his hat at home. Randall is greeted by an angry manager. The manager puts Randall to work right away, loading the rotisserie with raw chicken. Randall then moves to serving a customer who orders a freshly made salad. Randall is known for his salads and makes the salad to the customer's approval.

The manager asks Randall to take out the garbage and then make potato salad for the lunch-hour rush. On the way back from the garbage run, Randall tells the manager that his stomach is bothering him. The manager, thinking of his staff shortage, asks Randall to stick it out as long as he can. Randall agrees and gets out the ingredients for the potato salad. Then he heads to the restroom in hope of relieving his symptoms. After quickly rinsing his hands in the restroom, he finds that the paper towels have run out. Short of time, he wipes his hands on his apron.

The manager tells Randall to clean the few tables in the deli that are available for customers. When finished, Randall grabs a piece of chicken from the rotisserie for a snack. He takes the chicken with him to the prep area, so he can get back to making the potato salad.

1 What did Randall and his manager do wrong?

For answers, please turn to the Answer Key.

Apply Your Knowledge

CASE IN POINT

Kurt's Dilemma

Kurt had been awake off and on throughout the night with diarrhea and vomiting. When he woke up the next morning, he did not feel that much better, even though the vomiting and diarrhea had stopped. He decided that it might be a good idea to take the day off from the café where he worked. The café was a very popular place to eat among college students in a large university town.

Kurt's boss Jackie answered the phone when he called in. At first she could not believe what she was hearing. Kurt was calling in sick when he knew it was going to be an incredibly busy shift. The café was already running short of staff. Jackie questioned Kurt about his symptoms. Then she asked if he could come in long enough to get them through the rush. Jackie was not worried because Kurt was no longer vomiting and did not have diarrhea. Because he needed the money, Kurt decided to go into work with the promise that he could go home as soon as the lunch rush was over.

1 What did Jackie do wrong?

2 What should she have done differently?

For answers, please turn to the Answer Key.

4

Circle the best answer to each question.

1. After which activity must food handlers wash their hands?

   A Putting on gloves

   B Serving customers

   C Applying hand antiseptic

   D Clearing tables

2. What should food handlers do after prepping food and before using the restroom?

   A Wash their hands

   B Take off their hats

   C Change their gloves

   D Take off their aprons

3. Which piece of jewelry can be worn on a food handler's hand or arm?

   A Watch

   B Diamond ring

   C Plain band ring

   D Medical bracelet

4. When should hand antiseptics be used?

   A After washing hands

   B Before washing hands

   C When soap is unavailable

   D When gloves are not being used

5. A food handler will be wearing single-use gloves to chop lettuce for an hour. When must the food handler's hands be washed?

   A After putting on gloves

   B Before starting the task

   C Half-way through the task

   D Each time gloves are changed

6. A cook wore single-use gloves while forming raw ground beef into patties. The cook continued to wear them while slicing hamburger buns. What mistake was made?

   A The cook did not wear reusable gloves while handling the raw ground beef and hamburger buns.

   B The cook did not clean and sanitize the gloves before handling the hamburger buns.

   C The cook did not wash hands before putting on the same gloves to slice the hamburger buns.

   D The cook did not wash hands and put on new gloves before slicing the hamburger buns.

7. A food handler has diarrhea and has been diagnosed with an illness from *Shigella* spp. What should the manager tell this food handler to do?

   A Stay home until a doctor approves a return to work.

   B Wear gloves while handling food.

   C Work in a nonfood-handling position.

   D Wash hands frequently while handling food.

8. A food handler prepares and delivers meals to elderly individuals receiving cancer care services at home. What symptoms require this food handler to stay home from work?

   A Thirst with itching

   B Soreness with fatigue

   C Sore throat with fever

   D Headache with soreness

9 When is it acceptable to eat in an operation?

A   When prepping food

B   When washing dishes

C   When sitting in a break area

D   When handling utensils

10 What should a manager of a hospital cafeteria do if a cook calls in with a headache, nausea, and diarrhea?

A   Tell the cook to stay away from work and see a doctor.

B   Tell the cook to come in for a couple of hours and then go home.

C   Tell the cook to rest for a couple of hours and then come to work.

D   Tell the cook to go to the doctor and then immediately come to work.

For answers, please turn to the Answer Key.

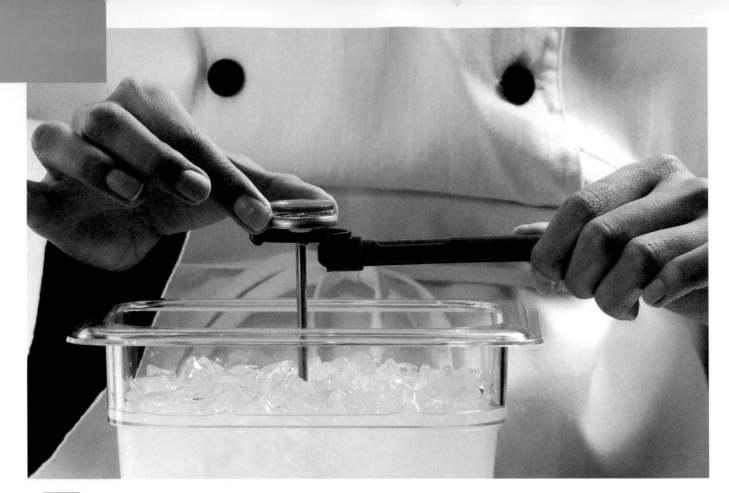

5 The Flow of Food: An Introduction

Cross-Contamination	Time-Temperature Control	
	— Avoiding Time- Temperature Abuse	— How to Calibrate Thermometers
	— Choosing the Correct Thermometer	— General Thermometer Guidelines

University Outbreak

An outbreak of *Salmonella* sickened 32 visitors to a university located in the northeastern United States. The sickened guests had attended a luncheon hosted by the chancellor during graduation weekend. Reports of illness flooded the local media, the university's on-campus clinic, and the local regulatory authority. Symptoms included stomach pain, nausea, diarrhea, chills, and vomiting.

It was determined that a new food handler at the dining facility had cross-contaminated romaine lettuce used for a chicken Caesar salad served at the luncheon. In her haste to catch up during a busy shift, the food handler chopped the lettuce on a cutting board that had been used to prep raw chicken for the salad. The cutting board had not been cleaned and sanitized between uses.

The university's contractor for foodservice announced that they would work closely with the local inspector to correct the problem. They would also immediately implement a program that would prevent cross-contamination in the future.

❶ **What could have been done to prevent this situation from occurring?**

For answers, please turn to the Answer Key.

INSIDE THIS CHAPTER

- Cross-Contamination
- Time-Temperature Control

OBJECTIVES

After completing this chapter, you should be able to identify the following:

- Ways of preventing cross-contamination
- Ways of preventing time-temperature abuse
- Different types of temperature-measuring devices and their uses
- How to calibrate and maintain different temperature-measuring devices
- General guidelines for thermometer use

KEY TERMS

- Flow of food
- Bimetallic stemmed thermometer
- Thermocouples
- Thermistors
- Time-temperature indicator (TTI)
- Calibration
- Ice-point method
- Boiling-point method

CROSS-CONTAMINATION

Many things can happen to food as it moves from purchasing and receiving through storing, prepping, cooking, holding, cooling, reheating, and serving. This path, as shown at left, is known as the flow of food.

Cross-contamination is a major hazard in the flow of food. Pathogens can be spread from food or unwashed hands to prep tables, utensils, equipment, or other food. Cross-contamination can occur at almost any point within the flow of food. When you know how and where it can happen, it is fairly easy to prevent. The most basic way is to keep raw and ready-to-eat food away from each other.

Here are some guidelines for doing this.

Using separate equipment   Use separate equipment when preparing each type of food. For example, use one set of cutting boards, utensils, and containers for raw poultry. Use another set for raw meat. Use a third set for produce. Colored cutting boards and utensil handles can help you keep equipment separate. The color tells food handlers which equipment to use with each food item. They might use yellow for raw chicken, red for raw meat, and green for produce, as the prep chef is doing in the photo at left.

Cleaning and sanitizing   Clean and sanitize all work surfaces, equipment, and utensils after each task. After cutting up raw chicken, for example, simply rinsing the cutting board is not enough. Pathogens, such as nontyphoidal *Salmonella*, can contaminate food through cross-contamination.
To prevent this, you need to wash, rinse, and sanitize equipment. See Chapter 12 for more information on cleaning and sanitizing.

Prepping food at different times   Sometimes you might need to use the same table to prep different types of food. If so, prep raw meat, fish, and poultry at different times from ready-to-eat food. For example, by prepping ready-to-eat food before raw food, the chance for cross-contamination can be minimized.

Buying prepared food   Buy food items that do not require much prepping or handling. For example, you could buy precooked chicken breasts or chopped lettuce, as shown in the photo at left.

Cross-Contamination	Time-Temperature Control	
	— Avoiding Time- Temperature Abuse	— How to Calibrate Thermometers
	— Choosing the Correct Thermometer	— General Thermometer Guidelines

TIME-TEMPERATURE CONTROL

Time-temperature abuse is another major hazard in the flow of food. Remember, TCS food has been time-temperature abused any time it remains between 41°F and 135°F (5°C and 57°C). This is called the temperature danger zone because pathogens grow in this range. They grow especially fast between 70°F and 125°F (21°C and 52°C). These ranges are shown in the illustration at left.

TCS food is being time-temperature abused whenever it is handled in the following ways:

* Cooked to the wrong minimum internal temperature

* Held at the wrong temperature

* Cooled or reheated incorrectly

Time also plays a critical role. The longer food stays in the temperature danger zone, the more time pathogens have to grow. To keep food safe, you must reduce the time food spends in this temperature range. TCS food must be thrown out if it stays in the temperature danger zone for four hours or more.

Avoiding Time-Temperature Abuse

Food handlers should avoid time-temperature abuse by following good policies and procedures. The ones you establish should cover the following areas.

Monitoring   Learn which food items should be checked, how often, and by whom. Then assign duties to food handlers in each area. Make sure they understand what to do, how to do it, and why it is important. For example, the manager in the photo at left is making sure the cook can check the temperature of a chicken breast.

Tools   Make sure the correct kinds of thermometers are available. Give food handlers their own thermometers. Have them use timers in prep areas to check how long food is in the temperature danger zone.

Recording   Have food handlers record temperatures regularly, as the chef is doing in the photo at left. Make sure they write down when the temperatures were taken. Print simple forms for recording this information. Post them on clipboards outside of coolers and freezers, near prep areas, and next to cooking and holding equipment.

Pathogens survive and grow

Pathogens grow rapidly

Time and temperature control   Have procedures that limit the time food spends in the temperature danger zone. This might include limiting the amount of food that can be removed from a cooler when prepping it.

Corrective actions   Make sure food handlers know what to do when time and temperature standards are not met. For example, if you hold soup on a steam table and its temperature falls below 135°F (57°C) after two hours, you might reheat it to the correct temperature or throw it out.

Choosing the Correct Thermometer

To keep food safe, you must control the amount of time it spends in the temperature danger zone. This requires monitoring food temperatures. The most important tool you have is the thermometer. There are many types of thermometers. Three types are commonly used in operations:

- Bimetallic stemmed thermometers
- Thermocouples
- Thermistors

Bimetallic Stemmed Thermometers

A bimetallic stemmed thermometer, shown in the photo at left, checks temperatures from 0°F to 220°F (–18°C to 104°C). This makes it useful for checking temperatures during the flow of food. For example, you can use it to check food temperatures both during receiving and in a hot- or cold-holding unit.

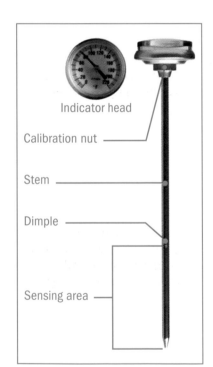

Indicator head

Calibration nut

Stem

Dimple

Sensing area

A bimetallic stemmed thermometer measures temperatures through a metal stem. When checking temperatures, insert the stem into the food up to the dimple. You must do this because the sensing area goes from the tip of the stem to the dimple. This trait makes the thermometer useful for checking the temperature of large or thick food. It is usually not practical for thin food, such as hamburger patties.

If you buy bimetallic stemmed thermometers for your operation, make sure they have the following features.

Calibration nut   You can make the thermometer accurate by adjusting its calibration nut.

Easy-to-read markings   Clear markings reduce the chance that someone will misread the thermometer. The thermometer must be scaled in at least two-degree increments.

Dimple   The dimple is the mark on the stem that shows the end of the temperature-sensing area.

Thermocouples and Thermistors

Thermocouples, such as the one in the photo at left, and thermistors check temperatures through a metal probe.

Temperatures are displayed digitally. The sensing area on thermocouples and thermistors is on the tip of their probe. This means you do not have to insert them into the food as far as bimetallic stemmed thermometers to get a correct reading. Thermocouples and thermistors are good for checking the temperature of both thick and thin food.

They are available in multiple sizes and styles. Many come with different types of probes, as shown below.

Immersion probes Use these to check the temperature of liquids. This could include soups, sauces, and frying oil.

Surface probes Use these to measure the temperature of flat cooking equipment, such as griddles.

Penetration probes Use these to check the internal temperature of food. They are especially useful for checking the temperatures of thin food, such as fish fillets or hamburger patties.

Air probes Use these to check the temperature inside coolers and ovens.

Infrared (Laser) Thermometers

Infrared thermometers, as shown in the photo at left, measure the temperatures of food and equipment surfaces. They are quick and easy to use.

Infrared thermometers do not need to touch a surface to check its temperature. This means there is less chance for cross-contamination and damage to food. However, these thermometers cannot measure air temperature or the internal temperature of food.

Follow these guidelines for using infrared thermometers.

Distance Hold the thermometer as close to the food or equipment as you can without touching it.

Barriers Remove anything between the thermometer and the food, food package, or equipment. Avoid taking readings through metal, such as stainless steel or aluminum. Do not take readings through glass either.

Manufacturer's directions Always follow the manufacturer's guidelines. This should give you the most accurate readings.

Other Temperature-Recording Devices

Other tools are available that can help you monitor temperature. A maximum registering thermometer is one type. This thermometer indicates the highest temperature reached during use. It is used where temperature readings cannot be continuously observed. It works well for checking final rinse temperatures of dishwashing machines.

Some devices monitor both time and temperature. The time-temperature indicator (TTI), shown in the photo at left, is an example. These tags are attached to packaging by the supplier. A color change appears in the TTI window if the food has been time-temperature abused during shipment or storage. This color change is not reversible, so you know if the item has been abused.

Some suppliers place temperature-recording devices inside their delivery trucks. These devices constantly monitor and record temperatures. You can check the device during receiving to make sure food remained at safe temperatures while it was being shipped.

How to Calibrate Thermometers

Thermometers can lose their accuracy when they are bumped or dropped. It can also happen when they go through a severe temperature change. When this happens, the thermometer needs calibration, or an adjustment, to give a correct reading. Thermometers that cannot be calibrated should be replaced. Others might need to be sent back to the manufacturer for calibration. Always follow the manufacturer's directions.

You have two ways to calibrate a thermometer. One is to adjust it based on the temperature at which water freezes. This is called the ice-point method. The other way is to adjust it based on the temperature at which water boils. This is called the boiling-point method.

Boiling-Point Method

To calibrate a thermometer using the boiling-point method, follow these steps:

1. Bring clean tap water to a boil in a deep pan.

2. Put the thermometer stem or probe into the boiling water. Make sure the sensing area is submerged. Wait 30 seconds or until the indicator stops moving. Do not let the stem or probe touch the container.

3. Adjust the thermometer so it reads 212°F (100°C). This temperature will vary depending on the boiling point for your elevation. Water's boiling point is about 1°F (about 0.5°C) lower for every 550 feet (168 meters) above sea level. If you are using a bimetallic stemmed thermometer, adjust it by holding the calibration nut with a wrench or other tool. If you are using a thermocouple or thermistor, some devices will let you press a reset button. Always follow the manufacturer's directions.

Ice-Point Method

Thermometers are often calibrated using the ice-point method. Follow these steps to use this method.

1. Fill a large container with crushed ice. Add tap water until the container is full.

   Note: Stir the mixture well.

2. Put the thermometer stem or probe into the ice water. Make sure the sensing area is submerged. Wait 30 seconds or until the indicator stops moving.

   Note: Do not let the stem or probe touch the container.

3. Adjust the thermometer so it reads 32°F (0°C).

   Note: If you are using a bimetallic stemmed thermometer, adjust it by holding the calibration nut with a wrench or other tool. If you are using a thermocouple or thermistor, some devices will let you press a reset button.

General Thermometer Guidelines

You should know how to use and care for each type of thermometer in your operation. You can follow the general guidelines below. However, you should always follow manufacturers' directions.

Cleaning and sanitizing   Thermometers must be washed, rinsed, sanitized (as shown in the photo at left), and air-dried.

Keep storage cases clean as well. Do these things before and after using thermometers to prevent cross-contamination. Be sure the sanitizing solution you are using is for food-contact surfaces. Always have plenty of clean and sanitized thermometers on hand.

Calibration   Make sure your thermometers are accurate by calibrating them regularly. Do this before each shift and before the first delivery arrives.

Accuracy   Thermometers used to measure the temperature of food need to be accurate to +/- 2°F or +/- 1°C. Thermometers used to measure air temperature in food storage equipment need to be accurate to +/- 3°F or +/- 1.5°C. A hanging thermometer in a walk-in cooler is an example.

Glass thermometers   Glass thermometers, such as candy thermometers, can be a physical contaminant if they break. They can only be used when enclosed in a shatterproof casing.

Checking temperatures   When checking the temperature of food, insert the thermometer stem or probe into the thickest part of the food, as shown in the photo at left. This is usually in the center. Also, take another reading in a different spot. The temperature may vary in different areas.

When using a bimetallic stemmed thermometer, insert the stem all the way into the food from the tip to the end of the sensing area. When checking the internal temperature of thin food, such as meat or fish patties, use a small diameter probe.

Before recording a temperature, wait for the thermometer reading to steady. Digital thermometers can display the temperature instantly. Bimetallic stemmed thermometers will take more time. Allow at least 15 seconds after you insert the thermometer stem into the food.

 Technology

Thermometers That Simulate Food

In the past few years, some U.S. thermometer manufacturers have begun producing thermometers with components that are meant to simulate food. The purpose of this is to determine what the product temperature of an item in a cooler is, rather than measuring the air temperature of the cooler, as a traditional thermometer would do.

In these thermometers, food is simulated by a silicone-based gel that surrounds the measuring unit. The gel freezes or liquefies similarly to food, depending on the temperature of the refrigeration unit.

Gel-based thermometers, like any other measuring instrument, must be NSF approved or the equivalent to comply with regulatory requirements. The thermometers have been popular in Europe for some time. Some proponents believe that operators who use these thermometers in their coolers may be able to save money by better understanding to what temperature a cooler really needs to be set to keep food safe.

SUMMARY

- The flow of food is the path food takes in your operation from purchasing to service. Many things can happen to food in its flow through the operation. Two major concerns are cross contamination and time-temperature abuse.

- To prevent cross-contamination, use separate equipment for each type of food. Also, you must clean and sanitize all work surfaces, equipment, and utensils after each task. Prepping ready-to-eat food before raw meat, poultry, and fish is one way to minimize the chance for cross-contamination. Similarly, you can buy food items that do not require much preparation or handling.

- Time-temperature abuse happens any time food remains between 41°F and 135°F (5°C and 57°C). This range is called the temperature danger zone. You must try to keep food out of this range.

- A thermometer is the most important tool you can use to prevent time-temperature abuse. You should regularly record food temperatures and the times they were taken.

- Always put the thermometer stem or probe into the thickest part of the food. A bimetallic stemmed thermometer should be put into food from the tip to the end of the sensing area. Before you record the temperature, wait for the thermometer reading to steady. Never use glass thermometers with food items unless they are enclosed in a shatterproof casing.

- Thermometers should be calibrated regularly. Most important, they must be cleaned and sanitized before and after each use.

Apply Your **Knowledge**	Use these questions to review the concepts presented in this chapter.
DISCUSSION QUESTIONS	① What are some ways food can be time-temperature abused? ② How can cross-contamination be prevented in the operation? ③ How is a thermometer calibrated using the ice-point method? *For answers, please turn to the Answer Key.*

5

Cross-Contamination Stops Truck in Its Tracks

CASE IN POINT

A popular food truck servicing the boardwalk area of a large beach resort community was cited for cross-contamination by the local regulatory authority.

The operator received violations for prepping raw chicken breasts and then fresh herbs on the same cutting board. The authorities also determined that he was using the same knife to trim raw meat and chop lettuce.

❶ What should the operator of the food truck have done differently?

For answers, please turn to the Answer Key.

Tour Cancelled by Outbreak

CASE IN POINT

A group of seniors from a local community decided to organize a tour of several nearby wineries. The seniors contracted with a coach bus service and worked out accommodations for the trip. They also ordered box lunches from a local catering company.

The lunches arrived just before 7:00 a.m. on a warm summer morning on the day of the tour. They were immediately placed in the luggage compartment of the bus. The boxes contained chicken salad, sliced ham sandwiches, a small cup of fresh fruit, a bag of baked chips, and a brownie.

The bus pulled over at a picnic area around noon and the box lunches were passed out to the seniors. Within the hour, 16 seniors got sick with nausea and vomiting. The remainder of the trip was canceled, and the bus returned to the senior center.

❶ What caused the illnesses?

❷ What could have been done to prevent them?

For answers, please turn to the Answer Key.

Study Questions

Circle the best answer to each question.

1 A food handler has finished trimming raw chicken on a cutting board and needs it to prep vegetables. What must be done to the cutting board?

A   It must be dried with a paper towel.

B   It must be turned over to the other side.

C   It must be washed, rinsed, and sanitized.

D   It must be rinsed in hot water and air-dried.

2 How far must a bimetallic stemmed thermometer be inserted into food to give an accurate reading?

A   Up to the tip of the thermometer stem

B   Just past the tip of the thermometer stem

C   Past the dimple of the thermometer stem

D   Up to the dimple of the thermometer stem

3 What probe should be used to check the temperature of a large stockpot of chili?

A   Air probe

B   Surface probe

C   Immersion probe

D   Penetration probe

4 What device can be used to record time-temperature abuse during the delivery of food?

A   Thermocouple

B   Thermistor

C   Time-temperature indicator

D   Bimetallic stemmed thermometer

5 At what temperatures do most foodborne pathogens grow most quickly?

A   Between 0°F and 41°F (-17°C and 5°C)

B   Between 45°F and 65°F (7°C and 18°C)

C   Between 70°F and 125°F (21°C and 52°C)

D   Between 130°F and 165°F (54°C and 74°C)

6 Which type of thermometer can read temperature without touching the item's surface?

A   TTI

B   Infrared

C   Air probe

D   Immersion probe

7 A thermometer used to measure the temperature of food must be accurate to what temperature?

A   +/- 2°F or +/- 1°C

B   +/- 4°F or +/- 3°C

C   +/- 6°F or +/- 5°C

D   +/- 8°F or +/- 7°C

For answers, please turn to the Answer Key.

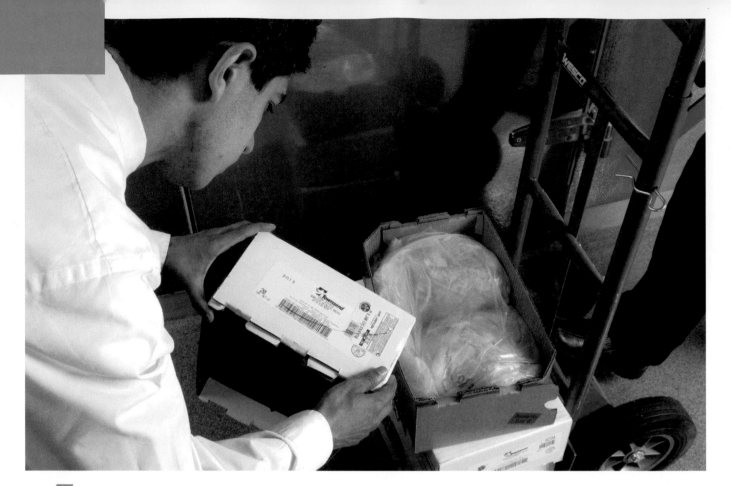

6 The Flow of Food: Purchasing and Receiving

Purchasing Considerations	Receiving Considerations	General Inspection Guidelines	Inspecting Specific Types of Food
	— Key Drop Deliveries — Rejecting Shipments	— Temperature — Packaging — Documents and Stamps — Food Quality	

Case in POINT

More Than They Bargained For

The chef at a newly opened seafood restaurant on the coast of California wanted to outdo her competition by providing the freshest seafood available. She could often be found down on the docks purchasing fresh seafood from the local fisherman. On a recent trip to the docks, she purchased some barracuda for the nightly special. That night, the chef told the servers to really push the item. The barracuda sold out quickly.

Several customers called the operation the next morning complaining of nausea and vomiting. Later, the same customers experienced joint and muscle pain and tingling in their fingers. All of them suffered from the reversal of hot and cold sensations. It was later discovered that the customers had contracted ciguatera fish poisoning.

1 What did the chef do wrong?

2 What should she have done differently?

For answers, please turn to the Answer Key.

INSIDE THIS CHAPTER

- Purchasing Considerations
- Receiving Considerations
- General Inspection Guidelines
- Inspecting Specific Types of Food

OBJECTIVES

After completing this chapter, you should be able to identify the following:

- Characteristics of an approved supplier
- Guidelines for receiving deliveries
- Requirements for key drop deliveries
- Procedure for handling food recalls
- Procedures for checking the temperatures of various food items
- Temperature requirements when receiving food
- Packaging requirements when receiving food
- Documentation required when receiving food
- Government inspection stamps required when receiving food
- Quality requirements when receiving food
- Receiving criteria for specific food items

KEY TERMS

- Approved suppliers
- Key drop delivery
- Shellstock identification tags
- Inspection stamp

6

Purchasing Considerations	Receiving Considerations	General Inspection Guidelines	Inspecting Specific Types of Food
	— Key Drop Deliveries — Rejecting Shipments	— Temperature — Packaging — Documents and Stamps — Food Quality	

PURCHASING CONSIDERATIONS

The final responsibility for the safety of food entering your operation resides with you. You can avoid many potential food safety hazards by using approved, reputable suppliers. Consider the following when making your selection.

Photo courtesy of Boskovich Farms, Inc.

Approved, reputable suppliers Food must be purchased from approved suppliers. These suppliers have been inspected and can show you an inspection report. Approved suppliers also meet applicable local, state, and federal laws. These standards apply to all suppliers in the food chain, which can include growers (such as the one shown in the photo at left), shippers, packers, manufacturers, distributors (trucking fleets and warehouses), and local markets. Develop relationships with all of your suppliers, and verify that they have good food safety practices.

Many operations establish supplier lists based on their company specifications, standards, and procedures. However, only approved, reputable suppliers should be included on these lists.

Inspection reports Consider reviewing suppliers' most recent inspection reports. These can be from the U.S. Department of Agriculture (USDA), the Food and Drug Administration (FDA), or a third-party inspector. They should be based on Good Manufacturing Practices (GMP) or Good Agricultural Practices (GAP).

GMPs are the FDA's minimum sanitation and processing requirements for producing safe food. They describe the methods, equipment, facilities, and controls used to process food. Both suppliers and their sources are subject to GMP inspections.

Make sure an inspection report reviews the following areas:

- Receiving and storage
- Processing
- Shipping
- Cleaning and sanitizing
- Personal hygiene
- Staff training
- Recall program
- HACCP program or other food safety system

Purchasing Considerations	Receiving Considerations	General Inspection Guidelines	Inspecting Specific Types of Food
	— Key Drop Deliveries — Rejecting Shipments	— Temperature — Packaging — Documents and Stamps — Food Quality	

RECEIVING CONSIDERATIONS

Having procedures in place for inspecting food can reduce hazards before they enter your operation. Here are some guidelines that can help you improve the way you receive deliveries.

Scheduling Suppliers should deliver food when staff have enough time to inspect it. Schedule deliveries at a time when they can be received correctly.

Staff needs Make specific staff responsible for receiving. Train them to follow food safety procedures, including checking items for correct temperatures, expired code dates, signs of thawing and refreezing, and pest damage. In the photo at left, a manager is training a food handler on inspecting produce. Staff should be able to accept, reject, and sign for deliveries. Also, provide them with the tools they need, including purchase orders, temperature logs, thermometers, and scales. Then make sure that enough trained staff is available to receive and inspect food promptly.

Good preparation Plan ahead for shipments. Have clean hand trucks, carts, dollies, and containers ready. Also make sure there is enough space in dry-storage and walk in areas for shipments.

Timing of inspections Visually inspect delivery trucks for signs of contamination. Then, look at each delivery right away to count quantities, check for damaged food, and look for items that might have been repacked or mishandled. Spot-check weights and take sample temperatures of all TCS food, as shown in the photo at left. Inspect and store each delivery before accepting another one. This will prevent temperature abuse in the receiving area.

Key Drop Deliveries

Some foodservice operations receive food after-hours when they are closed for business. This is often referred to as a key drop delivery. The supplier is given a key or other access to the operation to make the delivery. Products are then placed in coolers, freezers, and dry-storage areas. The delivery must be inspected once you arrive at the operation and must meet the following conditions:

- It is from an approved supplier.
- It was placed in the correct storage location to maintain the required temperature and was protected from contamination.
- It has not been contaminated.
- It is honestly presented.

Key Point

You have the right to refuse any delivery that does not meet your standards.

Rejecting Shipments

You can refuse any delivery that does not meet your standards. Staff should know how to reject an item or a shipment:

1 Set the rejected item aside from the items you are accepting.

2 Tell the delivery person exactly what is wrong with the item. Use your purchase agreement to support your decision.

3 Get a signed adjustment or credit slip from the delivery person before the item is removed.

4 Log the incident on the invoice or receiving document. Be specific about the action taken and the item involved.

Occasionally you may be able to recondition and use items that would have been rejected. For example, a shipment of cans with contaminated surfaces may be cleaned and sanitized, allowing them to be used. However, the same cans could not be reconditioned if the contamination was the result of damage to the cans.

Recalls

Food items you have received may sometimes be recalled by the manufacturer. This may happen when food contamination is confirmed or suspected. It can also occur when items have been mislabeled or misbranded. Often food is recalled when food allergens have not been identified on the label. Most vendors will notify you of the recall. However, you should also monitor recall notifications made by the FDA and the USDA. Follow these guidelines when notified of a recall:

- Identify the recalled food items by matching information from the recall notice to the item. This may include the manufacturer's ID, the time the item was manufactured, and the item's use-by date.

- Remove the item from inventory, and place it in a secure and appropriate location. That may be a cooler or dry-storage area. The recalled item must be stored separately from food, utensils, equipment, linens, and single-use items.

- Label the item in a way that will prevent it from being placed back in inventory. Some operations do this by including a Do Not Use and Do Not Discard label on recalled food items. Inform staff not to use the product.

- Refer to the vendor's notification or recall notice for what to do with the item. For example, you might be instructed to throw it out or return it to the vendor.

Purchasing Considerations	Receiving Considerations	General Inspection Guidelines	Inspecting Specific Types of Food
	— Key Drop Deliveries — Rejecting Shipments	— Temperature — Packaging — Documents and Stamps — Food Quality	

GENERAL INSPECTION GUIDELINES

When inspecting deliveries, focus on checking product temperatures, packaging, documentation, and the quality of the food. These can provide important evidence as to whether or not the food is safe.

Temperature

Use thermometers to check food temperatures. The following examples explain how to check the temperatures of various types of food.

Meat, poultry, and fish Insert the thermometer stem or probe into the thickest part of the food, as shown in the photo at left. The center is usually the thickest part.

Reduced-oxygen packaged (ROP) and bulk food Insert the thermometer stem or probe between two packages, as shown in the photo at left. If possible, fold the package around the thermometer stem or probe. Be careful not to puncture the package.

Other packaged food Open the package and insert the thermometer stem or probe into the food, as the food handler is doing with the carton of milk at left. Fully immerse the sensing area in the item. The stem or probe must not touch the package.

Temperature Requirements

Deliveries should be received at the temperatures indicated below.

Receiving Temperature Requirements for Various Types of Food	
Type of Food	**Temperature**
Cold TCS food	• 41°F (5°C) or lower, unless otherwise specified
Hot TCS food	• 135°F (57°C) or higher
Frozen food	• Should be frozen solid
Live shellfish	• Air temperature of 45°F (7°C) • Internal temperature no greater than 50°F (10°C) • Once received, cool it to an internal temperature of 41°F (5°C) or lower in four hours
Shucked shellfish	• 45°F (7°C) or lower • Must be cooled to 41°F (5°C) or lower in four hours
Milk	• 45°F (7°C) or lower • Must be cooled to 41°F (5°C) or lower in four hours
Shell eggs	• Air temperature of 45°F (7°C) or lower

Packaging

Both food items and nonfood items such as single-use cups, utensils, and napkins, must be packaged correctly when you receive them. Items should be delivered in their original packaging with a manufacturer's label. The packaging should be intact and clean, and it should protect food and food-contact surfaces from contamination.

Reject food and nonfood items if the packaging has any of the following problems.

Damage Reject items with tears, holes, or punctures in their packaging. Likewise, reject cans with labels that are not intact or that have bulging or swollen ends, rust, or dents. All food packaged in a reduced-oxygen environment, such as vacuum-packed meat, must be rejected if the packaging is bloated or leaking. An example is shown in the photo at left. Items with broken cartons or seals, or items with dirty or discolored packaging should also be rejected. Do not accept cases or packages that appear to have been tampered with.

Liquid Reject items with leaks, dampness, or water stains (which means the item was wet at some point). The flour bag shown at left has a water stain. Reject items if there are large ice crystals or frozen liquids on the packaging. This may be evidence of thawing and refreezing, which shows the food has been time-temperature abused.

Pests Reject items with signs of pests or pest damage.

Dates Food must be correctly labeled. Do not accept food that is missing use-by or expiration dates from the manufacturer. Reject items that have passed their use-by or expiration dates. Some operations label food items with the date the item was received to help with stock rotation during storage.

Documents and Stamps

Food items must be delivered with the correct documents. For example, shellfish must be received with shellstock identification tags. These tags indicate when and where the shellfish were harvested. They must be kept on file for 90 days from the date the last shellfish was used from its delivery container. A shellstock tag is shown in the photo at left.

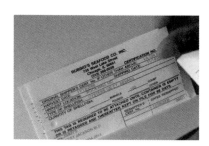

Fish that will be eaten raw or partially cooked must also be received with the correct documentation. These documents must indicate the fish was correctly frozen before you received it. Keep these documents for 90 days from the sale of the fish. If the fish was farm raised, it must have documentation that states the fish was raised to FDA standards. These documents must also be kept for 90 days from the sale of the fish.

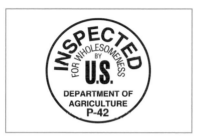

Inspection and Grading Stamps

Meat must be purchased from plants inspected by the USDA or a state department of agriculture. Note that "inspected" does not mean that the product is free of pathogens; rather, it means that the product and the processing plant have met defined standards.

Carcasses and packages of meat that have been inspected will have an inspection stamp with abbreviations for "inspected and passed" by the inspecting agency, along with a number identifying the processing plant. An example of this stamp appears in the top illustration at left.

Poultry is inspected by the USDA or the state department of agriculture in much the same way as meat. An example of a poultry inspection stamp is shown in the bottom illustration at left.

Liquid, frozen, and dehydrated eggs must also have a USDA inspection mark. These types of eggs are required by law to be pasteurized.

Note that grading stamps might also appear on packages of eggs, meat, and poultry. Grading of these types of products is voluntary and paid for by processors and packers.

Food Quality

Poor food quality can be a sign that the food has been time-temperature abused and, therefore, may be unsafe. Work with your suppliers to define specific safety and quality criteria for the food items you typically receive. Reject food if it has any of the following problems.

Appearance   Reject food that is moldy or has an abnormal color. Food that is moist when it should be dry, such as salami, should also be rejected. Do not accept any food item that shows signs of pests or pest damage. Reject frozen food that has large ice crystals on it. This may be evidence of thawing and refreezing. The food in the photo at left shows evidence of thawing and refreezing.

Texture   Reject meat, fish, or poultry that is slimy, sticky, or dry. Also reject it if it has soft flesh that leaves an imprint when you touch it.

Odor   Reject food with an abnormal or unpleasant odor.

In addition to the guidelines above, you should always reject any item that does not meet your company's standards for quality.

Resources

Global Food Safety Initiative (GFSI)

In May, 2000, a nonprofit foundation, the Global Food Safety Initiative (GFSI), was created in Belgium, partially in response to some large-scale foodborne-illness outbreaks. This initiative is coordinated through the Consumer Goods Forum (CGF), an industry network comprised of the CEOs and senior managers of over 650 companies in 70 countries.

The purpose of the initiative is to benchmark existing food standards against food safety criteria. It encourages merchants in the supply chain to exchange information that will raise awareness and review existing good practices. With the help of GFSI-defined food safety requirements, the initiative covers feed and distribution, as well as packaging. Members from across the globe frequently meet and contribute to the initiative's studies and resources. Learn more about the initiative at gfsi.com.

Purchasing Considerations	Receiving Considerations	General Inspection Guidelines	Inspecting Specific Types of Food
	— Key Drop Deliveries — Rejecting Shipments	— Temperature — Packaging — Documents and Stamps — Food Quality	

INSPECTING SPECIFIC TYPES OF FOOD

Certain types of food have specific criteria for accepting or rejecting it. An in-depth look at receiving criteria for specific products follows on the next several pages.

Receiving Criteria for Specific Types of Food

FRESH FISH

Accept criteria

- Color: bright red gills; bright shiny skin
- Texture: firm flesh that springs back when touched
- Odor: mild ocean or seaweed smell
- Eyes: bright, clear, full
- Packaging: product surrounded by crushed, self-draining ice

Reject criteria

- Color: dull gray gills; dull dry skin
- Texture: soft flesh that leaves an imprint when touched
- Odor: strong fishy or ammonia smell
- Eyes: cloudy, red-rimmed, sunken
- Product: tumors, abscesses, or cysts on the skin

SHELLFISH

Accept criteria

- Odor: mild ocean or seaweed smell
- Shells: closed and unbroken, indicating that the shellfish are alive
- Condition: if fresh, they must be received alive

Reject criteria

- Texture: slimy, sticky, or dry
- Odor: strong fishy smell
- Shells: excessively muddy or broken shells
- Condition: dead on arrival (open shells that do not close when tapped)

CRUSTACEANS

Accept criteria

- Odor: mild ocean or seaweed smell
- Condition: shipped alive, packed in seaweed, and kept moist

Reject criteria

- Odor: strong fishy smell
- Condition: dead on arrival

MEAT

Accept criteria

- Color
  - Beef: bright cherry red; aged beef may be darker; vacuum-packed beef will appear purplish
  - Lamb: light red
  - Pork: light pink meat; firm, white fat
- Texture: firm flesh that springs back when touched
- Odor: no odor
- Packaging: intact and clean

Reject criteria

- Color
  - Beef: brown or green
  - Lamb: brown, whitish surface covering the lean meat
  - Pork: excessively dark color; soft or rancid fat
- Texture: slimy, sticky, or dry
- Odor: sour odor
- Packaging: broken cartons; dirty wrappers; torn packaging; broken seals

POULTRY

Accept criteria

- Color: no discoloration
- Texture: firm flesh that springs back when touched
- Odor: no odor
- Packaging: should be surrounded by crushed, self-draining ice

Reject criteria

- Color: purple or green discoloration around the neck; dark wing tips (red are acceptable)
- Texture: stickiness under the wings and around joints
- Odor: abnormal, unpleasant odor

Continued on next page ▶

6

▶ *Continued from previous page*

| | | |

SHELL EGGS

Accept criteria
- Odor: no odor
- Shells: clean and unbroken

Reject criteria
- Odor: sulfur smell or off odor
- Shells: dirty or cracked

DAIRY PRODUCTS

Accept criteria
- Milk: sweetish flavor
- Butter: sweet flavor; uniform color; firm texture
- Cheese: typical flavor and texture; uniform color; clean and unbroken rind

Reject criteria
- Milk: sour, bitter, or moldy taste; off odor; expired sell-by date
- Butter: sour, bitter, or moldy taste; uneven color; soft texture; contains foreign matter
- Cheese: abnormal flavor or texture; uneven color; unnatural mold; unclean or broken rind

FRESH PRODUCE

Accept criteria
- Temperature: varies according to the product
- Condition: varies according to the product

Reject criteria
- Condition: evidence of mishandling or insects (including insect eggs and egg cases)
- Spoilage: mold, cuts, wilting, unpleasant odors, discoloration, etc. (will depend on the produce involved)

Business

Local Sourcing

Each year, the National Restaurant Association surveys thousands of members of the American Culinary Federation about trends in the industry. Since 2010, these chefs have identified locally sourced meat and seafood and locally sourced produce as the top two trends in the U.S. culinary world.

Successfully determining that locally sourced food is safe to purchase is strongly dependent on good communication and clear expectations between you and the local supplier. Here are some of the questions and concerns that anyone interested in local sourcing must consider to ensure the food to be purchased is safe.

- Is the seller required to be licensed by the state or local regulatory authority to be able to sell produce or homemade products to the foodservice industry?

- How is the homemade product processed? What are the ingredients? Is there an ingredient label on the item to help with allergen concerns?

- Does the produce look clean and free from debris? How is the produce grown? Are chemicals, herbicides, or other treatments used?

- Are the local meat products processed at an approved, USDA-inspected site? Is the meat stamped with a USDA inspection stamp?

- Are the local eggs inspected by the grower? How are they handled and processed?

As with any supplier, a local source must comply with all applicable laws and be able to show you good food safety practices.

SUMMARY

- It is your responsibility to check the quality and safety of food that comes into your operation.

- Food must be purchased from approved, reputable suppliers. These suppliers must be inspected and meet applicable local, state, and federal laws.

- Deliveries must be inspected by designated staff trained to follow food safety guidelines. That will include a visual inspection of food as well as checks to make sure the food has been received at the correct temperature.

- Sometimes food items will be recalled by the manufacturer. Identify these items, remove them from inventory, and secure them in an appropriate location. Mark them so that staff does not use them.

- Cold TCS food must be received at 41°F (5°C) or lower. Hot TCS food must be received at 135°F (57°C) or higher. Frozen food should always be received frozen. Some items have other temperature requirements. Received food should have the correct color, texture, and odor.

- The packaging of delivered food items must be intact and clean and it must protect food from contamination. There should also be no signs of pests or dampness. Food items should be correctly labeled and contain the correct documentation.

- Food items must be delivered with the correct documents. Shellfish must be delivered with shellstock tags identifying when and where the shellfish were harvested. Fish that will be eaten raw or partially cooked must be delivered with documentation indicating the fish was correctly frozen.

- Poor food quality can be a sign that the food has been time-temperature abused and, therefore, may be unsafe. Work with your suppliers to define specific safety and quality criteria for the food regarding its appearance, texture, and odor.

Apply Your Knowledge

Use these questions to review the concepts presented in this chapter.

DISCUSSION QUESTIONS

1. What are some general guidelines for receiving food safely?

2. What are correct methods for checking the temperatures of fresh poultry delivered on ice and a carton of milk? What should the temperature be for each?

3. What are three conditions that would result in rejecting a shipment of fresh poultry?

4. What types of external damage to cans are causes for rejection?

For answers, please turn to the Answer Key.

Apply Your Knowledge

A Decision to Make

CASE IN POINT

Two friends, who met in their senior year of hotel and restaurant management school, decided to become partners in a new fast-casual concept. The partners felt confident that their college and work experience had prepared them to open their new business—something they had been dreaming of for a long time.

All of the steps started to fall into place quickly. They identified a perfect location in a suburban strip mall, obtained financing, and developed a menu. The clock was ticking toward their projected opening date, yet they still had not selected their suppliers. Both partners turned their attention toward this important task.

1. What should the partners consider as they begin to select their suppliers?

For answers, please turn to the Answer Key.

Apply Your Knowledge

CASE IN POINT

Delivery Decision Could Cost Them

A large food delivery arrived at the Sunnydale Nursing Home during the busy lunch hour. It included cases of frozen ground beef patties, canned vegetables, frozen shrimp, fresh tomatoes, a case of potatoes, and fresh chicken.

Betty, the new assistant manager, thought the best thing to do was to put everything away and check it later as she was very busy. She told Ed, who was in charge of receiving, to sign for the delivery and put the food into storage. Ed asked her if it would be better to ask the delivery driver to come back later. Because she needed the chicken for dinner, Betty asked Ed to accept the delivery now, and then she went back to the front of the house.

Ed put the frozen shrimp and ground beef patties in the freezer and the fresh chicken in the refrigerator. Then he put the fresh tomatoes, potatoes, and canned vegetables in dry storage. When he was finished, he went back to work in the kitchen.

1 What was done incorrectly?

For answers, please turn to the Answer Key.

6

Circle the best answer to each question.

1. What is the most important factor in choosing a food supplier?

   A It has a HACCP program or other food safety system.

   B It has documented manufacturing and packing practices.

   C Its warehouse is close to the operation, reducing shipping time.

   D It has been inspected and complies with local, state, and federal laws.

2. What is the best method of checking the temperature of a delivery of fresh fish?

   A Feel the fish, making sure that it is cold to the touch.

   B Insert a thermometer probe into the thickest part of the fish.

   C Place a time-temperature indicator on the surface of the fish.

   D Use an infrared thermometer to check the fish's temperature.

3. What is the correct temperature for receiving cold TCS food?

   A 32°F (0°C) or lower

   B 41°F (5°C) or lower

   C 45°F (7°C) or lower

   D 50°F (10°C) or lower

4. Milk can be received at 45°F (7°C) under what condition?

   A It is thrown out after 2 days.

   B It is cooled to 41°F (5°C) or lower in 4 hours.

   C It is immediately cooled to 41°F (5°C) or lower.

   D It is served or used in the operation within 2 hours.

5. Frozen shrimp is rejected during receiving for having large ice crystals on the food and packaging. What is the problem that caused this?

   A Cross-contact

   B Cross-contamination

   C Time-temperature abuse

   D Incorrect cleaning and sanitizing

6. What is required when receiving fish that will be served raw or partially cooked?

   A It must be alive when received.

   B It must be thawed in the microwave.

   C It must be used within 24 hours of receiving.

   D It must be correctly frozen before you receive it.

7 Live shellfish must be received with what documentation?

A Shellstock identification tag

B USDA inspection stamp

C Certified fisheries tag

D USDA grading stamp

8 How should cartons of coleslaw be checked for the correct receiving temperature?

A Check the interior air temperature of the delivery truck.

B Open a carton and insert a thermometer stem into the food.

C Place a thermometer against the outside of the carton.

D Touch the carton to see if it is cold.

9 What should be done with an item that has been recalled?

A Throw it out.

B Arrange a pick-up from the vendor.

C Record the item's use-by date, and place the item in storage.

D Remove the item from inventory, and place it in a secure location.

10 Cleaning the surfaces of some cans of tomato sauce so that they can be accepted is an example of

A reconditioning.

B spot-inspecting.

C calibrating.

D documenting.

For answers, please turn to the Answer Key.

7 The Flow of Food: Storage

General Storage Guidelines	Storing Specific Food	
— Labeling	— Meat	— Fresh Produce
— Date Marking	— Poultry	— ROP Food
— Rotation	— Fish	— UHT and
— Temperatures	— Shellfish	Aseptically
— Preventing Cross-Contamination	— Eggs	Packaged Food
	— Milk	— Canned Goods
		— Dry Food

INSIDE THIS CHAPTER

- General Storage Guidelines
- Storing Specific Food

OBJECTIVES

After completing this chapter, you should be able to identify the following:

- Requirements for labeling and date marking food
- How to rotate food using first-in, first-out (FIFO)
- Temperature requirements for food in storage
- Practices that can prevent temperature-abuse during storage
- Locations where food should not be stored
- Practices that can prevent cross-contamination during storage
- Guidelines for storing specific types of food including meat, poultry, fish, shellfish, eggs, produce, and dry food

KEY TERMS

- Date marking
- First-in, first-out (FIFO)
- Reduced-oxygen packaged (ROP) food

General Storage Guidelines	Storing Specific Food	
– Labeling	– Meat	– Fresh Produce
– Date Marking	– Poultry	– ROP Food
– Rotation	– Fish	– UHT and
– Temperatures	– Shellfish	Aseptically
– Preventing Cross-Contamination	– Eggs	Packaged Food
	– Milk	– Canned Goods
		– Dry Food

GENERAL STORAGE GUIDELINES

When food is stored incorrectly and not used in a timely manner, quality and safety will suffer. The results can be serious.

In general, you must label and date mark your food correctly. You must also rotate food and store it at the correct temperature. Finally, you need to store items in a way that prevents cross-contamination.

Use the following general guidelines when storing food.

Labeling

Labeling food is important for many reasons. Illnesses have occurred when unlabeled chemicals were mistaken for food such as flour, sugar, and baking powder. Customers have also suffered allergic reactions when food was unknowingly prepped with a food allergen that was not identified on the label.

Labeling Food for Use On-Site

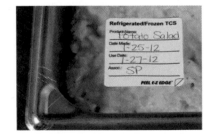

Any item not stored in its original container must be labeled. The label must include the common name of the food or a statement that clearly and accurately identifies it, as shown in the photo at left.

If a food is easily identifiable by sight and will not be mistaken for another item, it is not necessary to label the item. An example is dry pasta.

Labeling Food That is Packaged On-site for Retail Sale

Food packaged in the operation that is being sold to customers for use at home, such as bottled salad dressing, must be labeled. The label must include the following information:

- Common name of the food or a statement that clearly identifies it.

- Quantity of the food.

- List of ingredients and sub-ingredients in descending order by weight. This is necessary if the item contains two or more ingredients.

- List of artificial colors and flavors in the food. Chemical preservatives must also be listed.

- Name and place of business of the manufacturer, packer, or distributor.

- Source of each major food allergen contained in the food. This is not necessary if the source is already part of the common name of the ingredient.

These labeling requirements do not apply to customers' leftover food items placed in carry-out containers.

Key Point

Date mark ready-to-eat TCS food that will be held for longer than 24 hours.

Date Marking

Refrigeration slows the growth of most bacteria. Some types, such as *Listeria monocytogenes*, grow well at refrigeration temperatures. When food is refrigerated for long periods of time, these bacteria can grow enough to cause illness. For this reason, ready-to-eat TCS food must include date marking if it will be held for longer than 24 hours. The date marking must indicate when the food must be sold, eaten, or thrown out.

Ready-to-eat TCS food can be stored for only seven days if it is held at 41°F (5°C) or lower. The count begins on the day the food was prepared or a commercial container was opened. For example, a food handler that prepared and stored potato salad on October 1 would write a discard date of October 7 on the label.

Operations have a variety of systems for date marking. Some write the day or date the food was prepped on the label. Others write the use-by day or date on the label, as shown in the photo at left.

Commercially Processed Food

Sometimes commercially processed food will have a use-by date that is less than seven days from the date the container was opened. In this case, the container should be marked with this use-by date as long as the date is based on food safety.

Combining Food

When combining food in a dish with different use-by dates, the discard date of the dish should be based on the earliest prepared food.

Here is an example: a food handler is prepping jambalaya on December 4 using shrimp and sausage. The shrimp has a use-by date of December 8, and the sausage has a use-by date of December 10. So, the use-by date of the jambalaya is December 8.

Rotation

Food must be rotated while in storage to maintain quality and limit the growth of pathogens. Food items must be rotated so the items with the earliest use-by or expiration dates are used before those with later dates.

Many operations use the first-in, first-out (FIFO) method to rotate their refrigerated, frozen, and dry food during storage. Here is one way to use the FIFO method:

1 Identify the food item's use-by or expiration date.

2 Store items with the earliest use-by or expiration dates in front of items with later dates, as shown in the photo at left.

3 Once shelved, use those items stored in front first.

4 Throw out food that has passed its manufacturer's use-by or expiration date.

Temperatures

Pathogens can grow when food is not stored at the correct temperature. Follow these guidelines to keep food safe:

- Store TCS food at an internal temperature of 41°F (5°C) or lower, or 135°F (57°C) or higher. Randomly sample the internal temperature of stored food using a calibrated thermometer on a regular basis.

- Store meat, poultry, seafood, and dairy items in the coldest part of the unit, away from the door.

- Store frozen food at temperatures that keep it frozen.

- Make sure storage units have at least one air-temperature measuring device. It must be accurate to +/- 3°F or +/- 1.5°C. This device must be located in the warmest part of refrigerated units, and the coldest part of hot-holding units. The hanging thermometer in the photo at left is a common type of temperature measuring device used in coolers. Check cooler and freezer temperatures often.

- Do not overload coolers or freezers. Storing too many food items prevents good airflow and makes the units work harder to stay cold.

- Consider using cold curtains in walk-in coolers and freezers to help maintain temperatures.

- Use open shelving. Do not line shelves with aluminum foil, sheet pans, or paper. This restricts circulation of cold air in the unit.

- Monitor food temperatures in coolers regularly. Randomly sample the temperature of stored food to verify that the cooler is working.

- Defrost freezers regularly. They are more efficient when free of frost. Move food to another freezer while defrosting.

Storage Location

Food should be stored in a clean, dry location away from dust and other contaminants. Never store food in these areas to prevent contamination:

- Locker rooms or dressing rooms

- Restrooms or garbage rooms

- Mechanical rooms

- Under unshielded sewer lines or leaking water lines

- Under stairwells

Preventing Cross-Contamination

Food and nonfood items must be stored in ways that prevent cross-contamination. Follow these guidelines.

Supplies

Store food, linens, and single-use items (e.g., sleeve of single-use cups, single-use gloves), in designated storage areas. These items must be stored away from walls and at least six inches (15 centimeters) off the floor, as shown in the photo at left. Single-use items should be stored in the original packaging.

Containers

Store food in containers intended for food. The containers should be durable, leak-proof, and able to be sealed or covered. Never use empty food containers to store chemicals or put food in empty chemical containers.

Wrap or cover all food correctly. Leaving food uncovered can lead to cross-contamination.

Cleaning

Keep all storage areas clean and dry. Clean floors, walls, and shelving in coolers, freezers, dry-storage areas, and heated holding cabinets regularly, as shown in the photo at left. Clean up spills and leaks promptly to keep them from contaminating other food. Follow these guidelines:

- Clean dollies, carts, transporters, and trays often.
- Store food in containers that have been cleaned and sanitized.
- Store dirty linens away from food. Store them in clean, nonabsorbent containers. They can also be stored in washable laundry bags.

Storage Order

Store raw meat, poultry, and seafood separately from ready-to-eat food. If raw and ready-to-eat food cannot be stored separately, store ready-to-eat food above raw meat, poultry, and seafood. This will prevent juices from raw food from dripping onto ready-to-eat food.

Raw meat, poultry, and seafood can be stored with or above ready-to-eat food in a freezer if all of the items have been commercially processed and packaged. Frozen food that is being thawed in coolers must also be stored below ready-to-eat food.

Store raw meat, poultry, and seafood in coolers in the following top-to-bottom order: seafood, whole cuts of beef and pork, ground meat and ground fish, whole and ground poultry. This is shown in the photo below. This order is based on the minimum internal cooking temperature of each food. As an exception, ground meat and ground fish can be stored above whole cuts of beef and pork. To do this, make sure the packaging keeps out pathogens and chemicals. It also must not leak.

Ⓐ Ready-to-eat food

Ⓑ Seafood

Ⓒ Whole cuts of beef and pork

Ⓓ Ground meat and ground fish

Ⓔ Whole and ground poultry

General Storage Guidelines	Storing Specific Food	
— Labeling	— Meat	— Fresh Produce
— Date Marking	— Poultry	— ROP Food
— Rotation	— Fish	— UHT and
— Temperatures	— Shellfish	Aseptically
— Preventing Cross-Contamination	— Eggs	Packaged Food
	— Milk	— Canned Goods
		— Dry Food

STORING SPECIFIC FOOD

The general storage guidelines apply to most food. However, certain types of food have special requirements.

Meat

Immediately after delivery and inspection, store meat in its own storage unit or in the coldest part of the cooler. Fresh meat should be held at an internal temperature of 41°F (5°C) or lower. Frozen meat should be stored at a temperature that will keep it frozen.

If meat is removed from its original packaging, wrap it in airtight, moisture-proof material or place it in clean and sanitized containers, as shown in the photo at left.

Primal cuts, quarters, sides of raw meat, and slab bacon can be hung on clean and sanitized hooks or placed on sanitized racks. To prevent cross-contamination, do not store meat above other food.

Poultry

Store raw poultry at an internal temperature of 41°F (5°C) or lower. Frozen poultry should be stored at temperatures that will keep it frozen. If it has been removed from its original packaging, place it in airtight containers or wrap it in airtight material.

Ice-packed poultry can be stored in a cooler as is. Use self-draining containers. Change the ice and sanitize the container often.

Fish

Fresh fish is very sensitive to time-temperature abuse. It can spoil quickly if handled incorrectly.

Store fresh fish at an internal temperature of 41°F (5°C) or lower. Keep fillets and steaks in original packaging, or tightly wrap them in moisture-proof materials. Fresh, whole fish can be packed in flaked or crushed ice. Ice beds should be self-draining. Change the ice and clean and sanitize the container often. Store frozen fish at temperatures that will keep it frozen.

Key Point

Store fresh raw meat, poultry, and fish at an internal temperature of 41°F (5°C) or lower.

Shellfish

Store shucked shellfish at an internal temperature of 41°F (5°C) or lower.

Store live shellfish in its original container at an air temperature of 41°F (5°C) or lower. Keep shellstock identification tags on file for 90 days from the date the last shellfish was sold or served from the container.

You can store live shellfish, such as clams, oysters, mussels, and scallops, in a display tank under one of two conditions:

1 The tank has a sign stating that the shellfish are for display only.

2 For shellfish to be served to customers, a variance has been obtained from the local regulatory authority that allows the shellfish to be served to customers. You will need to show the following:

- Water from other tanks will not flow into the display tank.
- Using the display tank will not affect food quality or safety.
- Shellstock ID tags have been retained as required.

Eggs

Store shell eggs at an air temperature of 45°F (7°C) or lower. Maintain constant temperature and humidity levels in coolers used to store shell eggs. Here are some guidelines:

- Do not wash shell eggs before storing them. They are washed and sanitized at the packing facility.
- Plan to use all shell eggs within four to five weeks of the packing date.
- Keep shell eggs in cold storage until the time they are used. Take out only as many eggs as are needed for immediate use.
- Store frozen egg items at temperatures that will keep them frozen.
- Store liquid eggs according to the manufacturer's recommendations.
- Dried egg items can be stored in a cool dry-storage area. Once they are reconstituted (mixed with water), store them in the cooler at 41°F (5°C) or lower. Do not reconstitute more dried egg item than is needed for immediate use.

Milk

Store milk at 41°F (5°C) or lower.

Fresh Produce

Cut melons, cut tomatoes, and cut leafy greens are TCS food. Store them at 41°F (5°C) or lower.

Other fruit and vegetables have various temperature requirements for storage. While many raw, whole fruit and vegetables can be stored at 41°F (5°C) or lower, not all can be stored at this temperature. Work with your produce supplier to determine the best storage temperature for the items you purchase.

Raw, whole produce and raw, cut vegetables—such as celery, carrots, and radishes—delivered packed in ice can be stored as they are. Make sure the containers are self-draining. The ice should also be changed regularly. Follow these guidelines:

- Fruit and vegetables kept in the cooler can dry out quickly. Keep the relative humidity at 85 to 95 percent.

- Although most produce can be stored in the cooler, avocados, bananas, pears, and tomatoes ripen best at room temperature.

- Most produce should not be washed before storage. Moisture often promotes the growth of mold. Instead, wash produce before prepping or serving it.

- When soaking or storing produce in standing water or an ice-water slurry, do not mix different items or multiple batches of the same item.

- Store whole citrus fruit, hard-rind squash, eggplant, and root vegetables—such as potatoes, sweet potatoes, rutabagas, and onions—in a cool dry-storage area. Temperatures of 60°F to 70°F (16°C to 21°C) are best. Make sure containers are well ventilated. Store onions away from other vegetables that might absorb odor.

ROP Food

Always store reduced-oxygen packaged (ROP) food at temperatures recommended by the manufacturer or at 41°F (5°C) or lower. This includes modified atmosphere packaged (MAP), vacuum-packed, and *sous vide* food. An example is shown at left. Frozen items should be stored at temperatures that will keep them frozen. Store and handle these items carefully.

ROP items are especially susceptible to the growth of *Clostridium botulinum*. Throw the item away if the package shows any of the following characteristics:

- It is torn or slimy.

- It contains excessive liquid.

- The food item bubbles, indicating the possible growth of *Clostridium botulinum*.

Always check the expiration date before using ROP items. Labels should clearly list contents, storage temperature, prep instructions, and a use-by date.

Operators who package food in-house using a ROP process need to follow specific rules for packaging and labeling. Consult your local regulatory authority for guidance.

Key Point

When soaking or storing produce in standing water or an ice-water slurry, do not mix different items or multiple batches of the same item.

UHT and Aseptically Packaged Food

Food that has been pasteurized at ultra-high temperatures (UHT) and aseptically packaged can be stored at room temperature. The coffee creamers in the photo at left are an example. Once opened, store UHT and aseptically packaged food in the cooler at 41°F (5°C) or lower.

Store UHT items that are not aseptically packaged at an internal temperature of 41°F (5°C) or lower.

Canned Goods

Even canned food spoils over time. Higher storage temperatures may shorten shelf life. Acidic food, such as canned tomatoes, does not last as long as food that is low in acid. The acid can also form pinholes in the metal over time. Follow these guidelines:

- Discard damaged cans, as shown in the photo at left.
- Keep dry-storage areas dry. Too much moisture will cause cans to rust.
- Wipe cans clean with a sanitized cloth before opening them. This will help prevent dirt from falling into the contents of the can.

Dry Food

Keep flour, cereal, and grain items, such as pasta or crackers, in airtight containers. They can quickly become stale in a humid room. They can also become moldy with too much moisture.

Before using dry food, check containers or packages for damage from insects or rodents. Cereal and grain items are often targets for these pests.

If stored in the correct conditions, salt and sugar can be held almost indefinitely.

Business

What Happens On Television

The world of restaurants has never been more visible than it is today via the many television shows and competitions about culinary arts. If you are a fan of these shows, you might have noticed that some of the food safety principles you have been learning about in the ServSafe program do not always seem to be followed by the talented chefs and servers featured in the programs.

Why does this happen? No single answer can explain everything that you might see. But most shows are meant to be more entertaining than instructional. It is unlikely that someone washing his or her hands for 20 seconds is going to be featured, particularly when other exciting actions can be shown. The person involved might be doing the right thing, but it ends up on the cutting room floor. And while many of the people on competition shows are used to the high-pressure world of a dinner rush, it is also likely that they are facing an additional, unique combination of stress, scrutiny, and excitement, leading to some food safety mistakes in the heat of competition.

How does food safety "really" work? You might be tempted to assume that some of the actions that you see on TV—such as dipping a finger into a sauce, handling finished meat with bare hands, or putting thumbs onto the surfaces of plates being served—are only minor food safety risks. But in the real, everyday world of restaurants, no mistake is "minor." It only takes one unsafe action to make someone sick. The next time you watch a culinary-related program on television, make it a part of your food safety training. See if you could improve on what you see, or think about what might be happening off-camera. Then do everything that you can to avoid such infractions and keep the food that you handle safe, whether you have an audience or not.

SUMMARY

- Any item not stored in its original container must be labeled. The label must include the common name of the food or a statement that clearly and accurately identifies it.

- Ready-to-eat TCS food prepped in-house can be stored for up to seven days if held at 41°F (5°C) or lower. It must be date marked if held for longer than 24 hours. The label must indicate when the food must be sold, eaten, or thrown out.

- Do not overload coolers or freezers. This prevents good airflow and makes units work harder to stay cold.

- Food must be rotated so the items with the earliest use-by or expiration dates are used before those with later dates.

- Store TCS food at an internal temperature of 41°F (5°C) or lower, or 135°F (57°C) or higher. Randomly sample the internal temperature of stored food.

- Store raw meat, poultry, and seafood separately from ready-to-eat food. If raw and ready-to-eat food cannot be stored separately, store ready-to-eat food above raw meat, poultry, and seafood.

- Store food, linens, and single-use items in designated storage areas. These items must be stored away from walls and at least six inches (15 centimeters) off the floor.

Apply Your Knowledge

Use these questions to review the concepts presented in this chapter.

DISCUSSION QUESTIONS

1 What is the recommended top-to-bottom order for storing the following food in the same cooler: raw trout, an uncooked beef roast, raw chicken, pecan pie, and raw ground beef?

2 What are storage requirements for live shellfish?

3 Explain the labeling requirements for food packaged on-site for retail sale.

4 Explain the FIFO method of stock rotation.

For answers, please turn to the Answer Key.

Apply Your Knowledge

CASE IN POINT

Storage Problems at Enrico's

A shipment was delivered to Enrico's Italian Restaurant. Alyce, who was in charge of receiving, inspected the shipment and immediately proceeded to store the items. First, she carried the bags of shrimp to the freezer. She wondered who had left the freezer without making sure the door was completely shut.

Alyce then loaded a case of sour cream on the dolly and wheeled it over to the reach-in cooler. When she opened the cooler, she noticed that it was tightly packed. However, she was able to squeeze the case into a spot on the top shelf.

Next, she wheeled several cases of fresh ground beef and fresh salmon over to the walk-in cooler. Alyce pushed through the cold curtains in the cooler and bumped into a stockpot of soup stored on the floor. She moved the soup to a storage shelf and then made a space for the ground beef on a shelf next to the door. Alyce was able to put the salmon on the shelf above the soup. Then she spent a few minutes talking to Mary, who had just cleaned the shelving in the unit and was lining it with new aluminum foil.

① What storage errors occurred?

For answers, please turn to the Answer Key.

A Second Chance

CASE IN POINT

Ginny's Bistro, a longtime fixture on the food scene just outside of a large Midwestern city, had finally completed a major renovation of its kitchen. The bistro had been open for 44 years, and, except for some repairs along the way, not much had been done to improve the facilities in the back of the house. The kitchen staff was thrilled that the renovation work was nearly complete.

Chase, a young kitchen manager and Ginny's great grandson, jumped at the chance to review how food storage should be done in the newly renovated space. He set out to do a complete food storage review. Chase and his staff were determined to start fresh and ensure that they followed good food storage guidelines as they prepared for the reopening of their kitchen.

1 List some things that Chase and his staff should consider as they conduct a review of the new storage area.

For answers, please turn to the Answer Key.

Study Questions

1. What must be included on the label of TCS food that was prepped in-house?

   A Date that the food was received

   B Name of each TCS ingredient included

   C Date that the food should be thrown out

   D List of all potential ingredients in the food

2. How long can ready-to-eat TCS food that was prepped in-house be stored if it was held at 41°F (5°C) or lower?

   A 3 days

   B 5 days

   C 7 days

   D 9 days

3. When storing food using the FIFO method, where should the food with the earliest use-by dates be stored?

   A Below food with later use-by dates

   B Behind food with later use-by dates

   C In front of food with later use-by dates

   D Alongside food with later use-by dates

4. How far above the floor should food be stored?

   A At least 1" (3 cm)

   B At least 2" (5 cm)

   C At least 4" (10 cm)

   D At least 6" (15 cm)

5. What is the problem with storing raw ground beef above prepped salads?

   A Cross-contamination

   B Poor personal hygiene

   C Time-temperature abuse

   D Cross-contact with allergens

6. In top-to-bottom order, how should a fresh pork roast, fresh salmon, a container of lettuce, and a pan of fresh chicken breasts be stored in a cooler?

   A Lettuce, fresh salmon, fresh pork roast, fresh chicken breasts

   B Fresh salmon, fresh pork roast, fresh chicken breasts, lettuce

   C Lettuce, fresh chicken breasts, fresh pork roast, fresh salmon

   D Fresh salmon, lettuce, fresh chicken breasts, fresh pork roast

For answers, please turn to the Answer Key.

8 The Flow of Food: Preparation

Preparation	Cooking Food	Cooling and Reheating Food
— General Preparation Practices — Thawing — Prepping Specific Food — Prepping Practices That Have Special Requirements	— Minimum Internal Cooking Temperatures — Cooking TCS Food in the Microwave Oven — General Cooking Guidelines — Consumer Advisories — Partial Cooking During Prepping	— Temperature Requirements for Cooling Food — Methods for Cooling Food — Storing Food for Further Cooling — Reheating Food

INSIDE THIS CHAPTER

- Preparation
- Cooking Food
- Cooling and Reheating Food

OBJECTIVES

After completing this chapter, you should be able to identify the following:

- Correct ways for prepping food to prevent cross-contamination and time-temperature abuse
- Safe methods for thawing food
- The minimum internal cooking temperatures for TCS food
- The correct way to cook TCS food in a microwave oven
- The importance of informing consumers of risks when serving raw or undercooked food
- Requirements for partially cooking TCS food
- Methods and time-temperature requirements for cooling TCS food
- Time and temperature requirements for reheating TCS food

KEY TERMS

- Slacking
- Minimum internal temperature

Preparation	Cooking Food	Cooling and Reheating Food
— General Preparation Practices — Thawing — Prepping Specific Food — Prepping Practices That Have Special Requirements	— Minimum Internal Cooking Temperatures — Cooking TCS Food in the Microwave Oven — General Cooking Guidelines — Consumer Advisories — Partial Cooking During Prepping	— Temperature Requirements for Cooling Food — Methods for Cooling Food — Storing Food for Further Cooling — Reheating Food

PREPARATION

General Preparation Practices

Cross-contamination and time-temperature abuse can happen easily when you are prepping food. You can prevent pathogens from spreading and growing by making good food-prep choices.

Equipment   Make sure workstations, cutting boards, and utensils are clean and sanitized.

Quantity   Only remove as much food from the cooler as you can prep in a short period of time. This keeps ingredients from sitting out for long periods of time. In the photo at left, the food handler has taken out too much tuna salad.

Storage   Return prepped food to the cooler, or cook it as quickly as possible.

Additives   If you use food or color additives when prepping food, follow these guidelines:

* Only use additives that have been approved by your local regulatory authority. Never use more than is allowed by law. Never use additives to alter the appearance of the food.

* Do not sell produce that was treated with sulfites before it was received in the operation. Do not add sulfites to produce that will be eaten raw.

Presentation   Food should be offered to customers in a way that does not mislead or misinform them. Customers must be able to judge the true appearance, color, and quality of food. Do not use the following to misrepresent the appearance of food:

* Food additives or color additives

* Colored overwraps

* Lights

Food that has not been honestly presented should be thrown out.

Corrective actions   Food that has become unsafe should be thrown out unless it can be safely reconditioned. All food—especially ready-to-eat food—should be thrown out in the following situations:

* When it is handled by staff who have been restricted or excluded from the operation because of illness

* When it is contaminated by hands or bodily fluids from the nose or mouth

* When it has exceeded the time and temperature requirements designed to keep food safe

Sometimes food can be restored to a safe condition. This is called reconditioning. For example, a hot food that has not been held at the correct temperature may be reheated if it has not been in the temperature danger zone for more than two hours. This can return food to a safe condition.

Thawing

Freezing food does not kill pathogens. If frozen food is exposed to the temperature danger zone during thawing, any foodborne pathogens present will begin to grow. That is why food should not be thawed at room temperature.

For example, suppose a cook needs to thaw a 20-pound turkey. In a hurry, he places it on a prep table to thaw overnight, as shown in the photo at left. When the turkey begins to thaw, the skin and outer layers are exposed to the temperature danger zone even though the core of the turkey is still frozen. If there are pathogens on the turkey, they will grow to a level high enough to make the turkey unsafe.

To prevent pathogen growth, thaw TCS food in one of the following ways.

Cooler   Thaw food in a cooler keeping its temperature at 41°F (5°C) or lower. This requires advance planning. Larger items, such as a turkey, can take several days to thaw completely in a cooler.

Running water   Submerge the food under running drinkable water at a temperature of 70°F (21°C) or lower. The flow of the water should be strong enough to wash loose food into the drain. Always use a clean and sanitized prep sink when thawing food this way. The photo at left shows the correct way to thaw food under running water. Do not let the temperature of the food go above 41°F (5°C) for longer than four hours. This includes the time it takes to thaw the food plus the time to prep or cool it.

Microwave   Thaw food in a microwave oven if it will be cooked immediately after thawing. The food must be cooked in conventional cooking equipment, such as an oven, once it is thawed.

Cooking   Thaw food as part of the cooking process. Frozen hamburger patties, for example, can go straight from the freezer onto a grill without first being thawed. Frozen chicken can go straight into a deep fryer. These items cook quickly enough from the frozen state to pass through the temperature danger zone without harm. However, always verify the final internal cooking temperature with a thermometer.

Some frozen food may also be slacked before cooking. Slacking is the gradual thawing of frozen food to prep it for deep-frying. This allows even heating during cooking. For example, you might slack frozen breaded chicken breasts by having them warm from –10°F (–23°C) to 25°F (–4°C).

Slack food just before you cook it. Do not let it get any warmer than 41°F (5°C). If your regulatory authority allows slacking at room temperature, have a system that ensures the item does not exceed 41°F (5°C).

Thawing ROP Fish

Frozen fish may be supplied in reduced-oxygen packaging (ROP). This fish should usually remain frozen until ready for use. If this is stated on the label, the fish must be removed from the packaging at the following times:

- Before thawing it under refrigeration

- Before or immediately after thawing it under running water

Prepping Specific Food

Special care must be taken when handling meat, seafood, and poultry, as well as salads containing these items. Likewise, you will need to pay close attention when prepping eggs, batter and breading, and produce. Even ice needs special care.

Meat, Seafood, and Poultry

The sources of most cross-contamination in an operation are raw meat, poultry, and seafood. Your staff should follow specific procedures when handling these items.

Cleaning and sanitizing   Use clean and sanitized work areas, cutting boards, knives, and utensils. Prep raw meat, poultry, and seafood separately or at different times from fresh produce.

Portion control   Remove from refrigerated storage only as much of an item as can be prepped at one time. When prepping beef for stew, for example, take out and prep one portion, as shown in the photo at left. Then refrigerate it before taking out another portion.

Prompt action   Return raw, prepped meat directly to the cooler, or cook it as quickly as possible. Store these items correctly to prevent cross-contamination.

Salads Containing TCS Food

Chicken, tuna, egg, pasta, and potato salads have all been involved in foodborne-illness outbreaks. These salads are not usually cooked after prepping. This means you do not have a chance to reduce pathogens, such as *Staphylococcus aureus*, that may have gotten into the salad during preparation. Follow these guidelines.

Prepping small batches   Prep food in small batches so large amounts of food do not sit out at room temperature for long periods of time.

Using leftovers   Leftover TCS food, such as pasta, chicken, and potatoes, should only be used to make salads if it has been cooked, held, and cooled correctly.

Storing leftovers   Throw out leftover TCS food held at 41°F (5°C) or lower after seven days. Check the use-by date before using stored food items.

Chilling   Consider chilling all ingredients and utensils before using them to make the salad. For example, tuna, mayonnaise, and mixing bowls can be chilled before making tuna salad.

Refrigeration   Leave food in the cooler until all ingredients are ready to be mixed.

Eggs and Egg Mixtures

Historically the contents of whole, clean, uncracked shell eggs were considered bacteria-free. It is now known that in rare cases, a certain bacteria, *Salmonella* Enteritidis, can be found inside eggs.

Salmonella Enteritidis can live within a laying hen. It can also be deposited in an egg before the shell is formed. Only a small number of eggs produced in the United States are likely to carry this type of bacteria. However, all untreated eggs are considered TCS food. They are able to support the rapid growth of bacteria. When prepping eggs and egg mixtures, follow these guidelines.

Pooled eggs   Pooled eggs are eggs that are cracked open and combined in a common container, as shown in the photo at left. Handle them (if allowed) with special care because bacteria in one egg can be spread to the rest. Cook pooled eggs promptly after mixing or store them at 41°F (5°C) or lower. Wash and sanitize containers used to hold pooled eggs before using them for a new batch.

Pasteurized eggs   Consider using pasteurized shell eggs or egg products for egg dishes requiring little or no cooking. Examples are hollandaise sauce, Caesar salad dressing, tiramisu, and mousse.

High-risk populations   Operations that serve high-risk populations, such as hospitals and nursing homes, must take special care when using eggs. Use pasteurized eggs or egg products when dishes containing eggs will be served raw or undercooked. If shell eggs will be pooled for a recipe, they should also be pasteurized. Unpasteurized shell eggs may be used if the dish will be cooked all the way through, such as in an omelet or a cake.

Cleaning and sanitizing   Promptly clean and sanitize all equipment and utensils used to prep eggs.

Batters and Breading

Batters or breading prepped with eggs or milk, as shown in the photo at left, should be handled carefully. They run the risk of time-temperature abuse and cross-contamination. If you choose to make breaded or battered food from scratch, follow these guidelines.

Key Point

Batters or breading prepped with eggs or milk should be handled carefully. They run the risk of time-temperature abuse and cross-contamination.

Small batches   Prepping batters in small amounts prevents time-temperature abuse of both the batter and the food being coated. Store what you do not need in a covered container at 41°F (5°C) or lower.

Prompt storage   When breading food that will be cooked later, store it in the cooler as soon as possible.

Unused items   Create a plan to throw out unused batter or breading after a set time. This might be after using a batch or at the end of a shift.

Thorough cooking   The coating of battered and breaded food acts as an insulator that can prevent food from being thoroughly cooked. Cook this food all the way through. When deep-frying food, make sure the temperature of the oil recovers before loading each batch.

Overloading the basket also slows cooking time. This means items can be removed from the fryer before they are thoroughly cooked. Monitor oil and food temperatures using calibrated thermometers. Watch cooking time as well.

Fresh Juice

If you package fresh fruit and vegetable juice in-house for later sale, treat (e.g., pasteurize) the juice according to an approved HACCP plan. You will learn about HACCP plans in Chapter 10.

As an alternative to manufacturing under a HACCP plan, the juice can be labeled with the following: *Warning: This product has not been pasteurized and, therefore, may contain harmful bacteria that can cause serious illness in children, the elderly, and people with weakened immune systems.* An example is shown in the photo at left.

Produce

Handle fresh produce carefully to prevent foodborne illnesses. Viruses such as hepatitis A, bacteria such as shiga toxin-producing *E. coli*, and parasites such as *Cryptosporidium parvum* can survive on produce, especially cut produce. Follow these safeguards to minimize or eliminate the risk from these pathogens.

Key Point

When prepping raw vegetables, start with a clean, sanitized workstation. Prep vegetables away from raw meat, poultry, and seafood, as well as from ready-to-eat food.

Prepping   Make sure fruit and vegetables do not come in contact with surfaces exposed to raw meat, poultry, and seafood. Prep produce away from raw meat, poultry, and seafood, as well as from ready-to-eat food. Clean and sanitize the work space and all utensils that will be used during prepping.

Washing   Wash fruit and vegetables thoroughly under running water to remove dirt and other contaminants. Do this before cutting, cooking, or combining with other ingredients:

- The water should be slightly warmer than the temperature of the produce.

- Pay close attention to leafy greens, such as lettuce and spinach. Remove the outer leaves, and pull lettuce and spinach completely apart. Rinse them thoroughly.

- Clean and sanitize surfaces that were used to prep produce items for washing.

- Produce can be sanitized by washing it in water containing ozone. This treatment helps control pathogens. Check with your regulatory authority to see if this is allowed in your area.

Soaking or storing   When soaking or storing produce in standing water or an ice-water slurry, as shown in the photo at left, do not mix different items or multiple batches of the same item. Pathogens from contaminated produce can contaminate the water and the ice and can spread to other produce.

Refrigerating   Refrigerate and hold cut melons, cut tomatoes, and cut leafy greens at 41°F (5°C) or lower. They are TCS food.

High-risk populations   If your operation primarily serves high-risk populations, do not serve raw seed sprouts.

Ice

People often forget that ice is a food and can become contaminated just as easily as any other food. Ice must be made from water that is safe to drink. Do not use ice as an ingredient or to cool drinks if it was used to keep food cold.

When transferring ice from an ice machine, use a clean, sanitized scoop and container. Do not transfer ice in containers that have been used to store chemicals or raw meat, poultry, or seafood. Store ice scoops outside of the ice machine in a clean, protected location, as shown in the photo at left. Never touch ice with hands or use a glass to scoop ice.

Prepping Practices That Have Special Requirements

You will need a variance when prepping food in certain ways. A variance is a document issued by your regulatory authority that allows a regulatory requirement to be waived or changed. When applying for a variance, your regulatory authority may require you to submit a HACCP plan. The plan must account for any food safety risks related to the way you plan to prep the food item.

You will need a variance if your operation plans to prep food in any of the following ways:

* Packaging fresh juice on-site for sale at a later time, unless the juice has a warning label.

* Smoking food as a way of preserving it—not to enhance flavor.

* Using food additives or adding components such as vinegar to preserve or alter the food so that it no longer needs time and temperature control for safety.

* Curing food.

* Custom-processing animals for personal use. For example, a hunter brings a deer to a restaurant for dressing and takes the meat home for later use.

* Packaging food using a reduced-oxygen packaging (ROP) method. This includes MAP, vacuum-packed, and *sous vide* food. *Clostridium botulinum* and *Listeria monocytogenes* are risks to food packaged in these ways.

* Sprouting seeds or beans.

* Offering live shellfish from a display tank.

Regulatory

Butcher Blocks

Hardwood cutting boards, often known as butcher blocks, are popular with foodservice professionals. One common concern with these boards, however, is their potential for easy surface contamination. Where allowed, these surfaces can be used safely with the proper care.

Most acceptable surfaces are made of hard maple. Clean and sanitize it as you would any other food-contact surface. Make sure any "special" butcher block cleaners follow regulatory guidelines. The surface also must be planed or sanded regularly. Rubbing coarse salt over the surface can accomplish this. The gentle abrasion of the salt wears down the cuts and slits caused by knives, which can harbor pathogens. Also, the surface should be seasoned quarterly with food-grade mineral oil that is fresh and free from aroma or flavor.

The remaining surface must be free of pits, grooves, and cracks. Health inspectors look for any split in the wood or an uneven surface where pathogens might be able to grow. If they find a problem, the item must be thrown out.

Preparation	Cooking Food	Cooling and Reheating Food
— General Preparation Practices — Thawing — Prepping Specific Food — Prepping Practices That Have Special Requirements	— Minimum Internal Cooking Temperatures — Cooking TCS Food in the Microwave Oven — General Cooking Guidelines — Consumer Advisories — Partial Cooking During Prepping	— Temperature Requirements for Cooling Food — Methods for Cooling Food — Storing Food for Further Cooling — Reheating Food

COOKING FOOD

Minimum Internal Cooking Temperatures

The only way to reduce pathogens in food to safe levels is to cook it to its minimum internal temperature and hold that temperature for a specific amount of time. The temperature is different for each food. The FDA recommends cooking food to the minimum internal temperatures listed below. However, your operation or regulatory authority might require different temperatures. Keep in mind that while cooking can reduce pathogens in food to safe levels, it will not destroy spores or toxins they may have produced. For this reason, it is critical to handle food correctly before it is cooked.

Minimum Internal Cooking Temperature	Type of Food
165°F (74°C) for 15 seconds 	• Poultry—including whole or ground chicken, turkey, or duck • Stuffing made with fish, meat, or poultry • Stuffed meat, seafood, poultry, or pasta • Dishes that include previously cooked TCS ingredients (raw ingredients should be cooked to their minimum internal temperatures)
155°F (68°C) for 15 seconds 	• Ground meat—including beef, pork, and other meat • Injected meat—including brined ham and flavor-injected roasts • Mechanically tenderized meat • Ratites—including ostrich and emu • Ground seafood—including chopped or minced seafood • Shell eggs hot-held for service

145°F (63°C) for 15 seconds

- Steaks/chops of pork, beef, veal, and lamb
- Seafood—including fish, shellfish, and crustaceans
- Commercially raised game
- Shell eggs that will be served immediately

145°F (63°C) for 4 minutes

- Roasts of pork, beef, veal, and lamb
- Roasts may be cooked to these alternate cooking times and temperatures depending on the type of roast and oven used:
  - 130°F (54°C) 112 minutes
  - 131°F (55°C) 89 minutes
  - 133°F (56°C) 56 minutes
  - 135°F (57°C) 36 minutes
  - 136°F (58°C) 28 minutes
  - 138°F (59°C) 18 minutes
  - 140°F (60°C) 12 minutes
  - 142°F (61°C) 8 minutes
  - 144°F (62°C) 5 minutes

135°F (57°C)

- Fruit, vegetables, grains (rice, pasta), and legumes (beans, refried beans) that will be hot-held for service

175°F (80°C)

- Tea

Automatic iced tea and automatic coffee machine equipment: Tea leaves should remain in contact with the water for a minimum of one minute.

Traditional steeping method: Tea leaves should be exposed to the water for about five minutes.

Cooking TCS Food in the Microwave Oven

Meat, seafood, poultry, and eggs that you cook in a microwave oven must be cooked to 165°F (74°C). In addition, follow these guidelines:

- Cover the food to prevent its surface from drying out.
- Rotate or stir it halfway through the cooking process so that the heat reaches the food more evenly.
- Let the covered food stand for at least two minutes after cooking to let the food temperature even out.
- Check the temperature in at least two places to make sure that the food is cooked through.

General Cooking Guidelines

Here are general guidelines to follow when cooking food.

Time and temperature   Specify the cooking time and minimum internal temperature in all recipes.

Correct thermometer   Use a thermometer with a probe that is the correct size for the food. Check the temperature in the thickest part of the food, as shown in the photo at left. Take at least two readings in different locations.

Overloading   Avoid overloading ovens, fryers, and other cooking equipment. Overloading may lower the equipment or oil temperature and the food might not cook fully.

Equipment temperature   Let the cooking equipment's temperature recover between batches.

Consumer Advisories

You must cook TCS food to required minimum internal temperatures unless you inform customers that an item is raw or undercooked.

Disclosure   If your menu includes TCS items that are raw or undercooked, you must note it on the menu next to these items. This can be done by placing an asterisk next to the item that points customers to a footnote at the bottom of the menu. The footnote must include a statement that indicates the item is raw or undercooked, or contains raw or undercooked ingredients. The menu in the photo at left shows an example of disclosure.

Sesame Seared Ahi Tuna*
Avocado, mango-papaya salsa,
sweet soy, ginger vinaigrette

*THIS ITEM IS SERVED RAW OR UNDERCOOKED,
OR CONTAINS (OR MAY CONTAIN) RAW OR
UNDERCOOKED INGREDIENTS.

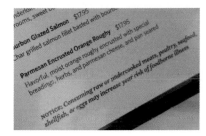

Reminder You must advise customers who order raw or undercooked food of the increased risk of foodborne illness. You can do this by posting a notice in your menu, as shown in the photo at left. You can also provide this information using brochures, table tents, signs or other written methods. Check your local regulatory requirements.

The Food and Drug Administration (FDA) advises against offering raw or undercooked meat, poultry, seafood, or eggs on a children's menu. This is especially true for undercooked ground beef, which may be contaminated with shiga toxin-producing *E. coli* O157:H7.

Operations that mainly serve a high-risk population, such as nursing homes or day-care centers, cannot serve raw or undercooked eggs, meat, or seafood. Examples include over-easy eggs, raw oysters, and rare hamburgers. Raw seed sprouts also should not be served.

Partial Cooking During Prepping

Some operations partially cook food during prep and then finish cooking it just before service.

Follow the steps below if you plan to partially cook meat, seafood, poultry, or eggs or dishes containing these items.

1 Do not cook the food for longer than 60 minutes during initial cooking.

2 Cool the food immediately after initial cooking.

3 Freeze or refrigerate the food after cooling it. If refrigerating the food, make sure it is held at 41°F (5°C) or lower.

4 Heat the food to its required minimum internal temperature before selling or serving it.

5 Cool the food if it will not be served immediately or held for service.

Your regulatory authority may require that you have written procedures explaining how food cooked in this way will be prepped and stored. They need to be approved by the regulatory authority and describe the following:

- How the requirements will be monitored and documented.

- Which corrective actions will be taken if requirements are not met.

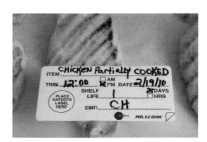

- How these food items will be marked after initial cooking to indicate they need further cooking. The chicken in the photo at left has been partially cooked and is marked to show this.

- How these food items will be separated from ready-to-eat food during storage, once initial cooking is complete.

Preparation	Cooking Food	Cooling and Reheating Food
— General Preparation Practices — Thawing — Prepping Specific Food — Prepping Practices That Have Special Requirements	— Minimum Internal Cooking Temperatures — Cooking TCS Food in the Microwave Oven — General Cooking Guidelines — Consumer Advisories — Partial Cooking During Prepping	— Temperature Requirements for Cooling Food — Methods for Cooling Food — Storing Food for Further Cooling — Reheating Food

COOLING AND REHEATING FOOD

Temperature Requirements for Cooling Food

As you know, pathogens grow well in the temperature danger zone. They grow even faster between 125°F and 70°F (52°C and 21°C). Food must pass through this temperature range quickly to reduce this growth.

Cool TCS food from 135°F to 41°F (57°C to 5°C) or lower within six hours.

135°F (57°C)
70°F (21°C)
2 hours

First, cool food from 135°F to 70°F (57°C to 21°C) within two hours.

70°F (21°C)
41°F (5°C)
4 hours

Then cool it from 70°F to 41°F (21°C to 5°C) or lower in the next four hours.

If food has not reached 70°F (21°C) within two hours, it must be reheated and then cooled again.

If you can cool the food from 135°F to 70°F (57°C to 21°C) in less than two hours, you can use the remaining time to cool it to 41°F (5°C) or lower. However, the total cooling time cannot be longer than six hours. For example, if you cool food from 135°F to 70°F (57°C to 21°C) in one hour, you have the remaining five hours to get the food to 41°F (5°C) or lower. Check your local regulatory requirements.

Methods for Cooling Food

The following factors affect how quickly food will cool.

Thickness or density of the food   The denser the food, the more slowly it will cool.

Size of the food   Large food items cool more slowly than smaller items. To let food cool faster, you should reduce its size. Cut large food items into smaller pieces. Divide large containers of food into smaller containers or shallow pans, as shown in the illustration at left.

Storage container   The container in which food is stored also affects how fast it will cool. Stainless steel transfers heat away from food faster than plastic. Shallow pans disperse heat faster than deep ones.

Do not cool large amounts of hot food in a cooler. Most coolers are not designed to cool large amounts of hot food quickly. Placing hot food in the cooler may also not move it through the temperature danger zone fast enough.

You can cool food quickly and safely in the following ways.

Ice-water bath   After dividing food into smaller containers, place them into a clean prep sink or large pot filled with ice water, as shown in the photo at left. Stir the food often to cool it faster and more evenly.

Ice paddle   Plastic paddles are available that can be filled with ice or with water and then frozen. Food stirred with these paddles will cool quickly, as shown in the photo at left.

Blast or tumble chiller   Blast chillers blast cold air across food at high speeds to remove heat. They are typically used to cool large amounts of food. Tumble chillers tumble bags of hot food in cold water. Tumble chillers work well on thick food, such as mashed potatoes.

Ice or cold water as an ingredient   When cooling soups or stews, the recipe is made with less water than required. Cold water or ice is then added after cooking to cool the food and provide the remaining water.

Storing Food for Further Cooling

Loosely cover food containers before storing them. Food can be left uncovered if stored in a way that protects it from contaminants. Storing uncovered containers above other food, especially raw meat, seafood, and poultry, will help prevent cross-contamination.

Reheating Food

How you reheat food depends on how you intend to use the food. Follow these guidelines when reheating food.

Food reheated for immediate service   You can reheat food that will be served immediately, such as beef for a beef sandwich, to any temperature. However, you must make sure the food was cooked and cooled correctly.

Food reheated for hot-holding   You must reheat TCS food for hot-holding to an internal temperature of 165°F (74°C) for 15 seconds. Make sure the food reaches this temperature within two hours from start to finish. The food handler in the photo at left is reheating clam chowder for hot-holding. These guidelines apply to all reheating methods, such as ovens or microwave ovens.

Reheat commercially processed and packaged ready-to-eat food to an internal temperature of at least 135°F (57°C). This includes items such as cheese sticks and deep-fried vegetables.

Business

Preventing Injuries

According to *Nation's Restaurant News*, cuts and burns to hands on the job cost the restaurant and foodservice industry approximately $300 million each year. Injuries threaten food safety, affect staffing, and clearly have an impact on an operation's bottom line.

Managers can help to reduce the likelihood of injuries by providing the correct training for equipment, providing staff with protective equipment (such as cut gloves and mitts), and making first aid training and supplies available. Encourage staff to use the protective equipment provided, and make sure everyone understands the connection between injuries and infection.

This will help to ensure that staff know what to do when they do suffer an injury. Cuts and burns that take place in food-prep areas must be addressed immediately, and the work space must be cleaned before prep can continue. Staff who arrive to work with injuries must cover them correctly, as discussed in chapter 4 of this text.

SUMMARY

- To protect food during preparation, you must handle it safely. The keys are time and temperature control and preventing cross-contamination.

- Freezing does not kill pathogens. Pathogens in the food will grow if exposed to the temperature danger zone during thawing. Thaw frozen food in the cooler, under running water, in a microwave oven, or as part of the cooking process. Never thaw food at room temperature.

- Prevent cross-contamination and time-temperature abuse when preparing food. Prep food in small batches and keep workstations and utensils clean and sanitized. Prepped food that is not going to be cooked immediately should be put back in the cooler.

- Cooking food can reduce pathogens in food to safe levels. You must cook food to minimum internal temperatures for a specific amount of time. These temperatures vary from food to food. Cooking does not kill the spores or toxins that some pathogens produce.

- You must advise customers who order food that is raw or undercooked of the increased risk of foodborne illness. You can do this in different ways. If your menu includes TCS items that are raw or undercooked, you must note it on the menu next to these items. The FDA advises against offering raw and undercooked food on children's menus.

- TCS food must be cooled from 135°F to 70°F (57°C to 21°C) within two hours. Then it must be cooled from 70°F to 41°F (21°C to 5°C) or lower in the next four hours.

- Before food is cooled, you should reduce its size. Cut large food items into smaller pieces. Divide large containers of food into smaller ones. Use an ice-water bath, stir food with ice paddles, or use a blast or tumble chiller to cool food safely.

- Reheated TCS food that will be hot-held must be heated to an internal temperature of 165°F (74°C) for 15 seconds. Make sure the food reaches this temperature within two hours.

Apply Your Knowledge

Use these questions to review the concepts presented in this chapter.

DISCUSSION QUESTIONS

1. What are the minimum internal cooking temperatures for poultry, fish, pork, and ground beef?

2. What are four correct methods for thawing food?

3. What methods can be used to cool cooked food?

4. What are the rules for correctly cooking food in a microwave oven?

For answers, please turn to the Answer Key.

Apply Your Knowledge

Something's Fishy

CASE IN POINT

On Friday, John went to work at The Fish House knowing he had a lot to do. After changing clothes and punching in, he took a case of frozen raw shrimp out of the freezer. To thaw it quickly, he put the frozen shrimp into the prep sink and turned on the hot water. While waiting for the shrimp to thaw, John took several fresh, whole fish out of the walk-in cooler. He brought them back to the prep area and began to clean and fillet them. When he finished, he put the fillets in a pan and returned them to the walk-in cooler. He rinsed off the boning knife and cutting board in the sink, and wiped off the worktable with a cloth towel.

Next John transferred the shrimp from the sink to the worktable using a large colander. On the cutting board, he peeled, deveined, and butterflied the shrimp using the boning knife. He put the prepared shrimp in a covered container in the cooler, and then started preparing fresh produce.

1. What did John do wrong?

For answers, please turn to the Answer Key.

8

Apply Your Knowledge

Chicken on the Fly

Aiden was a part-time line cook at Basil's Tavern, a popular meeting and drinking place in a small community. Happy hour was an extremely busy time, not just behind the bar, but in the kitchen as well. Basil's offered a huge variety of deep fried appetizers and other small plates at reduced prices.

Aiden always worried about running out of batter for their famous signature onion rings and chicken tenders. So he decided to make a double batch of the egg-based batter the day before a Happy Hour. He prepared it in a large plastic tub and added it to batter that was left from the previous day. Aiden covered the batter and placed it in the walk-in cooler.

The next day during Happy Hour, things got crazy in the kitchen. Tickets for chicken fingers were lining up and all three fryers were going full blast. In order to try to stay ahead, Aiden packed the fryer baskets with the battered chicken tenders and lowered the baskets quickly into the fryer. As each cooked batch came out of the fryer, a full basket of uncooked product was dropped in.

Plates started coming back almost as fast as they had left the kitchen. Customers were complaining that the chicken tenders were raw on the inside.

1. What did Aiden do wrong?

2. What should he have done differently?

For answers, please turn to the Answer Key.

Study Questions

1 What is the maximum water temperature allowed when thawing food under running water?

   A   70°F (21°C)

   B   65°F (18°C)

   C   60°F (16°C)

   D   55°F (13°C)

2 What must food handlers do to food immediately after thawing it in the microwave oven?

   A   Hold it.

   B   Cook it.

   C   Cool it.

   D   Freeze it.

3 What can occur if prep tables are not cleaned and sanitized between uses?

   A   Off flavors in food

   B   Cross-contamination

   C   Toxic-metal poisoning

   D   Time-temperature abuse

4 A food handler thaws several frozen turkeys on a prep table. What is the danger that this poses to the food?

   A   Off flavors in food

   B   Cross-contamination

   C   Toxic-metal poisoning

   D   Time-temperature abuse

5 A food handler pulled a hotel pan of tuna salad from the cooler and used it to prepare six tuna salad sandwiches. What is the problem with this situation?

   A   Cross-contamination

   B   Poor personal hygiene

   C   Time-temperature abuse

   D   Poor cleaning and sanitizing

6 What is the minimum internal cooking temperature for stuffed pork chops?

   A   135°F (57°C) for 15 seconds

   B   145°F (63°C) for 15 seconds

   C   155°F (68°C) for 15 seconds

   D   165°F (74°C) for 15 seconds

Continued on the next page ▶

▶ *Continued from previous page*

7 What is the minimum internal cooking temperature for eggs, meat, poultry, and seafood cooked in a microwave oven?

   A 135°F (57°C)

   B 145°F (63°C)

   C 155°F (68°C)

   D 165°F (74°C)

8 What is the minimum internal cooking temperature for eggs that will be hot-held for service?

   A 135°F (57°C) for 15 seconds

   B 145°F (63°C) for 15 seconds

   C 155°F (68°C) for 15 seconds

   D 165°F (74°C) for 15 seconds

9 What is the minimum internal cooking temperature for ground beef?

   A 135°F (57°C) for 15 seconds

   B 145°F (63°C) for 15 seconds

   C 155°F (68°C) for 15 seconds

   D 165°F (74°C) for 15 seconds

10 Which food should NOT be offered on a children's menu: a rare hamburger, fried chicken tenders, grilled cheese sandwich, or spaghetti with meat sauce?

   A Rare hamburger

   B Fried chicken tenders

   C Grilled cheese sandwich

   D Spaghetti with meat sauce

11 A food handler can cool a stockpot of clam chowder by placing it into a

   A cooler.

   B freezer.

   C sink of ice water.

   D cold-holding unit.

12 What temperature must TCS food be reheated to if it will be hot-held?

   A 135°F (57°C) for 15 seconds

   B 145°F (63°C) for 15 seconds

   C 155°F (68°C) for 15 seconds

   D 165°F (74°C) for 15 seconds

For answers, please turn to the Answer Key.

Notes

9 The Flow of Food: Service

Holding Food for Service	Serving Food Safely	Off-Site Service
— General Rules for Holding Food — Holding Food without Temperature Control	— Service Staff Guidelines — Kitchen Staff Guidelines — Preset Tableware — Re-serving Food Safely — Self-Service Areas	— Delivery — Catering — Temporary Units — Mobile Units — Vending Machines

Case in POINT

One Hundred Sickened by Norovirus Outbreak

A buffet attendant sickened over 100 guests at a large southwestern golf resort. Those that got sick had symptoms that included severe vomiting, diarrhea, and physical weakness. A food handler later tested positive for Norovirus. While the food handler was not experiencing symptoms at the time of the outbreak, he indicated that he had vomiting and diarrhea the week before.

Local regulatory authorities determined that the food handler contaminated items on the buffet line as he worked. The food handler failed to wash his hands correctly before moving from buffet station to buffet station. Authorities believed that utensils used by the guests had become contaminated by the food handler. This led to the outbreak.

① What could have been done to prevent this situation from occurring in the first place?

For answers, please turn to the Answer Key.

INSIDE THIS CHAPTER

- Holding Food for Service
- Serving Food Safely
- Off-Site Service

OBJECTIVES

After completing this chapter, you should be able to identify the following:

- Time and temperature requirements for holding hot and cold TCS food
- Ways of preventing time-temperature abuse and cross-contamination when displaying and serving food
- The requirements for using time rather than temperature as the only method of control when holding ready-to-eat food
- Ways of minimizing bare-hand contact with ready-to-eat food
- How to prevent staff from contaminating food during service
- How to prevent customers from contaminating self-service areas
- The possible hazards of transporting food and ways of preventing them
- The possible hazards of serving food off-site and ways of preventing them
- The possible hazards of vending food and ways of preventing them

KEY TERMS

- Sneeze guards
- Off-site service
- Temporary units
- Mobile units

| Holding Food for Service | Serving Food Safely | Off-Site Service |
| — General Rules for Holding Food
— Holding Food without
Temperature Control | — Service Staff Guidelines
— Kitchen Staff Guidelines
— Preset Tableware
— Re-serving Food Safely
— Self-Service Areas | — Delivery
— Catering
— Temporary Units
— Mobile Units
— Vending Machines |

HOLDING FOOD FOR SERVICE

General Rules for Holding Food

To keep food safe during holding, consider the following.

Temperature   Hold hot food at an internal temperature of 135°F (57°C) or higher. Hold cold food at an internal temperature of 41°F (5°C) or lower. These temperatures are shown in the illustrations at left.

Thermometer   Use a thermometer to check temperatures. Never use the temperature gauge on a holding unit to do it. It does not check the internal temperature of the food.

Time   Check food temperature at least every four hours. Throw out food that is not being held at the correct temperature. You can also check the temperature every two hours. This will leave time for corrective action. For example, hot TCS food that has been held below 135°F (57°C) can be reheated and then placed back in the hot-holding unit.

Reheating food   Never use hot-holding equipment to reheat food unless it is built to do so. Most hot-holding equipment does not pass food through the temperature danger zone quickly enough. Reheat food correctly. Then move it to the holding unit.

Food covers and sneeze guards   Cover food and install sneeze guards to protect food from contaminants. Covers, like the ones shown in the photo at left, will help maintain a food's internal temperature.

Policies   Create policies about how long the operation will hold food and when it will be thrown out.

Holding Food without Temperature Control

Your operation may want to display or hold TCS food without temperature control. Here are some examples of when you might hold food this way:

- When displaying food for a short time, such as at an off-site catered event, as shown in the photo at left
- When electricity is not available to power holding equipment

If your operation displays or holds TCS food without temperature control, it should do so under certain conditions. Also note that the conditions for holding cold food are different from those for holding hot food. Before using time as a method of control, check with your regulatory authority for specific requirements.

Cold Food

You can hold cold food without temperature control for up to six hours if you meet these conditions:

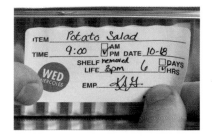

- Hold the food at 41°F (5°C) or lower before removing it from refrigeration.

- Label the food with the time you removed it from refrigeration and the time you must throw it out. The discard time on the label must be six hours from the time you removed the food from refrigeration. For example, if you remove potato salad from the cooler at 3:00 p.m. to serve at a picnic, the discard time on the label should be 9:00 p.m., as shown on the label at left.

- Make sure the food temperature does not exceed 70°F (21°C) while it is being served. Throw out any food that exceeds this temperature.

- Sell, serve, or throw out the food within six hours.

Hot Food

You can hold hot food without temperature control for up to four hours if you meet these conditions:

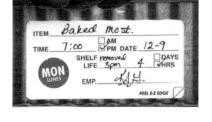

- Hold the food at 135°F (57°C) or higher before removing it from temperature control.

- Label the food with the time you must throw it out. The discard time on the label must be four hours from the time you removed the food from temperature control, as shown in the photo at left.

- Sell, serve, or throw out the food within four hours.

Business

Industry Communities

Dedicated to creating memorable experiences, the restaurant and foodservice industry places a lot of emphasis on making social connections on the job. So it is no surprise that there are a number of communities available to the industry's staff members to help them network and learn from each other. Examples include FohBoh.com, which provides a forum and resources for all levels of industry staff members. They also have separate communities for chefs and sommeliers. Foodservice.com also offers an online community, as well as the latest news and articles by featured writers. Many independent bloggers with forums and more informal communities can also be found through a simple online search.

As you continue in your career, you may develop a specialty, many of which also have online communities. For example, risk management professionals might join the Society for Risk Analysis at sra.org. Trainers can find many resources through the American Society for Training and Development, at astd.org. Restaurant designers might consider the Foodservice Consultants Society International at fcsi.org.

Holding Food for Service	Serving Food Safely	Off-Site Service
— General Rules for Holding Food — Holding Food without Temperature Control	— Service Staff Guidelines — Preset Tableware — Re-serving Food Safely — Kitchen Staff Guidelines — Self-Service Areas	— Delivery — Catering — Temporary Units — Mobile Units — Vending Machines

SERVING FOOD SAFELY

Service Staff Guidelines

Service staff can contaminate food simply by handling the food-contact areas of glasses, dishes, and utensils. Service staff should use these guidelines when serving food.

Guidelines for Handling Food and Tableware		
		• Hold dishes by the bottom or edge. • Hold glasses by the middle, bottom, or stem. • Do not touch the food-contact areas of dishes or glassware.
		• Carry glasses in a rack or on a tray to avoid touching the food-contact surfaces. • Do not stack glasses when carrying them.
		• Hold flatware by the handle. • Do not hold flatware by food-contact surfaces. • Store flatware so that servers grasp handles, not food-contact surfaces.
		• Avoid bare-hand contact with food that is ready to eat.
		• Use ice scoops or tongs to get ice. • Never scoop ice with your bare hands or a glass. A glass may chip or break.

Preset Tableware

If your operation presets tableware on dining tables, you must take steps to prevent it from becoming contaminated. This might include wrapping or covering the items as shown in the photo at left.

Table settings do not need to be wrapped or covered if extra (or unused) settings meet these requirements:

- They are removed when guests are seated.
- If they remain on the table, they are cleaned and sanitized after guests have left.

Re-serving Food Safely

Service and kitchen staff should also know the rules about re-serving food previously served to another customer.

Returned menu items   Do not re-serve food returned by a customer.

Plate garnishes   Do not re-serve plate garnishes such as fruit or pickles. Throw out served but unused garnishes.

Condiments   Serve condiments in their original containers or in containers designed to prevent contamination. Offering condiments in individual packets or portions can also help keep them safe.

Never re-serve uncovered condiments. Do not combine leftover condiments with fresh ones, as the food handler in the photo at left is doing. Throw away opened portions of condiments after serving them to customers. Salsa, butter, mayonnaise, and ketchup are examples.

Bread and rolls   Do not re-serve uneaten bread or rolls to other customers. Change linens used in bread baskets after each customer.

Prepackaged food   In general, you may re-serve only unopened, prepackaged food in good condition. This includes condiment packets, and wrapped crackers. You may also re-serve bottles of ketchup, mustard, and other condiments. The containers must remain closed between uses.

Kitchen Staff Guidelines

Train your kitchen staff to serve food in these ways.

Bare-hand contact   Food handlers must wear single-use gloves whenever handling ready-to-eat food. As an alternative, food can be handled with spatulas, tongs, deli sheets, or other utensils. The photo at left shows two ways to avoid bare-hand contact. Check your local regulatory requirements. Keep in mind that there are some situations where it may be acceptable to handle ready-to-eat food with bare hands, such as when a dish does not contain raw meat, seafood, or poultry and will be cooked to at least 145°F (63°C).

Serving Utensils   Use separate utensils for serving each food item. Clean and sanitize them after each serving task. If using utensils continuously, clean and sanitize them at least once every four hours.

Utensil storage   Store serving utensils in the food with the handle extended above the rim of the container, as shown in the photo at left. You can also place them on a clean and sanitized food-contact surface. Spoons or scoops used to serve food, such as ice cream or mashed potatoes, can be stored under running water that is at least 135°F (57°C).

Refilling take-home containers   Some jurisdictions allow food handlers to refill take-home containers brought back by a customer with food and beverages. Take-home containers can be refilled if they meet these conditions:

- They were designed to be reused
- They were provided to the customer by the operation
- They are cleaned and sanitized correctly

Take-home beverage containers can also be refilled as long as the beverage is not a TCS food and the container will be refilled for the same customer. The container must also meet these conditions:

- It can be effectively cleaned at home and in the operation
- It will be rinsed before refilling with fresh, hot water under pressure
- It will be refilled by staff in the operation or by the customer using a process that prevents contamination

Self-Service Areas

Self-service areas can be contaminated easily. Follow these guidelines to prevent contamination and time-temperature abuse.

Protection   Food on display can be protected from contamination using sneeze guards. They should be located 14 inches (36 centimeters) above the counter and extend 7 inches (18 centimeters) beyond the food, as shown in the photo at left.

Food can also be protected by placing it in display cases or by packaging it to protect it from contamination. Whole, raw fruits and vegetables and nuts in the shell that require peeling or hulling before eating do not require the protection measures discussed above.

Labels   Label food located in self-service areas. For example, place the name of salad dressings on ladle handles, as shown in the photo at left.

Raw and ready-to-eat food   Typically, raw unpackaged meat, poultry, and seafood cannot be offered for self-service. This does not apply to ready-to-eat food such as sushi or raw shellfish. Ready-to-cook portions that will be cooked and eaten immediately on the premises, such as at Mongolian barbecues, can also be offered raw and unpackaged. So can raw, frozen, shell-on shrimp or lobster.

Refills   Do not let customers refill dirty plates or use dirty utensils at self-service areas. Assign a staff member to monitor guests. Post signs reminding customers not to reuse plates and utensils.

Utensils   Stock food displays with the correct utensils for dispensing food. This might include tongs, ladles, or deli sheets.

Labeling Bulk Food

Label bulk food in self-service areas. The label must be in plain view of the customer. Include the manufacturer or processor label. As an alternative, you can provide this information using a card, sign, or other labeling method.

Bulk unpackaged food, such as bakery products and unpackaged food portioned for customers, does not need to be labeled if it meets these conditions:

- The product makes no claim regarding health or nutrient content.
- There are no laws requiring labeling.
- The food is manufactured or prepped on the premises.
- The food is manufactured or prepped at another food operation or processing plant owned by the same person. The operation must be regulated.

Holding Food for Service	Serving Food Safely	Off-Site Service
— General Rules for Holding Food — Holding Food without Temperature Control	— Service Staff Guidelines — Kitchen Staff Guidelines — Preset Tableware — Re-serving Food Safely — Self-Service Areas	— Delivery — Catering — Temporary Units — Mobile Units — Vending Machines

OFF-SITE SERVICE

Off-site service such as delivery, mobile/temporary kitchens, and vending machines can present special challenges. Those who operate these services need to follow the same food safety rules as permanent operations. Food should be protected from contamination and time-temperature abuse. Facilities and equipment used to prep food need to be clean and safe. Menu items should contribute to safe service. Food needs to be handled correctly as well.

Delivery

Many operations prep food at one location and then deliver it to remote sites. The longer the time between preparation and consumption, the greater the risk that food will be exposed to contamination or time-temperature abuse.

When transporting food, follow these safety procedures.

Containers Pack food in insulated, food-grade containers, as shown in the photo at left. They should be designed so food cannot mix, leak, or spill.

Delivery vehicles Clean the inside of delivery vehicles regularly.

Personal hygiene Practice good personal hygiene when distributing food.

Internal food temperatures Check internal food temperatures. If containers or delivery vehicles are not holding food at the correct temperature, reevaluate the length of the delivery route or the efficiency of the equipment being used.

Labels Label food with a use-by date and time, and reheating and service instructions for staff at off-site locations.

Storage Store raw meat, poultry, and seafood and ready-to-eat items separately. For example, store raw chicken separately from ready-to-eat salads.

Catering

Caterers must follow the same food safety rules as permanent operations. Food must be protected from contamination and time-temperature abuse. Facilities must be clean and sanitary. Food must be prepared and served correctly, and staff must follow good personal hygiene practices.

Catering often presents unique challenges. Follow these guidelines to keep food safe.

Utilities   Make sure the service site has the correct utilities:

- Safe water for cooking, dishwashing, and handwashing
- Garbage containers stored away from food-prep, storage, and serving areas

Insulated containers   Use insulated containers to hold TCS food. Raw meat should be wrapped and stored on ice. Deliver milk and dairy products in a refrigerated vehicle or on ice.

Cold food   Serve cold food in containers on ice or in chilled, gel-filled containers. If that is not desirable, the food may be held without temperature control according to the guidelines specified in this chapter.

Ready-to-eat food   Store ready-to-eat food separately from raw food.

Leftovers   If leftovers are given to customers, provide instructions on how they should be handled. Information such as a discard date and the food's storage and reheating instructions should be clearly labeled on the container.

Temporary Units

Temporary units typically operate in one location for less than 14 days. Foodservice tents or kiosks set up for food fairs, special celebrations, or sporting events may be temporary units. A temporary unit is shown in the photo at left.

In some areas, the definition also extends to units set up for longer periods. Temporary units usually serve prepackaged food or food requiring limited prepping, such as hot dogs. It is best to keep the menu simple to limit the amount of on-site food prep. Check with your regulatory authority for operating requirements.

Here are some additional guidelines:

- Temporary units should be constructed to keep dirt and pests out. If floors are made of dirt or gravel, cover them with mats or platforms to control dust and mud. Construct walls and the ceiling with materials that will protect food from weather and windblown dust.
- The safe-handling rules discussed throughout this book apply to food prep in temporary units.
- Safe drinking water also needs to be available for cleaning, sanitizing, and handwashing. Since dishwashing facilities will likely be limited too, it is best to use disposable, single-use items.

Mobile Units

Mobile units are portable facilities ranging from concession vans to elaborate field kitchens. Those serving only frozen novelties, candy, packaged snacks, and soft drinks need to meet basic sanitation requirements. However, mobile kitchens prepping and serving TCS food need to follow the same rules required of permanent foodservice kitchens. Both might be required to apply for a special permit or license from the regulatory authority.

Vending Machines

Vending operators should protect food from contamination and time-temperature abuse. This is especially important when prepping and packaging food and during transport and delivery. Follow these guidelines:

- Check product shelf life daily. Products often have an expiration or use-by date, such as that shown in the photo at left. If the date has expired, throw out the food immediately. Throw out refrigerated food prepped on-site if not sold within seven days of preparation.

- Keep TCS food at the correct temperature. It should be held at 41°F (5°C) or lower, or at 135°F (57°C) or higher. These machines must have controls that prevent TCS food from being dispensed if the temperature stays in the danger zone for a specified amount of time. This food must be thrown out.

- Dispense TCS food in its original container.

- Wash and wrap fresh fruit with edible peels before putting it in a machine.

Technology

Food Trucks

Food trucks are making inroads among some consumers, but have yet to enjoy widespread appeal. According to the National Restaurant Association's 2011 *Restaurant Trends Survey*, 6 percent of quick-service operators and 4 percent of fast-casual operators said they currently operate a food truck. In comparison, only 3 percent of casual-dining operators, 2 percent of family-dining operators, and less than 1 percent of fine-dining operators said they operate a food truck.

Fast-casual operators (22 percent) are the most likely to say they will start up a food truck in the next year or two, while 13 percent of quick-service and family-dining operators said they are likely to start up a food truck.

The food safety concerns for food trucks can vary from state to state. For example, some states allow food to be prepared directly on the truck, while others do not. The regulatory requirements that govern the trucks are also varied, but examples of what might be required include:

- Hot and cold drinkable water must be available on the truck.
- Every 24 hours, the truck must return to a commissary to clean, dump waste, and resupply.

As you can imagine, the confined space of a truck means that the space can get messy very quickly if staff are not diligent. "Clean as you go" is especially important.

At present, many operators consider food trucks competition and are not expanding their business via such an outlet. In fact, in the 2011 survey, most full-service operators do not believe food trucks will become more popular within their segment in the future. Only 16 percent of fine-dining operators and nearly three out of 10 family-dining and casual-dining operators think food trucks will grow in popularity in their segments. A higher proportion of fast-casual (47 percent) and quick-service operators (43 percent) think food trucks will become more popular in their segments.

SUMMARY

- When holding TCS food for service, keep hot food at 135°F (57°C) or higher. Never use hot-holding equipment to reheat food. Keep cold food at 41°F (5°C) or lower. Check the internal temperature of food at least every four hours. Throw food out if it is not at the correct temperature.

- Review the guidelines for keeping food safe when holding food without temperature control.

- In general, staff should be trained to avoid bare-hand contact with ready-to-eat food. They should also learn to use separate utensils for serving different food items.

- Teach staff the correct ways for handling service items and tableware. Staff should also be trained on the potential hazards of re-serving food such as plate garnishes, breads, or open dishes of condiments.

- Self-service areas can be contaminated by staff and customers. Protect food on display with sneeze guards, packaging, or other tools designed to keep food safe. Post self-service rules. Make it clear to customers that clean plates must be used for refills. Put the correct labels on displayed food and bulk food available for self-service. Make sure equipment holds food at the correct temperature.

- Follow safety procedures when prepping, delivering, or serving food off-site. Catering, mobile units, temporary units, and vending machines pose their own challenges to food safety. Learn and follow any regulatory requirements that may apply to your operation.

Apply Your Knowledge

Use these questions to review the concepts presented in this chapter.

DISCUSSION QUESTIONS

1. What can be done to minimize contamination in self-service areas?

2. What hazards are associated with the transportation of food and how can they be prevented?

3. What are the requirements for using time rather than temperature as the only method of control when holding ready-to-eat TCS food?

4. What practices should be followed to serve food correctly off-site?

For answers, please turn to the Answer Key.

Apply Your Knowledge

CASE IN POINT

In the Weeds

Jill, a line cook on the morning shift at Memorial Hospital, was busy helping the kitchen staff put food on display for lunch in the hospital cafeteria. Ann, the kitchen manager who usually supervised lunch in the cafeteria, was at an all-day seminar on food safety. Jill was also responsible for making sure meals were trayed and put into food carts for transport to the patients' rooms. The staff also packed two dozen meals each day for a neighborhood group that delivered them to homebound elderly people.

First, Jill looked for insulated food containers for the delivery meals. When she could not find them, she loaded the meals into cardboard boxes she found near the back door, knowing the driver would arrive soon to pick them up. The lunch hour was hectic. The cafeteria was busy, and the staff had many meals to tray and deliver.

As the lunch period was ending, Jill breathed a sigh of relief. She moved down the cafeteria serving line, checking food temperatures. One of the casseroles was at 130°F (54°C). Jill checked the water level in the steam table and turned up the thermostat. She then went to clean up the kitchen and finish her shift.

1 What did Jill do wrong?

2 What should she have done?

For answers, please turn to the Answer Key.

9

Megan's Day

CASE IN POINT

Megan, a new server at The Fish House, reported for work 10 minutes early on Thursday. She was excited about her new job and wanted to make a good impression.

Her shift started off well. One of her customers ordered a menu item that Megan had not tried yet. When the order came up, Megan dipped her finger into the sauce at the edge of the plate for a taste. As the shift progressed, Megan's station got busier. When the hostess came to ask how soon one of Megan's tables could be cleared, Megan decided to do it herself. She took the dirty dishes to a bus station and then wiped down the table with a serving cloth she kept in her apron.

The buser, John, finished another task and came to help her set the table. While he put out silverware and linens, Megan filled water glasses with ice by scooping the glasses into the ice bin in the bus station. Only one slice of bread and one pat of butter were missing from the basket that had been on a previous customer's table, so she put that on a tray with the water glasses and brought it to the table.

The table was reset in record time, and Megan soon had more guests. While taking their orders, Megan reached up to scratch a sore on her neck. Then she went to the kitchen to turn in the order and pick up a dessert order for another table.

① What errors did Megan make?

② What should she have done?

For answers, please turn to the Answer Key.

Circle the best answer to each question.

1. Which part of the plate should a food handler avoid touching when serving customers?

   A   Bottom

   B   Edge

   C   Side

   D   Top

2. An operation has a small salad bar with 8 different items on it. How many serving utensils are needed to serve the items on the salad bar?

   A   2

   B   4

   C   6

   D   8

3. At what maximum internal temperature should cold TCS food be held?

   A   0°F (-17°C)

   B   32°F (0°C)

   C   41°F (5°C)

   D   60°F (16°C)

4. What item must customers take each time they return to a self-service area for more food?

   A   Clean plate

   B   Extra napkins

   C   Hand sanitizer

   D   New serving spoon

5. At what minimum temperature should hot TCS food be held?

   A   115°F (46°C)

   B   125°F (52°C)

   C   135°F (57°C)

   D   145°F (63°C)

6. An operation is located in a jurisdiction that allows it to hold TCS food without temperature control. How many hours can it display hot TCS food without temperature control before the food must be sold, served, or thrown out?

   A   2

   B   4

   C   6

   D   8

7. Which food items can be displayed in a self-service area without the use of packaging, sneeze guards, or a display case to protect them from contamination?

   A   Bulk deli rolls

   B   Nuts in the shell

   C   Sushi-grade fish

   D   Cooked shrimp

8. What is the maximum distance that sneeze guards can be located from the self-service counter to protect food from contamination?

   A   8 inches (20 cm)

   B   10 inches (25 cm)

   C   12 inches (30 cm)

   D   14 inches (35 cm)

For answers, please turn to the Answer Key.

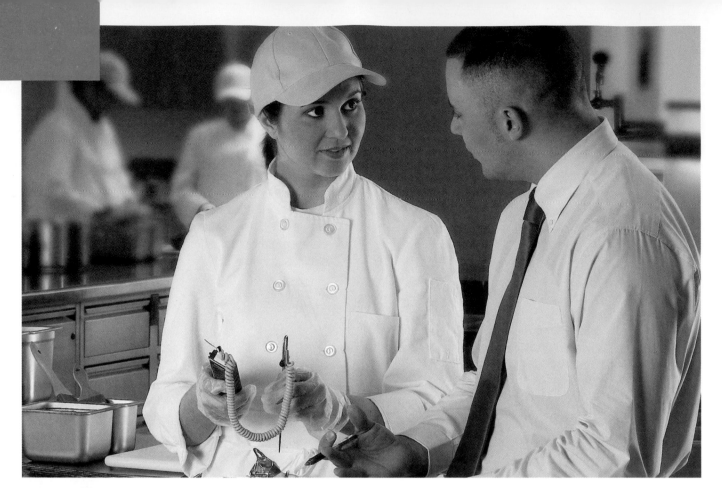

10 Food Safety Management Systems

Food Safety Management Systems	Active Managerial Control	Crisis Management	
	— The FDA's Public Health Interventions — HACCP	— Creating a Crisis-Management Team — Preparing for a Crisis — Crisis Response	— Crisis Recovery and Assessment — Imminent Health Hazards

Inside this Chapter

- Food Safety Management Systems
- Active Managerial Control
- Crisis Management

Objectives

After completing this chapter, you should be able to identify the following:

- Methods for achieving active managerial control
- The Food and Drug Administration's (FDA) public health interventions
- The seven HACCP principles for preventing foodborne illness
- How to prepare for, respond to, and recover from a crisis
- How to respond to a foodborne-illness outbreak
- How to respond to imminent health hazards including power outages, fire, flood, water interruption, and sewage

Key Terms

- Food safety management system
- Active managerial control
- HACCP
- HACCP plan
- Critical control points (CCPs)
- Variance
- Imminent health hazard

Food Safety Management Systems	Active Managerial Control	Crisis Management	
	— The FDA's Public Health Interventions — HACCP	— Creating a Crisis-Management Team — Preparing for a Crisis — Crisis Response	— Crisis Recovery and Assessment — Imminent Health Hazards

FOOD SAFETY MANAGEMENT SYSTEMS

A food safety management system is a group of practices and procedures intended to prevent foodborne illness. It does this by actively controlling risks and hazards throughout the flow of food.

Having some food safety programs already in place gives you the foundation for your system. The principles presented in the ServSafe program are the basis of these programs. Here are some examples of the programs your operation needs:

- Personal hygiene program
- Food safety training program
- Supplier selection and specification program
- Quality control and assurance programs
- Cleaning and sanitation program
- Standard operating procedures (SOPs)
- Facility design and equipment maintenance program
- Pest-control program

Key Point

A food safety management system helps you control risks and hazards throughout the flow of food.

Resources

OSHA

The Occupational Safety and Health Administration (OSHA) was created in 1970 by the U.S. Congress to ensure safe and healthful working conditions by setting and enforcing standards and by providing training, outreach, education, and assistance. It is part of the Department of Labor.

OSHA's role is apparent in every workplace in the United States: employers are required to post workers' rights as outlined in OSHA's "It's the Law" poster. Resources such as record keeping tools and educational materials are also available to employers to help them maintain compliance. The need to provide material safety data sheets to workers is an example of an OSHA requirement that foodservice operations must meet.

For more information about the prevention of workplace hazards, visit osha.gov.

Food Safety Management Systems	Active Managerial Control	Crisis Management	
	— The FDA's Public Health Interventions — HACCP	— Creating a Crisis-Management Team — Preparing for a Crisis — Crisis Response	— Crisis Recovery and Assessment — Imminent Health Hazards

ACTIVE MANAGERIAL CONTROL

Earlier, you learned that there are five common risk factors for foodborne illness:

1. Purchasing food from unsafe sources

2. Failing to cook food correctly

3. Holding food at incorrect temperatures

4. Using contaminated equipment

5. Practicing poor personal hygiene

Key Point

Managers must proactively control the risk factors for foodborne illness.

It is the manager's responsibility to actively control these and other risk factors for foodborne illness. This is called active managerial control. It is important to note that active managerial control is proactive rather than reactive. You must anticipate risks and plan for them.

There are many ways to achieve active managerial control in the operation. According to the Food and Drug Administration (FDA), you can use simple tools such as training programs, manager supervision, and the incorporation of SOPs. Active managerial control can also be achieved through more complex solutions, such as a HACCP Program.

Monitoring is critical to the success of active managerial control. Food will be safe if managers monitor critical activities in the operation. For example, the manager in the photo at left is monitoring a food handler as she carries out the critical task of cooling food correctly. Managers must take the necessary corrective action when required. They must also verify that the actions taken to control the risk factors for foodborne illness are actually working.

The FDA's Public Health Interventions

The FDA provides specific recommendations for controlling the common risk factors for foodborne illness. These are known as public health interventions. They are designed to protect public health.

Demonstration of knowledge   As a manager, you must be able to show that you know what to do to keep food safe. Becoming certified in food safety is one way to show this.

Staff health controls   Procedures must be put in place to make sure staff are practicing personal hygiene. For example, staff must understand that they must report illnesses and illness symptoms to management.

Controlling hands as a vehicle of contamination Controls must be put in place to prevent bare-hand contact with ready-to-eat food. This might include requiring the use of tongs to handle ready-to-eat food, as shown in the photo at left.

Time and temperature parameters for controlling pathogens Procedures must be put in place to limit the time food spends in the temperature danger zone. Requiring food handlers to check the temperature of food being hot-held every two hours is an example.

Consumer advisories Notices must be provided to customers if you serve raw or undercooked menu items. These notices must include a statement about the risks of eating these foods.

HACCP

There are many systems you can implement to achieve active managerial control of foodborne illness risk factors. Hazard Analysis Critical Control Point (HACCP) is one such system. HACCP (pronounced HASS-ip) is based on identifying significant biological, chemical, or physical hazards at specific points within a product's flow. Once identified, the hazards can be prevented, eliminated, or reduced to safe levels.

An effective HACCP system must be based on a written plan. This plan must be specific to each facility's menu, customers, equipment, processes, and operations. Since each HACCP plan is unique, a plan that works for one operation may not work for another.

The HACCP Approach

A HACCP plan is based on seven basic principles. They were created by the National Advisory Committee on Microbiological Criteria for Foods. These principles are the seven steps that outline how to create a HACCP plan.

The Seven HACCP Principles

Each HACCP principle builds on the information gained from the previous principle. You must consider all seven principles, in order, when developing your plan. Here are the seven principles:

1. Conduct a hazard analysis.
2. Determine critical control points (CCPs).
3. Establish critical limits.
4. Establish monitoring procedures.
5. Identify corrective actions.
6. Verify that the system works.
7. Establish procedures for record keeping and documentation.

Key Point

There are seven HACCP principles that must be considered when developing a HACCP plan.

In general terms, the principles break into three groups:

- Principles 1 and 2 help you identify and evaluate your hazards.

- Principles 3, 4, and 5 help you establish ways for controlling those hazards.

- Principles 6 and 7 help you maintain the HACCP plan and system, and verify its effectiveness.

The next few pages provide an introduction to these principles. They also present an overview of how to build a HACCP program. A real-world example has also been included for each principle. It shows the efforts of Enrico's, an Italian restaurant, as it implements a HACCP program. The example will appear after the explanation of each principle.

Principle 1: Conduct a Hazard Analysis

First, identify and assess potential hazards in the food you serve. Start by looking at how food is processed in your operation. Many types of food are processed in similar ways. Here are some common processes:

- Prepping and serving without cooking (salads, cold sandwiches, etc.)

- Prepping and cooking for same-day service (grilled chicken sandwiches, hamburgers, etc.)

- Prepping, cooking, holding, cooling, reheating, and serving (chili, soup, pasta sauce with meat, etc.)

Look at your menu and identify items that are processed like this. Next, identify the TCS food. Determine where food safety hazards are likely to occur for each TCS food. They can come from biological, chemical, or physical contaminants.

Principle 1 Example

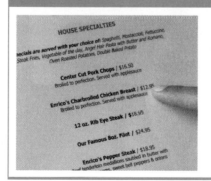

The management team at Enrico's decided to implement a HACCP program. They began by analyzing their hazards.

The team noted that many of their dishes were received, stored, prepared, cooked, and served the same day. The most popular of these items was the spicy charbroiled chicken breast.

The team determined that bacteria were the most likely hazard to food prepared this way.

Principle 2: Determine Critical Control Points (CCPs)

Find the points in the process where the identified hazard(s) can be prevented, eliminated, or reduced to safe levels. These are the critical control points (CCPs). Depending on the process, there may be more than one CCP.

Principle 2 Example

Enrico's management identified cooking as the CCP for food prepared and cooked for immediate service. This included the chicken breasts.

These food items must be handled correctly throughout the flow of food. However, correct cooking is the only step that will eliminate or reduce bacteria to safe levels.

Since the chicken breasts were prepared for immediate service, cooking was the only CCP identified.

Principle 3: Establish Critical Limits

For each CCP, establish minimum or maximum limits. These limits must be met to prevent or eliminate the hazard, or to reduce it to a safe level.

Principle 3 Example

With cooking identified as the CCP for Enrico's chicken breasts, a critical limit was needed. Management determined that the critical limit would be cooking the chicken to a minimum internal temperature of 165°F (74°C) for 15 seconds.

They decided that the critical limit could be met by cooking chicken breasts in the broiler for 16 minutes.

Principle 4: Establish Monitoring Procedures

Once critical limits have been created, determine the best way for your operation to check them. Make sure the limits are consistently met. Identify who will monitor them and how often.

Principle 4 Example

At Enrico's, each charbroiled chicken breast is cooked to order. The team decided to check the critical limit by inserting a clean and sanitized thermocouple probe into the thickest part of each chicken breast.

The grill cook must check the temperature of each chicken breast after cooking. Each chicken breast must reach the minimum internal temperature of 165°F (74°C) for 15 seconds.

Principle 5: Identify Corrective Actions

Identify steps that must be taken when a critical limit is not met. These steps should be determined in advance.

Principle 5 Example

If the chicken breast has not reached its critical limit within the 16 minute cook time, the grill cook at Enrico's must keep cooking the chicken breast until it has reached it.

This and all other corrective actions are noted in the temperature log.

Principle 6: Verify That the System Works

Determine if the plan is working as intended. Evaluate it on a regular basis. Use your monitoring charts, records, hazard analysis, etc., and determine if your plan prevents, reduces, or eliminates identified hazards.

Principle 6 Example

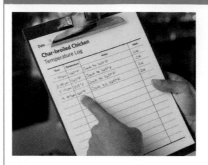

Enrico's management team performs HACCP checks once per shift. They make sure that critical limits were met and appropriate corrective actions were taken when needed.

They also check the temperature logs on a weekly basis to identify patterns. This helps to determine if processes or procedures need to be changed. For example, over several weeks they noticed problems toward the end of each week. The chicken breasts often failed to meet the critical limit. The appropriate corrective action was being taken.

Management discovered that Enrico's received chicken shipments from a different supplier on Thursdays. This supplier provided a six-ounce chicken breast. Enrico's chicken specifications listed a four-ounce chicken breast. Management worked with the supplier to ensure they received four-ounce breasts. The receiving procedures were changed to include a weight check.

Principle 7: Establish Procedures for Record Keeping and Documentation

Maintain your HACCP plan and keep all documentation created when developing it. Keep records for the following actions:

- Monitoring activities
- Taking corrective action
- Validating equipment (checking for good working condition)
- Working with suppliers (i.e., shelf-life studies, invoices, specifications, challenge studies, etc.)

Principle 7 Example

Enrico's management team determined that time-temperature logs would be kept for three months. Receiving invoices would be kept for 60 days. The team used this documentation to support and revise their HACCP plan.

Another HACCP Example

The Enrico's example shows one type of HACCP plan. Another plan may look very different when it deals with food that is processed more simply. Here is an example of the HACCP plan developed by The Fruit Basket for its signature item—the Melon Medley salad:

❶ Analyzing hazards   The HACCP team decided to look at hazards for the salad. The Melon Medley has fresh watermelon, honeydew, and cantaloupe. The team determined that bacteria pose a risk to these fresh-cut melons.

❷ Determining CCPs   The melons are prepped, held, and served without cooking. The team determined that prepping and holding are CCPs for the salad. They decided that cleaning and drying the melons' surfaces during prep, as shown in the photo at left, would reduce bacteria. Holding the melons at the correct temperature could prevent the bacteria's growth.

❸ Establishing critical limits   For the preparation CCP, the team decided the critical limit would be met by washing, scrubbing, and drying whole melons. For the holding CCP, the team decided that the salad must be held at 41°F (5°C) or lower because it includes cut melons.

❹ Establishing monitoring procedures   It was determined that the operation's team leader should monitor the salad's critical limits. This includes observing food handlers to ensure melons are prepped correctly. All surface dirt must be removed from the washed melons. Then food handlers must cut, mix, and portion the salad into containers. The finished salads are then put into the display cooler.

The team leader must monitor the temperature of the held salads to make sure the holding critical limit is met. The internal temperature must be 41°F (5°C) or lower. It must be checked three times per day, as shown in the photo at left.

❺ Identifying corrective actions   Some melons may still have surface dirt after preparation. The team decided that these melons must be rewashed. Before slicing, these melons must be approved by the team leader.

To correct a holding temperature higher than 41°F (5°C), the team leader must check the temperature of every salad in the cooler. Any salad that is above 41°F (5°C) must be thrown out.

❻ Verifying that the system works   The team leader reviews the Manager Daily HACCP Check Sheet at the end of each shift. He or she also confirms that all corrective actions have been taken and recorded. The Fruit Basket evaluates their HACCP system quarterly to see if it is working.

❼ Establishing procedures for record keeping   Because a foodborne illness associated with fresh produce can take as long as 16 weeks to emerge, the team decided that all HACCP records must be maintained for 16 weeks and kept on file.

Specialized Processing Methods and HACCP

Some food processes are highly specialized and can be a serious health risk if specific procedures are not followed. Typically these processes are carried out at processing plants:

- Smoking food as a method to preserve it (but not to enhance flavor).

- Using food additives or adding components, such as vinegar, to preserve or alter it so it no longer requires time and temperature control for safety.

- Curing food.

- Custom-processing animals. For example, this may include dressing deer in the operation for personal use.

- Packaging food using reduced-oxygen packaging (ROP) methods. This includes MAP, vacuum-packed, and *sous vide* food. *Clostridium botulinum* and *Listeria monocytogenes* are risks to food packaged in these ways.

- Treating (e.g., pasteurizing) juice on-site, and packaging it for later sale.

- Sprouting seeds or beans.

A variance from the regulatory authority will be required before processing food this way. A variance is a document that allows a requirement to be waived or changed.

A HACCP plan may also be required if the processing method carries a higher risk of causing a foodborne illness. There may also be dangers unique to these processes that are best addressed by HACCP.

If not done correctly, reduced-oxygen packaging (ROP) has a very high risk of causing a foodborne illness. Because of this, a HACCP plan is required when a variance has not been requested.

Check with your local regulatory authority before using any of these specialized processing methods on-site.

Key Point

Special processing methods will require a variance and may require a HACCP plan.

Regulatory

HACCP's Role in Food

"HACCP" was first developed in 1959 by the Pillsbury Company in response to the National Aeronautics and Space Administration's (NASA) need to ensure that the food served to astronauts in zero gravity was safe. NASA asked Pillsbury to produce food that was virtually 100 percent free of pathogens, known then as "zero defect." (Incidentally, NASA also wanted this food to be free of crumbs.)

NASA chose the HACCP system because of its scientific and logical approach toward identifying hazards, establishing controls for them, and then monitoring and verifying the system's effectiveness. Pillsbury modeled their approach after their engineering testing, which identified critical failure areas in equipment and then tried to eliminate them. Using this method for food was unique to the industry at the time. In 1971, Pillsbury presented the system to the National Conference on Food Protection with just three principles. Over time, with additional scientific groups, such as the National Advisory Committee on Microbiological Criteria for Foods, the system was refined and expanded to the framework of seven principles currently used.

Today, HACCP plans can be found internationally. They are widely used in food manufacturing. In some cases in the United States, HACCP plans are requirements by law (e.g., juice, seafood, and meat). A variety of resources are available online to help you learn more about HACCP, including fda.gov, fsis.usda.gov, and haccpalliance.org.

Food Safety Management Systems	Active Managerial Control	Crisis Management	
	— The FDA's Public Health Interventions — HACCP	— Creating a Crisis-Management Team — Preparing for a Crisis — Crisis Response	— Crisis Recovery and Assessment — Imminent Health Hazards

CRISIS MANAGEMENT

Putting the food safety principles you have learned into action can help keep food safe in your operation. However, despite your best efforts, a foodborne-illness outbreak or another type of crisis affecting food safety can still occur. How you respond can influence the outcome.

To handle these crises, you will need a crisis-management program. To be successful, the program needs to have a written plan that focuses on three phases: preparation, response, and recovery. For each phase, the plan should identify resources needed and procedures to be followed.

The time to prepare for a crisis is before one happens. There is no "off-the-shelf" disaster plan that works for everyone. Each plan needs to be customized to the operation.

A good way to ensure your plan works is to test it once it is complete. The results will help you identify potential gaps or problems. Testing the plan will also ensure it works as intended. You can do this yourself or hire a consulting firm with crisis-management experience. In either case, the test should simulate a crisis that will be as close as possible to what could happen.

Creating a Crisis-Management Team

To begin, create a crisis-management team. The size of the team will depend on the size of the operation. If your operation is large, the team may include representatives from the following departments:

- Senior management (president/CEO, etc.)
- Risk management (quality assurance, legal, etc.)
- Public relations
- Operations
- Finance
- Marketing
- Human resources

Smaller operations may include the chef, the general manager, and the owner/operator. Regardless of size, you should also consider using other external resources such as your regulatory authority and experts from your suppliers and manufacturers.

Preparing for a Crisis

Your crisis-management team should consider the following when preparing for a crisis.

Emergency contact list   Create an emergency contact list and post it by phones. It should include the names and numbers of all crisis-management team members; the media spokesperson; management or headquarters personnel; and outside resources such as testing labs, subject-matter experts, the police and fire departments, and the regulatory authority.

Crisis-communication plan   Develop a crisis-communication plan that includes the following:

- List of media responses or a question-and-answer sheet suggesting what to say for each crisis.

- Sample press releases that can be tailored quickly to each incident.

- List of media contacts to call for press conferences or news briefings. Include a media-relations plan with "dos and don'ts" for dealing with the media.

- Plan for communicating with staff during the crisis. Possibilities include shift meetings, email, a telephone tree, etc.

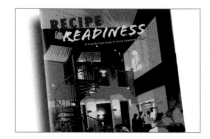

Several guides are available to help you develop a crisis-communication plan. One is shown at left.

You must appoint a single spokesperson to handle all media queries and communications. This usually results in more consistent messages. It also allows you to control media access to your staff. Crisis situations can be very stressful, and training will enable your spokesperson to handle it better. The spokesperson should also have interview skills as well so that he or she knows what to expect and how to respond.

Make sure your staff knows who the spokesperson is. Instruct them to direct questions to that person.

Crisis kit   Assemble a crisis kit for the operation. It can be a three-ring notebook or binder enclosing the plan's materials. Keep the kit in an accessible place, such as the manager's or chef's office.

Preparing for a Foodborne-Illness Outbreak

The greatest threat to your customers is foodborne illness. To prevent an outbreak, you need a food safety program. You also need to train your staff on policies and procedures that will keep the food you serve safe.

In the event of an outbreak, it will be critical to gather accurate information. To prepare for this, you should develop a foodborne illness incident report form, and train staff to complete it.

Develop the form with legal guidance and include all critical information. The form may contain the following:

- What and when the customer ate at the operation
- When the customer first got sick, what the symptoms were, and how long the customer experienced them
- When and where the customer sought medical attention, what the diagnosis was, and what treatment was received
- What other food was eaten by the customer

Crisis Response

A crisis-management plan should include response procedures to help manage a crisis more effectively. When a crisis occurs, gather your crisis-management team to implement your plan. Direct the team to collect information, plan courses of action, and manage events as they unfold.

Good communication is critical when handling a crisis. Consider the following to keep the situation under control.

Media relations   Work with the media. Make sure your spokesperson is fully informed before arranging a press conference. Contacting the media before they contact you also helps you control what they report. Stick to the facts and be honest. If you do not have all the facts, say so. Let the media know you will communicate with them as soon as you do have them. Keep calm and do not be defensive. The easiest way to worsen a crisis is to deny, lie, misinform, or change your story.

Direct communication   Communicate information directly to your key audiences. Do not depend on the media to relay all of the facts. Tell your side of the story to staff, customers, stockholders, and the community. Use newsletters, a Web site, flyers, and newspaper or radio advertising.

Solution   Fix the problem. Then communicate to both the media and your customers what you have done. Each time you take a step to resolve the problem, let the media know. Hold briefings when you have news. Go into each briefing or press conference with an agenda. Take control rather than simply responding to questions.

Responding to a Foodborne-Illness Outbreak

In the event of a foodborne-illness outbreak, you may be able to avoid a crisis by acting quickly. The table below shows how to respond to certain situations.

Foodborne-Illness Outbreak Responses

If	Then
A customer calls to report a foodborne illness.	• Take the complaint seriously and express concern. Do not admit responsibility or accept liability. • Ask for general contact information. Ask about the food that was eaten and when the person first became sick. Ask the person to describe symptoms. • Complete a foodborne-illness incident report form.
There are similar customer complaints of foodborne illness.	• Contact the crisis-management team. • Identify common food items to determine the potential source of the complaint. • Contact the regulatory authority to assist with the investigation if an outbreak is suspected.
The suspected food is still in the operation.	• Set aside the suspected product and identify it to prevent further sale. Include a label with Do Not Use and Do Not Discard. • Log information about the product including a description, product date, and lot number. The sell-by date and pack size should also be recorded • If possible, obtain samples of the suspect food from the customer.
The suspected outbreak is caused by a sick staff member.	• Maintain a list of food handlers scheduled at the time of the suspected contamination. Interview them about their health status. • Exclude the suspect staff member from the operation following requirements.
The regulatory authority confirms your operation is the source of the outbreak.	• Cooperate with the regulatory authority to resolve the crisis. Provide appropriate documentation including temperature logs, HACCP documents, staff files, etc.

Crisis Recovery and Assessment

The final step in a crisis-management plan is developing procedures for recovering from a crisis. Determine what you need to do to ensure both the operation and the food are safe. This is critical for getting your operation running again.

To recover from a foodborne-illness outbreak, you will need to take several steps. They should be planned in advance and include the following:

- Working with the regulatory authority to resolve issues, as shown in the photo at left.
- Cleaning and sanitizing all areas of the operation.
- Throwing out all suspect food.
- Investigating to find the cause of the outbreak.
- Reviewing food handling procedures to identify if standards are not being met or procedures are not working. Establish new procedures or revise existing ones based on the investigation results.
- Developing a plan to reassure customers that the food you serve is safe.

Imminent Health Hazards

In addition to foodborne-illness outbreaks, other crises can affect the safety of the food you serve. Among these are power outages, fire, and flood. Water interruption and sewage backup are also a concern. These are considered by the regulatory authority to be imminent health hazards. An imminent health hazard is a significant threat or danger to health that requires immediate correction or closure to prevent injury. If there is a significant risk to the safety or the security of your food, service must be stopped. Then the local regulatory authority must be notified. Spoiled or contaminated food must be thrown out, along with food in packaging that is not intact.

Power Outage

Power failures and refrigeration breakdowns can threaten your ability to control the temperature of TCS food. This can result in the growth of pathogens. Consider the following when planning for a power outage:

- Arrange access to an electrical generator and a refrigerated truck that you can use in the event of an emergency.
- Prepare a menu with items that do not require cooking to use in the event of an emergency.
- Develop a policy that addresses when cooler doors should be opened.

To manage your response to a power outage, consider the steps on the next page.

Power Outage Responses

If	Then
Refrigeration equipment stops working.	• Write down the time of the power outage. • Check and record food temperatures periodically. • Keep cooler and freezer doors closed. • Pack TCS food in ice bought from an approved, reputable supplier.
Ventilation hoods or fans stop working.	• Stop all cooking.
Hot-holding equipment stops working.	• Write down the time of the power outage. • Throw out all TCS food held below 135°F (57°C) for more than four hours. • Food can be reheated if the power outage was less than four hours.

You also need to plan for the recovery from a power outage. For example, refrigeration units will need to be checked often after the power has been restored to ensure the equipment can maintain product temperatures. TCS food will also have to be thrown out if it has been in the temperature danger zone for more than four hours.

Water Service Interruption

Broken water mains and breakdowns at water treatment facilities are a risk to the safety of food. Consider the following when planning for a water service interruption:

- Prepare a menu with items that require little or no water to be used in the event of an emergency.

- Keep a supply of single-use items.

- Keep a supply of bottled water. Also have a supplier who can provide bottled water in an emergency.

- Have a supplier who can provide ice in an emergency.

- Have emergency-contact information for your regulatory authority, plumber, and water department.

- Develop procedures that minimize water use during the emergency (e.g., use single-use items for service).

- Work with your regulatory authority to develop an emergency handwashing procedure for use during water service interruptions.

To manage your response to a water service interruption, consider the steps identified on the next page.

Water Service Interruption Responses

If	Then
Hands cannot be washed.	• Implement an emergency handwashing procedure.
Toilets do not flush.	• Find other restrooms for staff use during operating hours. • Stop operations if restrooms are not available.
Drinking water is not available or is contaminated.	• Use bottled water. • Use water from an approved, reputable supplier. • Keep water in a covered, sanitized container during hauling or storage.
Food items that require water during preparation cannot be made.	• Throw out any ready-to-eat food made with water before the contamination was discovered. • Use bottled or boiled water for ready-to-eat food.
Water is not available for food preparation and cooking.	• Use water from an approved, reputable supplier. • Use the emergency menu. • Use prewashed, packaged produce or frozen or canned fruit and vegetables. • Thaw food only in the cooler or microwave or as a part of the cooking process.
Ice cannot be made.	• Throw out existing ice. • Use ice from an approved, reputable supplier.
Equipment, utensils, and facility cannot be cleaned or sanitized.	• Use single-use items. • Use bottled water or water from an approved source to clean and sanitize.
Beverages made with water cannot be prepared.	• Stop using the drink machines that require water, such as the auto-fill coffee maker, etc.

When water is restored or the regulatory authority has lifted any boiled-water advisory, you should plan on taking these actions:

• Clean and sanitize equipment with water line connections such as spray misters, coffee or tea urns, ice machines, and others. Follow manufacturers' instructions.

• Flush water lines as required by the regulatory authority.

• Work with your regulatory authority to resume normal operations.

Fire

Consider the following when planning for a fire:

- Have emergency-contact information for the fire and police departments, the regulatory authority, and management or headquarters personnel.
- Post the fire department phone number by each phone so it is easy to see.

If a fire occurs, you must stop operating if you cannot prep food safely. Block off areas, equipment, utensils, and other items affected by the fire. Take the following into account when planning a recovery from a fire:

- Throw out all food affected by the fire.
- Throw out all damaged utensils, linens, or items that cannot be cleaned and sanitized.
- Clean and sanitize the operation.
- If needed, hire a janitorial service that specializes in areas exposed to fires.
- Check water lines. The use of fire hoses may have lowered water pressure in the area. This could cause backflow and water contamination.

Flood

Consider the following when planning for a flood:

- Have a plan to monitor and maintain flood-control equipment: plumbing, storm drains, sump pumps, etc.
- Have emergency-contact information for the regulatory authority, the plumber, utility companies, etc.
- Keep a supply of bottled water.

To manage your response to a flood, consider the steps identified below.

Flood Responses

If	Then
A water line leaks or water builds up on the floor, but food, utensils, etc., are not affected.	• Keep people away from the wet floor. • Repair the leak. • Block off areas, equipment, utensils, and other items affected by the flood.
A flood affects or damages food, utensils, etc.	• Stop all operations.
The flood is the result of a sewage backup in the prep area.	• Close the affected area right away. • Correct the problem. • Clean the area thoroughly.

Take the following into account when planning recovery from a flood:

- Throw out all damaged utensils, linens, or items that cannot be cleaned and sanitized.

- Throw out any food or food packaging that made contact with the water.

- Clean and sanitize the facility, utensils, equipment surfaces, floors, or other affected areas.

- If needed, hire a janitorial service that specializes in areas exposed to floods.

SUMMARY

- A food safety management system is a group of procedures and practices intended to prevent foodborne illness. It does this by actively controlling risks and hazards throughout the flow of food.

- It is the manager's responsibility to actively control the risk factors for foodborne illness. This is called active managerial control. It can be achieved by incorporating specific actions and procedures into the operation to prevent foodborne illness.

- The FDA provides specific recommendations for controlling the common risk factors for foodborne illness. These are known as public health interventions. They are designed to protect public health.

- HACCP is based on identifying significant biological, chemical, or physical hazards at specific points within a product's flow. Once identified, the hazards can be prevented, eliminated, or reduced to safe levels.

- A HACCP plan is based on seven basic principles. These principles are the seven steps that outline how to create a HACCP plan.

- Some food processes are highly specialized and can be a serious health risk if specific procedures are not followed. This includes processing methods such as curing food, or smoking food to extend shelf life. Always check with your local regulatory authority before using specialized processing methods on-site.

- Prepare for a crisis before one occurs. Start with a written plan that focuses on preparation, response, and recovery. For each of these phases, the plan should identify resources needed and procedures to be followed.

- Each crisis management plan needs to be customized to the operation. A good way to ensure your plan achieves what you need is to test it once it is complete. The results will help you identify potential gaps or problems.

Apply Your Knowledge

Use these questions to review the concepts presented in this chapter.

DISCUSSION QUESTIONS

① What types of food safety programs must be in place as a foundation for a food safety management system?

② What are some ways to achieve active managerial control?

③ List the seven HACCP principles in order.

④ What specialized food prep processes require a variance from the regulatory authority?

For answers, please turn to the Answer Key.

Apply Your Knowledge

Trouble at Nathan's

CASE IN POINT

Bryce, a restaurant owner, opened his morning paper and almost fell off his chair. He was shocked to see an article about foodborne illness at his friend Nathan's restaurant. Even though Nathan had a HACCP program in place and had passed a recent health inspection with flying colors, 23 people got sick after eating dinner at the restaurant. The regulatory authority closed the restaurant temporarily until the cause of the outbreak could be determined.

The article went on to say that even though the paper had called the restaurant several times to find out more about the outbreak, the restaurant manager did not return the calls. Direct calls to Nathan were also not returned. When interviewed, several staff members stated that they did not know what was going on and they had not heard anything from the owner or manager about the outbreak.

① What was wrong with how Nathan handled the crisis?

② What should have been done differently?

For answers, please turn to the Answer Key.

Apply Your Knowledge

Maria's Challenge

CASE IN POINT

Maria, an owner/operator of a local family restaurant, realized that she needed to do more to keep her place safe. That meant taking charge of food safety in a more formal way than before. It was time to develop a food safety management system. Though she had not had any formal training in HACCP, she wanted to develop a HACCP plan for her operation.

Maria began by reviewing her menu to try and identify CCPs for each menu item. Most dishes on the menu were grilled items that were prepared, cooked, and then served. Maria determined that risks to these items could best be controlled through cooking, so she identified cooking as the CCP. Next, she identified critical limits for each CCP. For grilled hamburgers, she determined that cooking them to 150°F (66°C) for 15 seconds would reduce pathogens to a safe level. For grilled chicken, she knew it was necessary to cook it to 165°F (74°C) for 15 seconds.

Maria decided to monitor the critical limits by having cooks press on the meat with their fingertips to check for doneness. As an additional safeguard, she required cooks to cut open product to check the color for doneness. Maria knew she needed to identify a corrective action for products that had not been cooked enough. She decided that if the meat did not feel right or if the color inside was not correct, cooks needed to keep cooking the meat. Maria knew that record keeping was often part of a HACCP program, but she was not sure what types of records to keep. She ended up deciding that for her operation, they really were not necessary.

1 What did Maria do wrong?

2 What should she have done differently?

For answers, please turn to the Answer Key.

Study Questions

Circle the best answer to each question.

1. The temperature of a roast is checked to see if it has met its critical limit of 145°F (63°C) for 4 minutes. This is an example of which HACCP principle?

   A Verification

   B Monitoring

   C Record keeping

   D Hazard analysis

2. The temperature of a pot of beef stew is checked during holding. The stew has not met the critical limit and is thrown out according to house policy. Throwing out the stew is an example of which HACCP principle?

   A Monitoring

   B Verification

   C Hazard analysis

   D Corrective action

3. A deli serves cold sandwiches in a self-serve display. Which step in the flow of food would be a critical control point?

   A Storage

   B Cooling

   C Cooking

   D Reheating

4. A chef sanitized a thermometer probe and then checked the temperature of minestrone soup being held in a hot-holding unit. The temperature was 120°F (49°C), which did not meet the operation's critical limit of 135°F (57°C). The chef recorded the temperature in the log and reheated the soup to 165°F (74°C) for 15 seconds within 2 hours. Which was the corrective action?

   A Reheating the soup

   B Checking the critical limit

   C Sanitizing the thermometer probe

   D Recording the temperature in the log

5. What is the purpose of a food safety management system?

   A Keep all areas of the facility clean and pest free

   B Identify, tag, and repair faulty equipment within the facility

   C Identify and control possible hazards throughout the flow of food

   D Identify, document, and use the correct methods for receiving food

6. Reviewing temperature logs and other records to make sure that the HACCP plan is working as intended is an example of which HACCP principle?

   A Monitoring

   B Verification

   C Hazard analysis

   D Record keeping

7. What is the first step in developing a HACCP plan?

   A Identify corrective actions.

   B Conduct a hazard analysis.

   C Establish monitoring procedures.

   D Determine critical control points.

8. What does an operation that wants to smoke food as a method of preservation need to have before processing food this way?

   A Food safety certificate

   B Crisis-management plan

   C Master cleaning schedule

   D Variance from the regulatory authority

For answers, please turn to the Answer Key.

Notes

11 Safe Facilities and Equipment

Designing a Safe Operation	Considerations for Other Areas of the Facility	Equipment Selection		Installing & Maintaining Kitchen Equipment	Utilities
— Construction Plan Review — Layout — Materials for Interior Construction — Flooring — Finishes for Interior Walls & Ceilings	— Dry Storage — Handwashing Stations — Sinks — Restrooms — Dressing Rooms and Lockers — Premises	— Equipment Standards — Dishwashing Machines — Three-Compartment Sinks — Coolers and Freezers	— Blast Chillers & Tumble Chillers — Cook-Chill Equipment Cutting Boards	— Installing Kitchen Equipment — Maintaining Equipment	— Water Supply — Hot Water — Plumbing — Lighting — Ventilation — Garbage

Case in POINT

Café Owners Stopped From Opening

The new owners of a small breakfast café were all set for their pre-opening inspection by the local regulatory authority. The owners had recently purchased the café, which had sat vacant for a number of years. While the owners were new to the foodservice business, they had done their best to get the café ready for opening on their limited budget. After the inspection, they were shocked to find out that they would not be able to open. The inspector had found a number of violations.

Several floor tiles were cracked, and a few ceiling tiles were missing. The coving between the floor and wall had also come away from the wall in several places. Some of the bulbs in the fluorescent lighting were burned out. The exhaust hoods in the kitchen were extremely dirty, and there was a buildup of grease on certain areas of the walls and ceilings.

There were also problems with the equipment in the café. Some of the equipment being used was household equipment, including the bread toasters. The wooden cutting boards had several large cracks, and the new milk dispenser that the owners had installed was simply sitting on the service counter in the wait station.

There were also some problems in other areas. Only the cold water worked at the handwashing sink in the restrooms and the Dumpster behind the café was missing a lid. The inspector told the owners that he would be back to reinspect the café once they had fixed the problems.

❶ **What do the owners need to fix in order to open for business?**

For answers, please turn to the Answer Key.

INSIDE THIS CHAPTER

- Designing a Safe Operation
- Considerations for Other Areas of the Facility
- Equipment Selection
- Installing and Maintaining Kitchen Equipment
- Utilities

OBJECTIVES

After completing this chapter, you should be able to identify the following:

- When a review of the construction plan is required
- Characteristics of correct flooring
- Characteristics of correct interior finishes including doors, walls, and ceilings
- Requirements for restrooms
- Requirements for handwashing stations
- Requirements for food-contact surfaces
- Organizations that certify equipment that meets sanitation standards
- Requirements for dishwashing facilities
- Requirements for installing equipment
- Approved water sources and testing requirements
- Methods for preventing cross-connection and backflow
- The correct response to a wastewater overflow
- Lighting-intensity requirements for different areas of the operation
- Ways of preventing lighting sources from contaminating food
- Ways of preventing ventilation systems from contaminating food and food-contact surfaces
- Requirements for handling garbage including correct storage and removal
- The importance of keeping physical facilities in good repair

KEY TERMS

- Porosity
- Resiliency
- Coving
- NSF
- Booster heater
- Cross-connection
- Backflow
- Air gap

11

Designing a Safe Operation	Considerations for Other Areas of the Facility	Equipment Selection		Installing & Maintaining Kitchen Equipment	Utilities
– Construction Plan Review – Layout – Materials for Interior Construction – Flooring – Finishes for Interior Walls & Ceilings	– Dry Storage – Handwashing Stations – Sinks – Restrooms – Dressing Rooms and Lockers – Premises	– Equipment Standards – Dishwashing Machines – Three-Compartment Sinks – Coolers and Freezers	– Blast Chillers & Tumble Chillers – Cook-Chill Equipment – Cutting Boards	– Installing Kitchen Equipment – Maintaining Equipment	– Water Supply – Hot Water – Plumbing – Lighting – Ventilation – Garbage

DESIGNING A SAFE OPERATION

When designing or remodeling a facility, consider how both the building and its equipment will be kept clean. Poorly designed areas are generally harder to clean and can become a breeding ground for pathogens. Food passing through these areas runs a much higher risk of contamination.

This chapter focuses on four topics related to the safe layout and design of equipment and facilities:

- Designing and arranging equipment and fixtures to comply with sanitation standards
- Selecting wall, floor, and ceiling materials that are easier to clean
- Designing utilities to prevent contamination and make cleaning easier
- Managing garbage correctly to avoid contaminating food and attracting pests

Construction Plan Review

Before starting any new construction or a large remodeling project, you must check with your regulatory authority. You will need approval of your construction plans before construction begins. While mandatory, a regulatory review of the plans has several benefits:

- It ensures the design meets regulatory requirements.
- It ensures a safe flow of food.
- It may save time and money.
- It assures that contractors are constructing the facility correctly and approved equipment is being used.

In addition to submitting your construction plans to the regulatory authority, you should also check with your local building department to see what is required.

Key Point

You must have the regulatory authority review construction plans before new construction or remodeling.

Layout

A well-designed kitchen will address the following factors.

Work flow   Establish a work flow that will minimize the time food spends in the temperature danger zone. It should also minimize the number of times food is handled. For example, locate storage areas near the receiving area, as shown in the illustration below, to prevent delays in storing food. Locate prep tables near coolers and freezers for the same reason.

Contamination   A good layout will minimize the risk of cross-contamination. Place equipment in a way that will prevent splashing or spilling from one piece of equipment onto another. For example, avoid placing the dirty-utensil table next to the salad-prep sink.

Equipment accessibility   Hard-to-reach areas are less likely to be cleaned. A well-planned layout will ensure that equipment is accessible for cleaning.

Materials for Interior Construction

When selecting materials for interior construction, the most important consideration is how easy the operation will be to clean and maintain. Sound-absorbent surfaces that resist grease and moisture and reflect light will probably create an environment acceptable to your regulatory authority.

Flooring

Each area of your operation has its own flooring needs. Flooring should be smooth, durable, nonabsorbent, and easy to clean. It should resist wear and help prevent slips. Once installed, flooring should be kept in good condition and be replaced if damaged or worn.

The flooring's porosity is another important factor. Porosity is the extent to which a material will absorb liquids. Avoid high-porosity flooring. Its absorbency often makes it ideal for pathogen growth. High-porosity flooring can also cause people to slip or fall. It often deteriorates quickly as well.

To prevent these problems, use nonabsorbent flooring in the following areas:

- Walk-in coolers
- Prep and food-storage areas
- Dishwashing areas
- Restrooms
- Dressing and locker rooms

Nonporous, Resilient Flooring

In most areas of the operation, nonporous, resilient flooring is the best choice. Resiliency means a material can react to a shock without breaking or cracking.

Nonporous, resilient materials, such as vinyl or rubber tiles, are relatively inexpensive. They are also easy to clean and maintain, as shown in the photo at left. If individual tiles break, they can be easily replaced. They can also handle heavy traffic and resist grease and alkalis.

However, this type of flooring does have disadvantages. Sharp objects can easily damage it. It also tends to be slippery when wet. It is usually a poor choice for dining rooms or public areas. It is more practical for break rooms, staff dressing rooms, and foodservice offices. See the table below for characteristics and recommended uses of nonporous, resilient flooring.

Characteristics of Nonporous, Resilient Flooring				
	Where to Use	Durability	Advantages	Disadvantages
Rubber tile	Kitchens; restrooms	Less durable and less resistant to grease and alkalis	Nonslip; resilient; easy to clean	Can only be used in moderate-traffic areas
Vinyl sheet	Offices; kitchens; corridors	Less resistant to grease and alkalis	Very resilient; easy to clean	Can only be used in light- or moderate-traffic areas
Vinyl tile	Offices; staff restrooms	Wears out quickly with high traffic	Very resilient; easy to clean	Requires waxing and machine buffing

Key Point

Hard-surface flooring is nonabsorbent and very durable, making it a good choice for high-dirt areas.

Hard-Surface Flooring

Because it is durable and nonabsorbent, hard-surface flooring is often used in foodservice operations. These types of flooring—especially quarry and ceramic tile—are excellent for public restrooms or high-dirt areas.

Still, these flooring materials have their disadvantages. They may crack or chip if heavy objects are dropped on them. They do not absorb sound, and they are expensive to install and maintain. Finally, hard-surface flooring is somewhat difficult to clean.

While most hard-surface floors, especially marble, can be slippery, unglazed tiles can provide a hard, slip-resistant surface. See the table below for characteristics and recommended uses of hard-surface flooring.

Characteristics of Hard-Surface Flooring				
	Where to Use	Durability	Advantages	Disadvantages
Marble; terrazzo	Public corridors; dining rooms; public restrooms	Wear resistant	Nonporous; good appearance	Nonresilient; heavy; expensive; requires special care; difficult to install
Quarry tile	Kitchen; service, dishwashing, and receiving areas; offices; restrooms; dining rooms	Wear resistant	Nonporous	Nonresilient; heavy; expensive; slippery when wet unless an abrasive is added
Wood	Offices; dining rooms	Durable in lower-traffic areas	Good appearance and sound absorption	Requires frequent polishing and periodic refinishing to maintain surface qualities

Carpeting

Carpeting is a popular choice for certain areas, such as dining rooms, because it absorbs sound. However, it is not recommended in high-dirt areas such as waitstaff service areas, tray and dish drop-off areas, beverage stations, and major traffic aisles.

Carpet can be maintained by simple vacuuming. Areas prone to heavy traffic and moisture will require routine cleaning. You can also purchase special carpet for areas where sanitation, dirt, moisture, and fire safety are concerns.

Special Flooring Needs

Use nonslip surfaces in traffic areas. Nonslip surfaces are ideal for the entire kitchen as well, because slips and falls are a potential hazard.

For safety reasons, rubber mats are allowed in areas where standing water may occur, such as in the dish room. When scrubbing floors, pick up rubber mats and clean them separately.

Coving is required in operations using resilient or hard-surface flooring materials. Coving is a curved, sealed edge placed between the floor and the wall to eliminate sharp corners or gaps that would be impossible to clean. An example is shown in the photo at left. The coving tile or strip should adhere tightly to the wall. This will help eliminate hiding places for insects. It will also prevent moisture from deteriorating the wall.

Finishes for Interior Walls and Ceilings

Interior finishes are the materials used on the surface of an operation's walls and ceilings. As with flooring, these finishes need to be smooth, nonabsorbent, durable, and easy to clean.

Consider the location when selecting finishes for walls and ceilings. A material that might be suitable in one area may be a poor choice for another. Walls and ceilings in prep areas should be light in color to distribute light and to make it easier to spot dirt when cleaning. They should also be kept free of cracks, holes, and peeling paint.

The best wall finish in cooking areas is ceramic tile, as shown in the photo at left. However, it needs to be monitored for grout loss and regrouted when needed. Stainless steel is used occasionally because it is durable and moisture resistant.

The most common ceiling materials are acoustic tile, painted drywall, painted plaster, and exposed concrete.

Wall and ceiling support structures (studs, joists, and rafters) as well as pipes should not be exposed unless finished and sealed for cleaning.

Flexible materials such as paper, vinyl, and thin wood veneers are often used for walls and ceilings. Vinyl wall coverings are popular because they are attractive, relatively inexpensive, easy to clean, and durable. They are also rated for flammability by testing agencies.

Plaster or cinder-block walls that have been sealed and painted with oil-resistant, easy-to-wash, glossy paints are appropriate for dry areas of the facility.

Designing a Safe Operation	Considerations for Other Areas of the Facility	Equipment Selection		Installing & Maintaining Kitchen Equipment	Utilities
— Construction Plan Review — Layout — Materials for Interior Construction — Flooring — Finishes for Interior Walls & Ceilings	— Dry Storage — Handwashing Stations — Sinks — Restrooms — Dressing Rooms and Lockers — Premises	— Equipment Standards — Dishwashing Machines — Three-Compartment Sinks — Coolers and Freezers	— Blast Chillers & Tumble Chillers — Cook-Chill Equipment — Cutting Boards	— Installing Kitchen Equipment — Maintaining Equipment	— Water Supply — Hot Water — Plumbing — Lighting — Ventilation — Garbage

Technology

LED Lights

Light-emitting diode (LED) lights are semi-conductor light sources. LED lights are energy-efficient products that convert electricity to light. They contain no filaments, which is why they don't get very hot. LED lighting is being used outside and inside restaurants, including in refrigeration display cases. This type of lighting is considered more attractive than traditional lighting and lasts longer. In fact, LED bulbs have a lifetime expectancy of 50,000 hours or more in continuous operation.

LED bulbs cost anywhere from $25 to $60 per bulb. As lighting can account for 11% of a restaurant's energy bill (on average), LED lighting is a simple and cost-effective way to reduce energy consumption in foodservice establishments while maintaining the volume of light needed to ensure food is handled safely.

In the following examples, all of these organizations were able to make choices that conserved energy, reduced costs, and maintained regulatory requirements for lighting needs. See how:

- A national, casual-dining chain recently replaced 12,000 standard incandescent and halogen lights in 150 of their restaurants with LED lighting. The company has stated that it saves approximately $120,000 on lighting bills annually.

- Another company recently refitted all 31 of its New York restaurants with LED lights, using both exterior and interior LED lightbulbs. The organization reduced the average kilowatt hour light by 80%.

CONSIDERATIONS FOR OTHER AREAS OF THE FACILITY

Dry Storage

Construct dry-storage areas with easy-to-clean materials that allow good air circulation. Shelving, tabletops, and bins for dry ingredients should be made of corrosion-resistant metal or food-grade plastic.

Any windows in the dry-storage area should have frosted glass or shades. Direct sunlight can increase the area's temperature and affect food quality.

Steam pipes, water lines, and other conduits do not belong in a well-designed dry-storage area. Dripping condensation or leaks in overhead pipes can promote pathogen growth in such normally stable items as crackers, flour, and baking powder. Leaking overhead sewer lines can also contaminate food. Hot-water heaters or steam pipes can raise the area's temperature to levels that allow foodborne pathogens to grow as well.

Dry food is also susceptible to attack by insects and rodents. Cracks and crevices in floors or walls should therefore be filled. Doors leading to the building's exterior should be self-closing. Screens for windows and doors should be 16 mesh to the inch without any tears or holes.

Dry-Storage Example

Handwashing Stations

Handwashing stations should be put in areas that make it easy for staff to wash their hands often. These stations are required in restrooms or directly next to them. Handwashing stations are also required in areas used for food prep, service, and dishwashing. Handwashing sinks must be used only for handwashing and not for any other purpose.

Make sure these stations work correctly and are well stocked and maintained. They must also be available at all times. Handwashing stations cannot be blocked by portable equipment or stacked full of dirty kitchenware, as shown in the photo at left. A handwashing station must include the items listed below.

Requirements for a Handwashing Station	
	Hot and cold running water The water must be drinkable and meet temperature and pressure requirements.
	Soap The soap can be liquid, bar, or powder.
	A way to dry hands Disposable paper towels or a continuous towel system that supplies the user with a clean towel can be used. Hands can also be dried with a hand dryer using either warm air or room-temperature air delivered at high velocity.
	Garbage container Garbage containers are required if disposable paper towels are used.
	Signage A clearly visible sign or poster must tell staff to wash hands before returning to work. The message should be in all languages used by staff in the operation.

Some jurisdictions allow the use of automatic handwashing facilities in an operation. Check with your local regulatory authority for more information.

Sinks

To prevent cross-contamination, staff must use each sink in an operation for its intended purpose. Handwashing sinks are for handwashing. Prep sinks are for prepping food. Service sinks are for cleaning mops and disposing of wastewater. At least one service sink or curbed drain area is required for disposing of dirty water, as shown in the photo at left.

Restrooms

If possible, provide separate restrooms for staff and customers. If this is not possible, the operation must be designed so patrons do not pass through prep areas to reach the restroom. Otherwise, they could contaminate food or food-contact surfaces.

Restrooms should be convenient, sanitary, and have self-closing doors. They must be adequately stocked with toilet paper. Garbage containers must be provided if disposable paper towels are used. Women's restrooms also need covered garbage containers for disposing sanitary supplies.

Dressing Rooms and Lockers

Dressing rooms are not required. If available, they should not be used for prepping food, storage, or utensil washing. Lockers should be located in a separate room or one where food, equipment, utensils, linens, and single-service items cannot be contaminated.

Premises

Grade the parking lot and walkways so standing pools of water do not form. They should also be surfaced to minimize dirt and blowing dust.

Concrete and asphalt are recommended for walkways and parking lots. Gravel, while acceptable, is not recommended.

Customer traffic through prep areas is prohibited, although guided tours are allowed. Do not allow the premises to be used for living or sleeping quarters.

 Technology

Low-Flow Faucet Aerators

Using a low-flow aerator does not mean skimping on the water needed to ensure food safety. Sinks with low-flow aerators cut water use and save on water-heating costs without affecting your ability to work with food correctly. Low-flow aerators mix air with the water coming out of the faucet. This reduces the amount of water used without compromising its pressure.

At least one major quick-service restaurant chain has been using these since 2006. This company requires low-flow faucets/taps for all of its new restaurants. They state that this change has saved about 182.1 million gallons of water annually.

Learn more about water conservation at conserve.restaurant.org.

Designing a Safe Operation	Considerations for Other Areas of the Facility	Equipment Selection		Installing & Maintaining Kitchen Equipment	Utilities
— Construction Plan Review — Layout — Materials for Interior Construction — Flooring — Finishes for Interior Walls & Ceilings	— Dry Storage — Handwashing Stations — Sinks — Restrooms — Dressing Rooms and Lockers — Premises	— Equipment Standards — Dishwashing Machines — Three-Compartment Sinks — Coolers and Freezers	— Blast Chillers & Tumble Chillers — Cook-Chill Equipment — Cutting Boards	— Installing Kitchen Equipment — Maintaining Equipment	— Water Supply — Hot Water — Plumbing — Lighting — Ventilation — Garbage

EQUIPMENT SELECTION

Equipment Standards

Foodservice equipment must meet certain standards if it will come in contact with food. NSF is an organization that creates these national standards. NSF is accredited by the American National Standards Institute (ANSI). NSF/ANSI standards for food equipment require that it be nonabsorbent, smooth, and corrosion resistant. Food equipment must also be easy to clean, durable, and resistant to damage. The NSF Mark, shown at left, will appear on equipment that meets these standards.

Only commercial foodservice equipment should be used in operations. Household equipment is not built to withstand heavy use.

Dishwashing Machines

Dishwashing machines vary widely by size, style, and method of sanitizing. High-temperature machines sanitize with extremely hot water. Chemical-sanitizing machines use a chemical solution.

The following machines are common in foodservice operations.

Single-tank, stationary-rack machine, with doors   This machine holds a stationary rack of tableware and utensils. Items are washed by detergent and water from below, and sometimes from above, the rack. The wash cycle is followed by a hot-water or chemical-sanitizer final rinse.

Conveyor machine   With this machine, a conveyor moves racks of items through the various cycles of washing, rinsing, and sanitizing. The machine may have a single tank or multiple tanks.

Carousel or circular-conveyor machine   This multiple-tank machine moves tableware and utensils on a peg-type conveyor or in racks.

Flight type   This is a high-capacity, multiple-tank machine with a peg-type conveyor. It may also have a built-in dryer.

Batch-type, dump   This stationary-rack machine combines the wash and rinse cycles in a single tank. Each cycle is timed. The machine automatically dispenses both the detergent and the sanitizing chemical or hot water. Wash and rinse water are drained after each cycle.

Recirculating, door-type, non-dump machine   This stationary-rack machine is not fully drained of water between cycles. The wash water is diluted with fresh water and reused from cycle to cycle.

Dishwasher Selection and Installation Guidelines

Consider these guidelines when selecting and installing dishwashers.

Installation   Dishwashers must be installed so that they are reachable and conveniently located. That installation must also keep utensils, equipment, and other food-contact surfaces from becoming contaminated. The machine should be raised at least six inches (15 centimeters) off the floor to permit easy cleaning beneath. Always follow the manufacturer's instructions when installing, operating, and maintaining dishwashers.

Plumbing   Water pipes to the dishwashing machine should be as short as possible to prevent the loss of heat.

Chemicals   Use detergents and sanitizers approved by the regulatory authority.

Settings   Purchase dishwashers that can measure the following:

- Water temperature
- Water pressure
- Cleaning and sanitizing chemical concentration

Information about the correct settings should be posted on the machine. The label in the photo at left shows an example.

Thermometer   The machine's thermometer should be located so it is readable with a scale in increments no greater than 2°F (1°C).

Cleaning   Dishwashers should be easy to clean. They should be cleaned as often as necessary. Follow the manufacturer's recommendations and local regulatory requirements.

Three-Compartment Sinks

Many operations use three-compartment sinks to clean and sanitize items manually in the operation. Purchase sinks that can accommodate large equipment and utensils. Have other ways of cleaning these items as well, such as cleaning a large piece of equipment in place.

Coolers and Freezers

There are several types of cooler and freezer units. The two most common are walk-in and reach-in coolers and freezers. The doors should withstand heavy use and close with a slight nudge.

A drain must be provided and maintained for disposal of condensation and defrost water as well. A correctly plumbed, indirect drain can be used in the walk-in cooler. You can minimize any excess condensation by maintaining a flush-fitting floor sweep (gasket) under the door.

Courtesy of Hobart Corporation

Courtesy of Hobart Corporation

Considerations When Purchasing Coolers or Freezers

In addition to the sanitation standards discussed in this chapter, consider these factors when purchasing a cooler or freezer unit.

Installation   Make sure walk-in units can be sealed to the floor and wall. They should offer no access to moisture or rodents.

Reach-ins   Purchase reach-in cooler or freezer units with legs that elevate them six inches (15 centimeters) off the floor. Otherwise, mount and seal them on a masonry base. Caster wheels are often preferred or required by regulatory authorities, as shown in the photo at left. They make it easier to move the unit for cleaning.

Temperature   Make sure the unit meets the temperature requirements of the food you store. Built-in thermometers should be easy to locate and read. They should also be accurate to within +/- 3°F or +/- 1.5°C.

Blast Chillers and Tumble Chillers

Blast chillers cool food quickly. Many can cool food from 135°F to 37°F (57°C to 3°C) within 90 minutes. A blast chiller is shown in the photo at left. Most units allow the operator to set target chill temperatures and monitor the temperature of food throughout the chill cycle. Once chilled to safe temperatures, the food can then be stored in conventional coolers or freezers.

Tumble chillers cool food quickly as well. Prepackaged hot food is placed into a drum that rotates inside a reservoir of chilled water. The tumbling action increases the effectiveness of the chilled water in cooling the food.

Cook-Chill Equipment

Some operations prep food using a cook-chill system. By this method, food is partially cooked, rapidly chilled, and then held in refrigerated storage. When needed, the food is simply reheated. A cook-chill unit is an integrated piece of equipment that can cook, cool, and reheat food.

Cutting Boards

Many regulatory authorities allow the use of either wooden or synthetic cutting boards. If the regulatory authority allows wooden cutting boards and baker's tables, they need to be made from a nonabsorbent hardwood, such as maple or oak. They need to be nontoxic and free of cracks and seams as well.

Designing a Safe Operation	Considerations for Other Areas of the Facility	Equipment Selection		Installing & Maintaining Kitchen Equipment	Utilities
— Construction Plan Review — Layout — Materials for Interior Construction — Flooring — Finishes for Interior Walls & Ceilings	— Dry Storage — Handwashing Stations — Sinks — Restrooms — Dressing Rooms and Lockers — Premises	— Equipment Standards — Dishwashing Machines — Three-Compartment Sinks — Coolers and Freezers	— Blast Chillers & Tumble Chillers — Cook-Chill Equipment — Cutting Boards	— Installing Kitchen Equipment — Maintaining Equipment	— Water Supply — Hot Water — Plumbing — Lighting — Ventilation — Garbage

INSTALLING AND MAINTAINING KITCHEN EQUIPMENT

Stationary equipment should be easy to clean and easy to clean around. In the photo at left, the dishwasher is installed so that the floor underneath can be cleaned easily.

Installing Kitchen Equipment

Follow the manufacturer's directions when installing equipment. Also check with your regulatory authority for requirements.

In general, stationary equipment should be installed as follows.

Floor-mounted equipment Put floor-mounted equipment on legs at least 6 inches (15 centimeters) high. Another option is to seal it to a masonry base.

Tabletop equipment Put tabletop equipment on legs at least 4 inches (10 centimeters) high. Or seal it to the countertop.

Also seal all cracks or seams to prevent food buildup or pests. However, do not use sealant to cover wide gaps from faulty construction or repairs. Any gaps should be correctly repaired before equipment is installed.

Maintaining Equipment

Once you have installed equipment, make sure it is maintained regularly by qualified people. Also set up a maintenance schedule with your supplier or manufacturer. Check equipment regularly to be sure it is working correctly.

Designing a Safe Operation	Considerations for Other Areas of the Facility	Equipment Selection		Installing & Maintaining Kitchen Equipment	Utilities
– Construction Plan Review – Layout – Materials for Interior Construction – Flooring – Finishes for Interior Walls & Ceilings	– Dry Storage – Handwashing Stations – Sinks – Restrooms – Dressing Rooms and Lockers – Premises	– Equipment Standards – Dishwashing Machines – Three-Compartment Sinks – Coolers and Freezers	– Blast Chillers & Tumble Chillers – Cook-Chill Equipment – Cutting Boards	– Installing Kitchen Equipment – Maintaining Equipment	– Water Supply – Hot Water – Plumbing – Lighting – Ventilation – Garbage

UTILITIES

An operation uses many utilities and building systems. Utilities include water, electricity, gas, sewage, and garbage disposal. Building systems include plumbing, lighting, and ventilation. There must be enough utilities to meet the needs of the operation. In addition, the utilities and systems must work correctly. If they do not, the risk of contamination is greater.

Water Supply

Each regulatory authority establishes standards for water in its jurisdiction. Only water that is drinkable can be used for prepping food and come in contact with food-contact surfaces.

This water may come from the following sources:

- Approved public water mains
- Private water sources that are regularly tested and maintained
- Closed, portable water containers
- Water transport vehicles

If your operation uses a private water supply, such as a well, rather than an approved public source, check with your regulatory authority for information on inspections, testing, and other requirements. Nonpublic water systems should be tested at least each year. The report should also be kept on file in the operation.

Hot Water

Providing a continuous supply of hot water can be a problem for many operations serving the public. Evaluate water heaters often to make sure they can meet peak demands. Consider how quickly the heater produces hot water as well. Also take into account the size of the holding tank and the heater's location in relation to sinks or dishwashing machines.

Most general-purpose water heaters will not heat water to temperatures required for hot-water sanitizing. You might then need a booster heater to maintain water temperature. Many dishwashing machines now come with booster heaters.

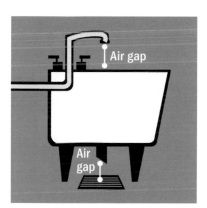

Plumbing

Incorrectly installed or poorly maintained plumbing has been implicated in outbreaks of typhoid fever, hepatitis A, Norovirus, and other illnesses. For this reason, only licensed plumbers should install and maintain plumbing.

Cross-Connections

The greatest challenge to water safety comes from cross-connections. A cross-connection is a physical link between safe water and dirty water, which can come from drains, sewers, or other wastewater sources.

A cross-connection is dangerous because it can let backflow occur. Backflow is the reverse flow of contaminants through a cross-connection into a drinkable water supply. Backflow can be the result of pressure pushing contaminants back into the water supply. It can also happen when high water use in one area of an operation creates a vacuum in the plumbing system that sucks contaminants back into the water supply. This is called backsiphonage. A running faucet below the flood rim of a sink is an example of a cross-connection that can lead to backsiphonage. A running hose in a mop bucket is another example, as shown in the illustration at left.

Backflow Prevention

The best way to prevent backflow is to avoid creating a cross-connection. Do not attach a hose to a faucet unless a backflow prevention device, such as a vacuum breaker, is attached. A vacuum breaker is a mechanical device that prevents backsiphonage. It does this by closing a check valve and sealing the water supply line shut when water flow is stopped.

Other mechanical devices are used to prevent backflow. These include double check valve and reduced pressure zone backflow preventers. These devices include more than one check valve for sealing off the water supply. They also provide a way to determine if the check valves are operational.

Backflow prevention devices must be checked periodically to make sure they are working correctly. This must be done by a trained and certified technician. And, the work must be documented. Always follow local requirements and manufacturer's recommendations. The only sure way to prevent backflow is to create an air gap. An air gap is an air space that separates a water supply outlet from a potentially contaminated source. A sink that is correctly designed and installed usually has two air gaps, as shown in the illustration at left. One is between the faucet and the flood rim of the sink. The other is between the drainpipe of the sink and the floor drain of the operation.

Key Point

A backup of raw sewage is cause for immediate closure of the affected area, correction of the problem, and thorough cleaning.

Grease Condensation and Leaking Pipes

Grease condensation in pipes is another common problem in plumbing systems. Grease traps are often installed to prevent the buildup of grease from creating a drain blockage. An example is shown in the photo at left. If used, grease traps must be easily accessible. They must also be installed by a licensed plumber and cleaned periodically according to the manufacturer's recommendations. If traps are not cleaned or are not cleaned correctly, a backup of wastewater could lead to odor and contamination.

Overhead wastewater pipes or fire-safety sprinkler systems can also leak and become a source of contamination. Even overhead lines carrying drinkable water can be a problem. Water can condense on the pipes and drip onto food. Check all pipes often to ensure they appear in good condition and do not leak. They should be serviced immediately when leaks occur.

Sewage

Sewage and wastewater contain pathogens, dirt, and chemicals. It is absolutely essential to prevent them from contaminating food or food-contact surfaces.

If there is a backup of raw sewage in the operation, the affected area should be closed right away. Then the problem must be corrected and the area thoroughly cleaned. If the backup is a significant risk to the safety of food, service must be stopped. Then the local regulatory authority must be notified.

The facility must have adequate drainage to handle all wastewater. Any area subjected to heavy water exposure should have its own floor drain. The drainage system should be designed to prevent floors from flooding.

Lighting

Lighting intensity—how bright the lights are in the operation—is usually measured in units called foot-candles or lux. Different areas of the facility have different lighting-intensity requirements. Regulatory authorities usually require prep areas to be brighter than other areas. This allows staff to recognize the condition of food. It also helps staff identify items that need cleaning. Lighting intensity requirements are shown in the table below. Contact the regulatory authority for requirements in your jurisdiction.

Minimum Lighting Intensity	Area
50 foot-candles (540 lux)	• Prep areas
20 foot-candles (215 lux)	• Handwashing or dishwashing areas • Buffets and salad bars • Displays for produce or packaged food • Utensil-storage areas • Wait stations • Restrooms • Inside some pieces of equipment (e.g., reach-in refrigerators)
10 foot-candles (108 lux)	• Inside walk-in coolers and freezer units • Dry-storage areas • Dining rooms (for cleaning)

Once the correct level of lighting has been installed in each area, you need to monitor it. Replace any bulbs that have burned out. Make sure they are the correct size as well. All lights should have shatter-resistant lightbulbs or protective covers, as shown in the photo at left. These products prevent broken glass from contaminating food or food-contact surfaces.

Ventilation

Ventilation improves the air inside an operation. It removes heat, steam, and smoke from cooking lines. It also eliminates fumes and odors. If ventilation systems are not working correctly, grease and condensation will build up on walls and ceilings.

To prevent this, clean and maintain ventilation systems according to manufacturer's recommendations and/or your local regulatory requirements.

Mechanical ventilation must be used in areas for cooking, frying, and grilling. Ventilation must be designed so that hoods, fans, guards, and ductwork do not drip onto food or equipment. Hood filters or grease extractors need to be tight fitting and easy to remove. They should be cleaned often. The hood and ductwork should be cleaned periodically by professionals as well.

Garbage

Garbage can attract pests and contaminate food, equipment, and utensils if not handled correctly. To control contamination from garbage, consider the following.

Garbage removal   Garbage should be removed from prep areas as quickly as possible to prevent odors, pests, and possible contamination. Staff must be careful when removing garbage so they do not contaminate food or food-contact surfaces. The food handler in the photo at left has not been careful and may contaminate the prep table.

Cleaning of containers   Clean the inside and outside of garbage containers frequently. This will help prevent the contamination of food and food-contact surfaces. It will also reduce odors and pests. Do not clean garbage containers near prep or food-storage areas.

Indoor containers   These must be leak proof, waterproof, and pest proof. They also should be easy to clean. Containers must be covered when not in use.

Designated storage areas   Waste and recyclables must be stored separately from food and food-contact surfaces. The storage of these items must not create a nuisance or a public health hazard.

Outdoor containers   Place garbage containers on a surface that is smooth, durable, and nonabsorbent. Asphalt and concrete are good choices, as shown in the photo at left. Make sure the containers have tight-fitting lids and are kept covered at all times. Keep their drain plugs in place.

Summary

- Plans for new construction or extensive remodeling must be reviewed and approved by the local regulatory authority and the local building department.

- Choose flooring, wall, and ceiling materials that are smooth and durable. This will make cleaning easier. Replace and maintain these materials when necessary.

- Make sure equipment that will come in contact with food is smooth, nonabsorbent, and easy to clean. Floor-mounted equipment must be put on legs at least six inches high or sealed to a masonry base. Tabletop equipment must be put on legs at least four inches high or sealed to the countertop.

- Dishwashing machines must be installed so that they prevent contamination of utensils, equipment, and other food-contact surfaces.

- Handwashing stations are required in areas used for food prep, service, and dishwashing. They must be used only for handwashing and should never be blocked for use.

- Handwashing stations should include hot and cold running drinkable water, soap, and a way to dry hands. They should also include a garbage container if paper towels are provided, and signage reminding staff to wash hands before returning to work.

- Plumbing must always be installed and maintained by a licensed plumber. This will help prevent cross-connections from occurring. A cross-connection is dangerous because it can let backflow occur. Backflow is the reverse flow of contaminants through a cross-connection into a drinkable water supply.

- The best way to prevent backflow is to avoid creating a cross-connection. Vacuum breakers, double check valve backflow preventers, and reduced pressure zone backflow preventers can all be used to prevent backflow. However, an air gap is the best way to prevent backflow.

- Garbage must be removed from prep areas as quickly as possible to prevent odors, pests, and possible contamination. Garbage containers must be leak proof, waterproof and pest proof. They must be cleaned, inside and out, frequently. Facilities must also be regularly maintained. Clean them on a regular basis, and make sure there are no leaks, holes, or cracks in the floors, foundation, or ceilings.

Apply Your Knowledge

Use these questions to review the concepts presented in this chapter.

DISCUSSION QUESTIONS

1. What is one of the most important considerations when choosing flooring for food-preparation areas?

2. What action must be taken in the event of a backup of raw sewage in an operation?

3. What can be done to prevent backflow in an operation?

4. What are some approved water sources for an operation? What are the testing requirements for nonpublic water systems?

5. What are the requirements of a handwashing station? In what areas of an operation are handwashing stations required?

6. What are the requirements for installing stationary equipment?

For answers, please turn to the Answer Key.

11

Apply Your Knowledge

Go or No-Go

CASE IN POINT

A food handler walked to the ingredient prep area in the back of the gourmet sandwich shop where he worked. He was shocked to see a small puddle of sewage that had formed around a floor drain. He watched the drain closely, but nothing else backed up. He quickly told a manager who evaluated the situation. Because it appeared the sewage had not contaminated food or equipment, the manager decided to remain open. However, no new sandwich ingredients were prepared. Instead the shop sold sandwiches made from remaining ingredients. When they had used these up, they sold premade sandwiches from the display case. The manager assigned one of the staff members to clean up the spill. She then contacted the building management, who quickly sent out a licensed plumber.

1 Did the manager handle the situation correctly? Why or why not?

For answers, please turn to the Answer Key.

Apply Your Knowledge

Where There's Smoke

CASE IN POINT

A regional manager for a small quick-service chain had stopped to check in on one of her stores. Unfortunately, she had not visited the store for several months. As the manager walked around, she noticed that there was a buildup of grease on the kitchen walls and ceilings. She also noticed condensation dripping from these areas.

1 What is the problem?

2 What should the regional manager do to fix it?

For answers, please turn to the Answer Key.

Study Questions

Circle the best answer to each question.

1 What are the most important food safety features to look for when selecting flooring, wall, and ceiling materials?

A   Absorbent and durable

B   Hard and durable

C   Porous and durable

D   Smooth and durable

2 What organization creates national standards for foodservice equipment?

A   CDC

B   EPA

C   FDA

D   NSF

3 When installing tabletop equipment on legs, the space between the base of the equipment and the tabletop must be at least

A   2 inches (5 centimeters).

B   4 inches (10 centimeters).

C   6 inches (15 centimeters).

D   8 inches (20 centimeters).

4 Besides information on chemical concentration and water temperature, what other machine setting information should be posted on dishwashing machines?

A   Water pH

B   Water salinity

C   Water pressure

D   Water hardness

5 Signage posted at a handwashing station must include a reminder to staff to

A   wash hands before returning to work.

B   use hot running water when washing.

C   scrub hands and arms for 10 to 15 seconds.

D   avoid touching faucet handles after washing.

6 What is the only completely reliable method for preventing backflow?

A   Air gap

B   Ball valve

C   Cross-connection

D   Vacuum breaker

7 A food handler drops the end of a hose into a mop bucket and turns the water on to fill it. What has the food handler done wrong?

A   Created a cross-connection

B   Created an air gap separation

C   Prevented backflow

D   Prevented atmospheric vacuuming

8 Which area of the operation is usually required to be the brightest?

A   Dry storage

B   Preparation

C   Refrigerated storage

D   Service

Continued on the next page ▶

► *Continued from previous page*

9 An operation has a buildup of grease and condensation on the walls and ceiling. What is the most likely problem?

A The ventilation system is not working correctly.

B The cleaning chemicals are not being used correctly.

C The staff are not cleaning the walls correctly.

D The grill is not being operated at a high-enough temperature.

10 An operation received a violation in the outside area of the facility. The manager reviewed the area and saw that the Dumpster was placed on a freshly graveled drive. The lids were closed, and the drain plug was in place to prevent the Dumpster from draining. What was the problem?

A The Dumpster lids should have been open to allow it to air out.

B The drain plug should have been removed to allow the Dumpster to drain correctly.

C The surface underneath the Dumpster should have been paved with concrete or asphalt.

D The Dumpster should have been freshly painted so that food debris would not stick to surfaces.

11 A broken water main has caused the water in an operation to appear brown. What should the manager do?

A Boil the water for 1 minute before use.

B Contact the local regulatory authority before use.

C Use the water for everything except dishwashing.

D Use the water for everything except handwashing.

For answers, please turn to the Answer Key.

Notes

12 Cleaning and Sanitizing

Cleaning	Sanitizing	Dishwashing	Cleaning the Premises	Developing a Cleaning Program
— Factors That Affect Cleaning — Types of Cleaners	— Heat Sanitizing — Chemical Sanitizing — Sanitizer Effectiveness — How and When to Clean and Sanitize	— Machine Dishwashing — Manual Dishwashing — Storing Tableware and Equipment	— Nonfood-Contact Surfaces — Cleaning Tools and Supplies	— Identifying Cleaning Needs — Creating a Master Cleaning Schedule — Choosing Cleaning Materials — Implementing the Cleaning Program

Case in POINT

Slicer Tied to Outbreak

Twenty people got sick after dining at a small quick-service restaurant. The culprit—*Salmonella* on a slicer used to slice meat and other products. Investigators found the bacteria after swabbing the equipment in the operation. When interviewed, food handlers at the operation stated that they had wiped the machine down between uses. However, they had not completely disassembled the machine when cleaning and sanitizing it.

1 How could the outbreak have been prevented?

For answers, please turn to the Answer Key.

INSIDE THIS CHAPTER

- Cleaning
- Sanitizing
- Dishwashing
- Cleaning the Premises
- Developing a Cleaning Program

OBJECTIVES

After completing this chapter, you should be able to identify the following:

- Correct cleaners for specific tasks
- Approved sanitizers including chlorine, iodine, and quats
- Factors affecting the efficiency of sanitizers (e.g., contact time, water temperature, concentration, water hardness, and pH)
- How to clean and sanitize food-contact surfaces
- Required frequency for cleaning and sanitizing food-contact surfaces
- Correct machine-dishwashing procedures
- How to clean and sanitize items in a three-compartment sink
- How to clean nonfood-contact surfaces
- Storage and disposal requirements for chemicals
- How to store clean and sanitized tableware and equipment
- How to clean the premises
- How to develop a cleaning program

KEY TERMS

- Cleaning
- Detergents
- Degreasers
- Delimers
- Abrasive cleaners
- Sanitizing
- Concentration
- Water hardness
- Material Safety Data Sheet (MSDS)

Cleaning	Sanitizing	Dishwashing	Cleaning the Premises	Developing a Cleaning Program
— Factors That Affect Cleaning — Types of Cleaners	— Heat Sanitizing — Chemical Sanitizing — Sanitizer Effectiveness — How and When to Clean and Sanitize	— Machine Dishwashing — Manual Dishwashing — Storing Tableware and Equipment	— Nonfood-Contact Surfaces — Cleaning Tools and Supplies	— Identifying Cleaning Needs — Creating a Master Cleaning Schedule — Choosing Cleaning Materials — Implementing the Cleaning Program

CLEANING

If you do not keep your facility and equipment clean and sanitary, food can easily become contaminated. It all starts with correct cleaning.

Factors That Affect Cleaning

Everything in your operation must be kept clean. Cleaning removes food and other dirt from a surface. There are several factors that affect the cleaning process.

Type and condition of the dirt   Certain types of dirt require special cleaning methods. The condition of the dirt also affects how easily it can be removed. For example, dried or baked-on dirt will be more difficult to remove.

Water hardness   Cleaning is more difficult in hard water. Minerals react with the detergent and decrease how effective it is. Hard water can also cause scale or lime deposits to build up on equipment. This can require the use of lime-removal cleaners, as shown in the photo at left.

Water temperature   In general, the higher the water temperature, the better a detergent will dissolve and the better it will loosen dirt.

Surface   Different surfaces call for different cleaners. Some cleaners work well in one situation but not in another. The wrong cleaner might even damage equipment.

Agitation or pressure   Scouring or scrubbing a surface helps remove the outer layer of dirt. This allows the cleaner to penetrate deeper.

Length of treatment   The longer dirt on a surface is exposed to a cleaner, the easier it is to remove.

Types of Cleaners

Cleaners are chemicals that remove food, dirt, rust, stains, minerals, or other deposits. They must be stable, noncorrosive, and safe to use. Ask your supplier to help you pick cleaners that meet your needs.

To use cleaners correctly, follow these guidelines:

* Follow manufacturers' instructions carefully, as the manager in the photo at left is doing. If not used the correct way, cleaners may not work and can even be dangerous.

* Do not use one type of cleaner in place of another unless the intended use is the same.

Cleaners are divided into four categories: detergents, degreasers, delimers, and abrasive cleaners. Some categories may overlap. For example, most abrasive cleaners and some delimers contain detergents. Some detergents may also contain degreasers.

Detergents

Different detergents are used for different cleaning tasks. However, all detergents contain surfactants (surface acting agents) that reduce surface tension between the dirt and the surface being cleaned. These allow the detergent to quickly penetrate and soften the dirt.

General-purpose detergents are mildly alkaline cleaners that remove fresh dirt from floors, walls, ceilings, prep surfaces, and most equipment and utensils. Heavy-duty detergents are highly alkaline cleaners that remove wax, aged or dried dirt, and baked-on grease. Dishwashing detergents, for example, are highly alkaline.

Degreasers

Degreasers are detergents that contain a grease-dissolving agent. These cleaners work well in areas where grease has been burned on, such as grill backsplashes, oven doors, and range hoods. A degreaser is being used in the photo at left.

Delimers

Delimers are used on mineral deposits and other dirt that other cleaners cannot remove. They are often used to remove scale in dishwashing machines and on steam tables. Follow the instructions carefully and use delimers with caution.

Abrasive Cleaners

Abrasive cleaners contain a scouring agent that helps scrub hard-to-remove dirt. These cleaners are often used to remove baked-on food in pots and pans. Use abrasives with caution because they can scratch surfaces.

Technology

Using Ozone to Clean

Ozone is an odorless gas that occurs naturally in the atmosphere. Scientists sometimes talk about ozone in relationship to the UV-light protection that it provides to the planet; other times, when ozone is occurring in lower levels of the atmosphere, scientists will point out the dangerous effects that ozone can have as an air pollutant.

In the industrial world, ozone has long been an agent to purify water (in which its properties act differently than they do in air). Some industries also use ozone systems that mix ozone and water to clean and sanitize equipment and surfaces. Currently, the systems are physically quite large and relatively expensive, which makes them difficult to install and maintain in smaller spaces, such as the back of the house of a restaurant.

Additionally, ozone is an approved antimicrobial agent used in the treatment, storage, and processing of fruit and vegetables. This is an alternative method to using chemicals for washing these types of food. Still, due to its size and cost, it is mostly a method currently found at the manufacturing and processing levels rather than at the foodservice level.

Cleaning	Sanitizing	Dishwashing	Cleaning the Premises	Developing a Cleaning Program
– Factors That Affect Cleaning – Types of Cleaners	– Heat Sanitizing – Chemical Sanitizing – Sanitizer Effectiveness – How and When to Clean and Sanitize	– Machine Dishwashing – Manual Dishwashing – Storing Tableware and Equipment	– Nonfood-Contact Surfaces – Cleaning Tools and Supplies	– Identifying Cleaning Needs – Creating a Master Cleaning Schedule – Choosing Cleaning Materials – Implementing the Cleaning Program

SANITIZING

Sanitizing reduces pathogens on a surface to safe levels. Food-contact surfaces must be sanitized after they have been cleaned and rinsed. This can be done by using heat or chemicals.

Heat Sanitizing

One way to sanitize items is to soak them in hot water. For this method to work, the water must be at least 171°F (77°C). The items must be soaked for at least 30 seconds. You may need to install a heating device to maintain this temperature. Another way to sanitize items is to run them through a high-temperature dishwasher.

Chemical Sanitizing

Tableware, utensils, and equipment can be sanitized by soaking them in a chemical sanitizing solution. Or you can rinse, swab, or spray them with sanitizing solution, as shown in the photo at left.

Three common types of chemical sanitizers are chlorine, iodine, and quaternary ammonium compounds, or quats. Chemical sanitizers are regulated by state and federal environmental protection agencies (EPAs). For requirements, check with your local regulatory authority.

In some cases, you can use detergent-sanitizer blends to sanitize. Operations that have two-compartment sinks often use these. If you use a detergent-sanitizer blend, use it once to clean. Then use it a second time to sanitize.

Sanitizer Effectiveness

Several factors influence the effectiveness of chemical sanitizers. The most critical include concentration, water temperature, contact time, water hardness, and pH.

Concentration   Sanitizer solution is a mix of chemical sanitizer and water. The concentration of this mix—the amount of sanitizer to water—is critical. Too little sanitizer may make the solution weak and useless. Too much sanitizer may make the solution too strong and unsafe. It can also leave a bad taste on items or corrode metal.

Concentration is measured in parts per million (ppm). To check the concentration of a sanitizer solution, use a test kit, as shown in the photo at left. Make sure it is made for the sanitizer being used. These kits are usually available from the chemical manufacturer or supplier.

Hard water, food bits, and leftover detergent can reduce the solution's effectiveness. Change the solution when it looks dirty or its concentration is too low. Check the concentration often.

Temperature   The water in sanitizing solution must be the correct temperature. Follow manufacturers' recommendations.

Contact time   For a sanitizer solution to kill pathogens, it must make contact with the object being sanitized for a specific amount of time. The bain in the photo at left is being sanitized in an iodine sanitizing solution. It must be in contact with the solution for at least 30 seconds.

Water hardness   Water hardness can affect how well a sanitizer works. Water hardness is the amount of minerals in your water. Find out what your water hardness is from your municipality. Then work with your supplier to identify the correct amount of sanitizer to use for your water.

pH   Water pH can also affect a sanitizer. Find out what the pH of your water is from your municipality. Then work with your supplier to find out the correct amount of sanitizer to use for your water.

General Guidelines for the Effective Use of Chlorine, Iodine, and Quats

	Chlorine		Iodine	Quats
Water temperature	≥100°F (38°C)	≥75°F (24°C)	68°F (20°C)	75°F (24°C)
Water pH	≤10	≤8	≤5 or as per manufacturer's recommendation	As per manufacturer's recommendation
Water hardness	As per manufacturer's recommendation		As per manufacturer's recommendation	≤500 ppm or as per manufacturer's recommendation
Sanitizer concentration	50-99 ppm	50-99 ppm	12.5-25 ppm	As per manufacturer's recommendation
Sanitizer contact time	≥7 sec	≥7 sec	≥30 sec	≥30 sec

How and When to Clean and Sanitize

All surfaces must be cleaned and rinsed. This includes walls, storage shelves, and garbage containers. However, any surface that touches food, such as knives, stockpots, cutting boards, or prep tables, must be cleaned and sanitized.

How to clean and sanitize   To clean and sanitize a surface, follow these steps.

1 Scrape or remove food bits from the surface.

- Use the correct cleaning tool, such as a nylon brush or pad, or a cloth towel.

2 Wash the surface.

- Prepare the cleaning solution with an approved cleaner.
- Wash the surface with the correct cleaning tool, such as a cloth towel.

3 Rinse the surface.

- Use clean water.
- Rinse the surface with the correct cleaning tool, such as a cloth towel.

4 Sanitize the surface.

- Use the correct sanitizing solution.
- Prepare the concentration per manufacturer requirements.
- Use the correct tool, such as a cloth towel, to sanitize the surface.
- Make sure the entire surface has come in contact with the sanitizing solution.

5 Allow the surface to air-dry.

When to clean and sanitize   All food-contact surfaces need to be cleaned and sanitized at these times:

* After they are used

* Before food handlers start working with a different type of food

* Any time food handlers are interrupted during a task and the items being used may have been contaminated

* After four hours if items are in constant use

Cleaning and Sanitizing Stationary Equipment

Equipment manufacturers will usually provide instructions for cleaning and sanitizing stationary equipment, such as a slicer. In general, follow these steps:

* Unplug the equipment.

* Take the removable parts off the equipment. Wash, rinse, and sanitize them by hand. You can also run the parts through a dishwasher if allowed.

* Scrape or remove food from the equipment surfaces.

* Wash the equipment surfaces. Use a cleaning solution prepared with an approved detergent. Wash the equipment with the correct cleaning tool such as a nylon brush or pad, or a cloth towel.

* Rinse the equipment surfaces with clean water. Use a cloth towel or other correct tool.

* Sanitize the equipment surfaces. The food handler in the photo at left is spraying sanitizer on the surfaces of a piece of equipment. Make sure the sanitizer comes in contact with each surface. The concentration of the sanitizer must meet requirements.

* Allow all surfaces to air-dry. Put the unit back together.

Clean-in-Place Equipment

Some pieces of equipment, such as soft-serve yogurt machines, are designed to have cleaning and sanitizing solutions pumped through them. Because many of them hold and dispense TCS food, they must be cleaned and sanitized every day unless otherwise indicated by the manufacturer. You should also check your local regulatory requirements.

Cleaning	Sanitizing	Dishwashing	Cleaning the Premises	Developing a Cleaning Program
— Factors That Affect Cleaning — Types of Cleaners	— Heat Sanitizing — Chemical Sanitizing — Sanitizer Effectiveness — How and When to Clean and Sanitize	— Machine Dishwashing — Manual Dishwashing — Storing Tableware and Equipment	— Nonfood-Contact Surfaces — Cleaning Tools and Supplies	— Identifying Cleaning Needs — Creating a Master Cleaning Schedule — Choosing Cleaning Materials — Implementing the Cleaning Program

DISHWASHING

There are two methods used by operations to wash dishes: machine dishwashing and manual dishwashing.

Machine Dishwashing

Tableware and utensils are often cleaned and sanitized in a dishwashing machine. The effectiveness of your dishwashing program will depend on the following factors:

- Well-planned layout in the dishwashing area, including a scraping and soaking area and enough space for both dirty and clean items

- Sufficient water supply, especially hot water

- Separate area for cleaning pots and pans

- Devices that indicate water pressure and temperature of the wash and rinse cycles

- Protected storage areas for clean tableware and utensils

- Staff trained to operate and maintain the equipment and use the correct chemicals

High-Temperature Machines

High-temperature machines use hot water to clean and sanitize. If the water is not hot enough, items will not be sanitized. If the water is too hot it can bake food onto the items.

The temperature of the final sanitizing rinse must be at least 180°F (82°C). For stationary rack, single-temperature machines, it must be at least 165°F (74°C). The dishwasher must have a built-in thermometer which checks water temperature at the manifold, as shown in the photo at left. This is where the water sprays into the tank.

Chemical-Sanitizing Machines

Chemical-sanitizing machines can clean and sanitize at much lower temperatures. Different sanitizers require different temperatures, so follow the manufacturer's dishwashing guidelines.

Items washed and rinsed at these lower temperatures may take longer to air-dry. You may also need more room at the clean end of the machine and more tableware during peak periods.

Dishwashing Machine Operation

Operate your dishwasher according to the manufacturer's recommendations, and keep it in good repair. However, no matter what type of machine you use, you should follow these guidelines.

Cleanliness   Clean the machine as often as needed, checking it at least once a day. Clear spray nozzles of food and foreign objects. Remove mineral deposits when needed. Fill tanks with clean water, and make sure detergent and sanitizer dispensers are filled.

Preparation   Scrape, rinse, or soak items before washing. Presoak items with dried-on food.

Loading   Use the correct dish racks. Load them so the water spray will reach all surfaces, as shown in the photo at left. Never overload dish racks.

Air-drying   Air-dry all items. Never use a towel to dry items. You could recontaminate them.

Monitoring   Check water temperature, pressure, and sanitizing levels. Take appropriate corrective action if necessary. Operations using high-temperature dishwashing machines must provide staff with an easy and quick way to measure surface temperatures of items being sanitized. The method used must provide an irreversible record of the highest temperature reached during the sanitizing rinse. This ensures that the dishwasher can reach correct sanitizing temperatures during operation. Maximum registering thermometers or heat sensitive tape are good tools for checking temperatures.

Manual Dishwashing

Operations often use a three-compartment sink to clean and sanitize large items. The sink needs to be set up correctly before use, as shown in the photo at left. Follow these procedures:

- Clean and sanitize each sink and drain board.

- Fill the first sink with detergent and water. The water temperature must be at least 110°F (43°C). Follow the manufacturer's recommendations.

- Fill the second sink with clean water. This is not necessary if items will be spray-rinsed instead of being dipped.

- Fill the third sink with water and sanitizer to the correct concentration. Hot water can be used as an alternative. Follow the guidelines on pages 12-4 and 12-5 and the manufacturer's recommendations.

- Provide a clock with a second hand. This will let food handlers time how long items have been in the sanitizer.

How to Use a Three-Compartment Sink

Follow these steps to clean and sanitize items in a three-compartment sink.

1 Rinse, scrape, or soak items before washing them.

- If items are being soaked in the first sink, change the solution when food bits start to build up or the suds are gone.
- Do not soak wood surfaces in detergent solutions.

2 Wash items in the first sink.

- Use a brush, cloth towel, or nylon scrub pad to loosen dirt. Change the water and detergent when the suds are gone or the water is dirty.

3 Rinse items in the second sink.

- Spray the items with water or dip them in it. Make sure to remove all traces of food and detergent from the items being rinsed.
- If dipping the items, change the rinse water when it becomes dirty or full of suds.

4 Sanitize items in the third sink.

- Change the sanitizing solution when the temperature of the water or the sanitizer concentration falls below requirements.
- Never rinse items after sanitizing them. This could contaminate their surfaces. The only exception to this rule is when you are washing items in a dishwasher that can safely rinse items after they have been sanitized.
- Do not soak wood surfaces in sanitizing solutions.

5 Air-dry items on a clean and sanitized surface.

- Place items upside down so they will drain.

Storing Tableware and Equipment

Once utensils, tableware, and equipment have been cleaned and sanitized, they must be stored in a way that will protect them from contamination. Follow these guidelines.

Storage Store tableware and utensils at least six inches (15 centimeters) off the floor. Protect them from dirt and moisture.

Storage surfaces Clean and sanitize drawers and shelves before storing clean items.

Glasses and flatware Store glasses and cups upside down on a clean and sanitized shelf or rack. Store flatware and utensils with handles up, as shown in the photo at left. Staff can then pick them up without touching food-contact surfaces.

Trays and carts Clean and sanitize trays and carts used to carry clean tableware and utensils. Check them daily, and clean as often as needed.

Stationary equipment Keep the food-contact surfaces of stationary equipment covered until ready for use.

Cleaning	Sanitizing	Dishwashing	Cleaning the Premises	Developing a Cleaning Program
– Factors That Affect Cleaning – Types of Cleaners	– Heat Sanitizing – Chemical Sanitizing – Sanitizer Effectiveness – How and When to Clean and Sanitize	– Machine Dishwashing – Manual Dishwashing – Storing Tableware and Equipment	– Nonfood-Contact Surfaces – Cleaning Tools and Supplies	– Identifying Cleaning Needs – Creating a Master Cleaning Schedule – Choosing Cleaning Materials – Implementing the Cleaning Program

CLEANING THE PREMISES

Keeping your operation clean means using the correct tools, supplies, and storage to prevent contamination. Many of the chemicals you will use are hazardous, so you also have to know how to handle them to prevent injury.

For all of your cleaning efforts to come together, you need a master cleaning schedule. Making this schedule work also means training and monitoring your staff to be sure they can follow it.

Nonfood-Contact Surfaces

Nonfood-contact surfaces must be cleaned regularly. Examples include floors, ceilings, equipment exteriors, restrooms, and walls, as shown in the photo at left. Regular cleaning prevents dust, dirt, and food residue from building up.

Cleaning Up after People Who Get Sick

If a person has diarrhea or vomits in the operation, these spills must be cleaned up the correct way. Vomit and diarrhea can carry Norovirus, which is highly contagious. Correct cleanup can prevent food from becoming contaminated. It will also keep others from getting sick. Check with your local regulatory authority regarding requirements for cleaning up vomit and diarrhea. In many jurisdictions, a written cleanup plan may be required.

The way you clean up vomit and diarrhea is different from the way you clean other items in the operation. There are several things to think about when developing a plan for cleaning these substances:

- How you will contain liquid and airborne substances, and remove them from the operation

- How you will clean, sanitize, and disinfect surfaces

- When to throw out food that may have been contaminated

- What equipment is needed to clean up these substances, and how it will be cleaned and disinfected after use

- When a food handler must wear personal protective equipment

- How staff will be notified of the correct procedures for containing, cleaning, and disinfecting these substances

- How to segregate contaminated areas from other areas

- When staff must be restricted from working with or around food or excluded from working in the operation

- How sick customers will be quickly removed from the operation

- How the cleaning plan will be implemented

Cleaning Tools and Supplies

Cleaning tools can contaminate surfaces if not handled carefully. You can help prevent this by cleaning the tools before storing them and by designating tools for tasks.

For example, some operations assign one set of tools for cleaning food-contact surfaces and another for nonfood-contact surfaces. Likewise, one set of tools can be used for cleaning and another for sanitizing.

Color-coding each set of tools helps reinforce their different uses. Always use a separate set of tools for the restroom.

Storing Cleaning Tools and Supplies

Cleaning tools and supplies must be stored in a separate area away from food and prep areas. The storage area should have the following:

- Good lighting so staff can see chemicals easily
- Hooks for hanging mops, brooms, and other cleaning tools
- Utility sink for filling buckets and washing cleaning tools
- Floor drain for dumping dirty water, as shown in the photo at left

To prevent contamination, never clean mops, brushes, or other tools in sinks used for handwashing, food prep, or dishwashing. Additionally, never dump mop water or other liquid waste into toilets or urinals.

When storing cleaning tools, consider the following:

- Air-dry towels overnight.
- Hang mops, brooms, and brushes on hooks to air-dry.
- Clean and rinse buckets. Let them air-dry, and then store them with other tools.

Wiping Towels

Never use towels meant for wiping up food spills for any other purpose. Store wiping towels in a sanitizer solution between uses, as shown in the photo at left. Keep towels that come in contact with raw meat, fish, or poultry separate from other cleaning towels.

Using Foodservice Chemicals

Many of the chemicals used in the operation can be hazardous, especially if they are used the wrong way. To reduce your risk, you should only use chemicals that are approved for use in a foodservice operation. You should also follow these guidelines.

Storage and labeling   Store chemicals in their original containers away from food and prep areas. Separate by spacing or partitioning. If chemicals are transferred to a new container, the label on that container must list the common name of the chemical.

Disposal   When throwing out chemicals, follow the instructions on the label and any requirements from your local regulatory authority.

Material Safety Data Sheets

The Occupational Safety and Health Administration (OSHA) has requirements for using chemicals. OSHA requires chemical manufacturers and suppliers to provide a Material Safety Data Sheet (MSDS) for each hazardous chemical they sell.

An MSDS contains the following information about the chemical:

- Safe use and handling
- Physical, health, fire, and reactivity hazards
- Precautions
- Appropriate personal protective equipment (PPE) to wear when using the chemical
- First-aid information and steps to take in an emergency
- Manufacturer's name, address, and phone number
- Preparation date of MSDS
- Hazardous ingredients and identity information

MSDS are often sent with the chemical shipment. You can also request them from your supplier or the manufacturer. Staff have a right to see an MSDS for any hazardous chemical they work with. Therefore, you must keep these sheets where they can be accessed. The photo at left shows how one operation makes them available to staff.

Business

Color Coding Across the Operation

As you have learned, using color-coded cutting boards to prepare products can help to reduce cross-contamination in the kitchen. Some organizations take color coding farther than just boards. The possibilities can be found everywhere in the kitchen: knives, tongs, scoops, measuring cups, fryer baskets, spray bottles, storage containers, brushes, pans with colored handles, and gloves are just some of the options offered by equipment manufacturers.

The color coding helps with more than just cross-contamination. Cross-contact can also be avoided by assigning a color to equipment used for food that contains allergens. Some operations build standard operating procedures around color coding to help produce more consistent menu items. Others also use color coding for cleaning equipment. This can help to ensure that the correct tools are used in the correct areas (for example, restroom cleaning equipment will not get used in the kitchen). It also can help staff to understand which cleaning chemicals are appropriate for use in which areas, making cleaning safer for everyone.

Cleaning	Sanitizing	Dishwashing	Cleaning the Premises	Developing a Cleaning Program
— Factors That Affect Cleaning — Types of Cleaners	— Heat Sanitizing — Chemical Sanitizing — Sanitizer Effectiveness — How and When to Clean and Sanitize	— Machine Dishwashing — Manual Dishwashing — Storing Tableware and Equipment	— Nonfood Contact Surfaces — Cleaning Tools and Supplies	— Identifying Cleaning Needs — Creating a Master Cleaning Schedule — Choosing Cleaning Materials — Implementing the Cleaning Program

DEVELOPING A CLEANING PROGRAM

A clean and sanitary operation is a foundation for a successful food safety management system. You can keep your operation in this condition with an effective cleaning program.

To develop your program, first identify what the operation needs. Then create a master cleaning schedule. Also train staff to clean equipment and surfaces correctly. Lastly, monitor the program to ensure that it is effective.

Identifying Cleaning Needs

Identify cleaning needs using the following guidelines:

- Review the facility to identify all surfaces, tools, and equipment that need cleaning.

- Look at how cleaning is currently done. Get input from staff. Ask them how and why they clean a certain way. Find out which procedures can be improved.

- Estimate the time and skills needed for each task. Some jobs may be done more efficiently by two or more people. Others might require an outside contractor. Determine cleaning frequency as well.

Creating a Master Cleaning Schedule

Use the information you gather while identifying your cleaning needs to develop a master cleaning schedule. The schedule should include the following.

What should be cleaned   Arrange the schedule so that nothing is left out. List all cleaning jobs in one area, or list jobs in the order they should be performed. Keep the schedule flexible enough so you can adjust it if needed.

Who should clean it   Assign each task to a specific person. In general, staff should clean their own areas. Rotate other cleaning tasks to distribute them fairly.

When it should be cleaned   Staff should clean and sanitize as needed. Schedule major cleaning when food will not be contaminated or service interrupted—usually after closing. Schedule work shifts to allow enough time as well. Staff rushing to clean before the end of their shifts may cut corners.

How it should be cleaned Provide clearly written procedures for cleaning. Guide staff through the process. Always follow manufacturers' instructions when cleaning equipment. Specify cleaning tools and chemicals by name. Post cleaning instructions near the item to be cleaned.

Choosing Cleaning Materials

Consider the following when selecting cleaning tools and supplies for your operation.

Correct tools and cleaners Select tools and cleaners according to what is identified in the master cleaning schedule. Ask suppliers to suggest which tools and supplies are correct for your operation.

Worn tools Replace worn tools. Dirty or worn equipment may not clean or sanitize surfaces correctly.

Protective gear Provide staff with the correct protective gear, such as aprons, goggles, and rubber gloves.

Implementing the Cleaning Program

Training is critical to the success of a cleaning program. Staff need to understand the tasks you want them to perform and the quality that you expect. Follow these guidelines for a successful cleaning program.

Kickoff meeting Schedule a kickoff meeting to introduce your program to staff. Explain the reason behind it. Stress how important cleanliness is to food safety. If they understand why they are supposed to do something, they will be more likely to do it.

Training Schedule enough time for training. Work with small groups, as shown in the photo at left, or conduct training by area. Show staff how to clean equipment and surfaces in each area.

Motivation Provide lots of motivation. Reward staff for any job well done. Create small incentives for staff members or teams, such as a Clean Team of the Month award. Tie performance to specific goals or measurements, such as achieving high marks during regulatory inspections.

Monitoring Once you have implemented the cleaning program, monitor it to make sure it is working. This includes the following:

* Supervising daily cleaning routines

* Checking the daily completion of all cleaning tasks against the master cleaning schedule

* Modifying the master schedule to reflect any changes in menu, procedures, or equipment

* Requesting staff input on improving the program

Summary

- Cleaning removes food and other dirt from a surface. Sanitizing reduces the number of harmful pathogens on a surface to safe levels. You must clean and rinse a surface before it can be sanitized. Surfaces can be sanitized with hot water or a chemical-sanitizing solution. Then the surface must be allowed to air-dry.

- All surfaces should be cleaned and rinsed. Food-contact surfaces must be cleaned and sanitized after every use. You should also clean and sanitize each time you begin working with a different type of food or when a task is interrupted. If items are in constant use, they must be cleaned and sanitized every four hours.

- Tableware and utensils can be washed in dishwashers or by hand in a three-compartment sink. Always follow manufacturers' instructions when using dishwashers. Make sure your machine is clean and in good working condition. Check the temperature and pressure of wash and rinse cycles daily.

- Three-compartment sinks and drain boards must be cleaned and sanitized before they are used for dishwashing. Items washed in a three-compartment sink should be rinsed or scraped clean before washing. They should then be washed in a detergent solution and rinsed in clean water. Next, they should be sanitized in either hot water or in a chemical-sanitizing solution for a specific amount of time. Finally, they should be air-dried. Once cleaned and sanitized, tableware and equipment should be protected from contamination.

- Make sure chemicals are clearly labeled. Keep MSDS for each chemical in a location accessible to all staff while on the job.

- Create a master cleaning schedule listing all cleaning tasks. Monitor the cleaning program to keep it effective and supervise cleaning procedures. Make adjustments as needed.

Apply Your Knowledge

Use these questions to review the concepts presented in this chapter.

DISCUSSION QUESTIONS

1. When should food-contact surfaces be cleaned and sanitized?

2. What is the difference between cleaning and sanitizing?

3. What are the steps that should be taken (in order) when cleaning and sanitizing items in a three-compartment sink?

4. How should clean and sanitized tableware, utensils, and equipment be stored?

5. What factors affect the efficiency of a sanitizer?

For answers, please turn to the Answer Key.

Apply Your Knowledge

Another Way

CASE IN POINT

The kitchen staff in the university cafeteria had scraped and rinsed every piece of tableware, placed them in racks, and fed them into the high-temperature dishwashing machine. When the wash and rinse cycles were complete, one of the staff noticed that the items were spotted.

The thermometer registering the final rinse temperature for the sanitizing cycle had a reading of 140°F (60°C), rather than the required 180°F (82°C) indicated on the machine. The staff member went to inform the manager who called for service.

1. What alternative methods could be used to clean and sanitize the tableware as the machine is not functioning correctly?

For answers, please turn to the Answer Key.

Apply Your
Knowledge

CASE IN POINT

Keep it Separate

A local regulatory authority noted that a routine sample of soft-serve ice cream from a restaurant tested high for bacteria. The health inspector and manager examined all aspects of the ice-cream mix, the soft-serve machine, and the maintenance and cleaning of the machine. Everything appeared to be in order. The mix was fine, the machine was in perfect working order, and the staff cleaned and sanitized the machine every night according to the manufacturer's specifications.

The source of the bacteria was eventually found in the utility closet. A new staff member responsible for cleaning and sanitizing the machine had been using a brush that was also used for heavy cleaning of the operation itself, including the restrooms. Each night as he cleaned the machine with the dirty brush, the staff member was unknowingly contaminating the machine with bacteria.

❶ What could have been done to prevent this situation?

For answers, please turn to the Answer Key.

Circle the best answer to each question.

1. What is required for measuring the sanitizing rinse temperature in a high-temperature dishwashing machine?

   A Infrared thermometer

   B Time-temperature indicator

   C Maximum registering thermometer

   D Thermocouple with immersion probe

2. What is sanitizing?

   A Reducing dirt from a surface

   B Reducing the pH of a surface

   C Reducing the hardness of water

   D Reducing pathogens to safe levels

3. If food-contact surfaces are in constant use, how often must they be cleaned and sanitized?

   A Every 4 hours

   B Every 5 hours

   C Every 6 hours

   D Every 7 hours

4. What must food handlers do to make sure sanitizing solution for use on food-contact surfaces has been made correctly?

   A Test the solution with a sanitizer kit.

   B Use very hot water when making the solution.

   C Try out the solution on a food-contact surface.

   D Mix the solution with equal parts of water.

5. A food handler was assigned to clean a slicer that was too difficult to move. The slicer was unplugged. Then the removable parts were taken off the slicer and cleaned and sanitized in a three-compartment sink. Food bits on the slicer were removed. After the machine was wiped down with detergent and water, it was sanitized and allowed to air-dry. Then the food handler put the machine back together. What mistake did the food handler make?

   A Failed to dry the machine with a clean cloth after sanitizing it

   B Failed to sanitize the machine before taking the removable parts off

   C Failed to rinse the machine after wiping it down with detergent and water

   D Failed to wash the machine with detergent and water before taking it apart

6. What should be done when throwing away chemicals?

   A Seal the container and recycle it.

   B Seal the container in a bag and place it in the garbage.

   C Follow label instructions and regulatory requirements.

   D Pour leftover chemicals into a drain and throw the container away.

7 How should flatware and utensils that have been cleaned and sanitized be stored?

   A With handles facing up

   B Below cleaning supplies

   C In drawers that have been washed and rinsed

   D Four inches (10 centimeters) from the floor

8 What is the correct way to clean and sanitize a prep table?

   A Remove food from the surface, wash, rinse, sanitize, air-dry

   B Remove food from the surface, sanitize, rinse, wash, air-dry

   C Remove food from the surface, wash, sanitize, air-dry, rinse

   D Remove food from the surface, air-dry, wash, rinse, sanitize

For answers, please turn to the Answer Key.

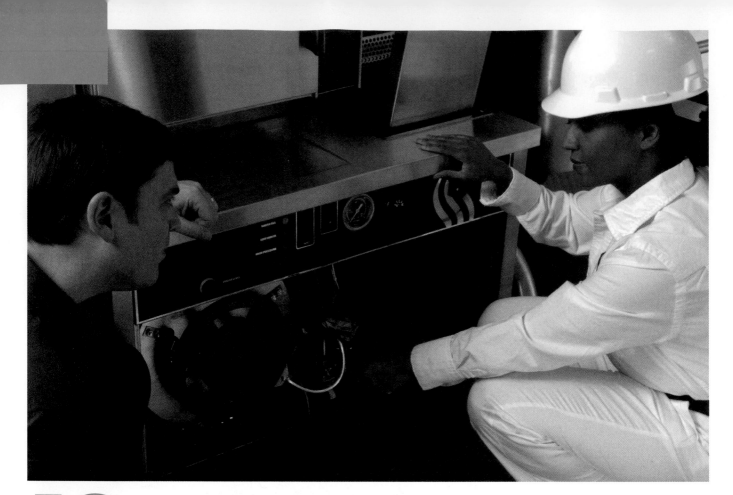

13 Integrated Pest Management

Integrated Pest Management (IPM) Programs	Identifying Pests	Working with a Pest Control Operator (PCO)	Treatment	Using and Storing Pesticides
— Deny Pests Access to the Operation — Deny Food and Shelter	— Flies — Cockroaches — Rodents	— How to Choose a PCO	— Control Measures	

Case in POINT

Rats!

Construction of new subway tunnels had several nearby restaurateurs up in arms. They blamed the construction project for a significant increase in rat activity outside their operations. The restaurateurs contacted the engineers for the project and the regulatory authority. They wanted assurances that the rats would be kept out of their operations.

① What are some methods that might be used to keep the rats out?

For answers, please turn to the Answer Key.

INSIDE THIS CHAPTER

- Integrated Pest Management (IPM) Programs
- Identifying Pests
- Working with a Pest Control Operator (PCO)
- Treatment
- Using and Storing Pesticides

OBJECTIVES

After completing this chapter, you should be able to identify the following:

- Methods for denying pests access to an operation
- Methods for denying pests food and shelter
- Signs of pest infestation and activity
- How to correctly store pesticides
- How to select a pest control operator (PCO)

KEY TERMS

- Infestation
- Integrated pest management (IPM)
- Pest control operator (PCO)
- Air curtains
- Pesticides

Integrated Pest Management (IPM) Programs	Identifying Pests	Working with a Pest Control Operator (PCO)	Treatment	Using and Storing Pesticides
— Deny Pests Access to the Operation — Deny Food and Shelter	— Flies — Cockroaches — Rodents	— How to Choose a PCO	— Control Measures	

INTEGRATED PEST MANAGEMENT (IPM) PROGRAMS

Pests, such as insects and rodents, can pose serious problems for restaurants and foodservice operations. Beyond being unsightly to customers, they damage food, supplies, and facilities. The greatest danger from pests is that they can spread diseases, including foodborne illnesses.

Once pests have entered the operation in large numbers—an infestation—they can be difficult to eliminate. Developing and implementing an integrated pest management (IPM) program is the key. An IPM program uses prevention measures to keep pests from entering the operation and control measures to eliminate those that do get inside.

The best way to ensure your IPM program succeeds is to work closely with a licensed pest control operator (PCO), as shown in the photo at left. These professionals use safe, current ways of preventing and controlling pests.

Prevention is critical in pest control. If you wait until there is evidence of pests in your operation, they may already be there in large numbers.

An IPM program has three basic rules:

❶ Deny pests access to the operation.

❷ Deny pests food and shelter.

❸ Work with a licensed PCO to eliminate pests that do enter.

Deny Pests Access to the Operation

Pests can enter an operation by traveling inside with deliveries or by entering through openings in the building itself.

Deliveries

Here is how to prevent pests from entering with deliveries:

- Use approved, reputable suppliers.
- Check all deliveries before they enter your operation.
- Refuse shipments that have pests or signs of pests, such as egg cases and body parts (legs, wings, etc.).

Doors, Windows, and Vents

Address the following to prevent pests from entering through doors, windows, and vents.

Screens   Screen all windows and vents with at least 16 mesh per square inch screening. Anything larger might let in mosquitoes or flies. Check screens often. Clean, patch, or replace them as needed.

Self-closing devices and door sweeps   Install self-closing devices and door sweeps on all doors. Repair gaps and cracks in door frames and thresholds, such as the one in the photo at left. Use weather stripping on the bottoms of doors with no threshold.

Air curtains   Install air curtains (also called air doors or fly fans) above or alongside doors. These devices blow a steady stream of air across the entryway. This creates an air shield around doors left open.

Exterior openings   Keep all exterior openings tightly closed. Close drive-through windows when not in use.

Pipes

Rodents and insects use pipes as highways through an operation. Consider the following methods of prevention.

Concrete   Use concrete to fill holes or sheet metal to cover openings around pipes. The pipes in the photo at left have been sealed with concrete to keep out pests.

Screens   Install screens over ventilation pipes and ducts on the roof.

Grates   Cover floor drains with hinged grates to keep rodents out. Rats are good swimmers. They can enter buildings through drainpipes.

Floors and Walls

Rodents often burrow into buildings through decaying masonry or cracks in foundations. They move through floors and walls the same way. Seal all cracks in floors and walls, as shown in the photo at left. Use a permanent sealant recommended by your PCO or regulatory authority. Seal spaces or cracks where stationary equipment is fitted to the floor. Use an approved sealant or concrete, depending on the size of the spaces.

Deny Food and Shelter

Pests are attracted to damp, dark, dirty places. A clean operation offers them no food or shelter. The stray pest that might get in cannot thrive or multiply in a clean kitchen. Stick to your master cleaning schedule and follow these additional guidelines.

Garbage   Dispose of garbage quickly and correctly. Garbage attracts pests and provides them with a breeding ground. Keep garbage containers clean. Make sure outdoor containers are tightly covered. Clean spills around garbage containers right away. Wash and rinse containers often.

Recyclables   Store recyclables in clean, pest-proof containers as far from your building as regulatory requirements allow. Bottles, cans, paper, and packaging material provide shelter and food for pests.

Storage   Keep food and supplies away from walls and at least six inches (15 centimeters) off the floor. Rotate food items so pests do not have time to settle into them and breed.

Cleaning   Careful cleaning eliminates pests' food supply and destroys insect eggs. It also reduces the places where pests can safely take shelter. The food handler at left is cleaning underneath equipment to eliminate a possible food supply for pests. Here are some guidelines:

- Clean food and beverage spills right away, including crumbs and scraps.
- Clean toilets and restrooms as often as needed.
- Train staff to keep lockers and break areas clean.
- Keep cleaning tools and supplies clean and dry. Store wet mops on hooks rather than on the floor; otherwise roaches can hide in them.
- Empty water from buckets to keep from attracting rodents.

Grounds and Outdoor Dining Areas

Birds, flies, bees, and wasps can be both annoying and dangerous to your customers. As with indoor pests, the key to controlling them is to deny them food and shelter. Here are some guidelines:

- Mow the grass, pull weeds, get rid of standing water, and pick up litter.
- Cover all outdoor garbage containers.
- Remove uneaten food and dirty dishes from tables. Clean dishes as quickly as possible.
- Clean spills as quickly as possible.
- Do not allow staff or customers to feed birds or wildlife on the grounds.
- Locate electronic insect eliminators, or zappers, away from food, customers, staff, and serving areas.
- Call your PCO to remove hives and nests.

Integrated Pest Management (IPM) Programs	Identifying Pests	Working with a Pest Control Operator (PCO)	Treatment	Using and Storing Pesticides
— Deny Pests Access to the Operation — Deny Food and Shelter	— Flies — Cockroaches — Rodents	— How to Choose a PCO	— Control Measures	

IDENTIFYING PESTS

Pests may still get into your operation even if you try to prevent them. They hide in delivery boxes and even ride in on staff's clothing or personal belongings.

It is important to spot signs of pests and determine which type you are dealing with. When you detect pests, record the date, time, and location. Then inform your PCO. Early detection allows the PCO to start treatment as soon as possible.

Key Point

Flies can spread pathogens such as *Shigella* spp.

Flies

Flies are a threat to human health because they feed on garbage and animal waste. For this reason, flies can spread pathogens such as *Shigella* spp.

Cockroaches

Roaches often carry disease-causing pathogens such as *Salmonella* Typhi, fungi, parasite eggs, and viruses. They reproduce quickly and can adapt to certain pesticides. This makes them difficult to control. Many people are also allergic to residue that roaches leave on food and surfaces. There are several types of roaches. Most live and breed in dark, warm, moist, hard-to-clean places. You will often find them in the following areas:

- Behind coolers, freezers, and stoves
- In sink and floor drains
- In spaces around hot-water pipes
- Inside equipment, often near motors and other electrical devices
- Under shelf liners and wallpaper
- Underneath rubber mats
- In delivery bags and boxes
- Behind unsealed coving (especially rubber-based)

Roaches generally feed in the dark. If you see a cockroach in daylight, you may have a major infestation, because only the weakest roaches come out during the day. If you suspect you have a roach problem, check for the following signs:

- Strong oily odor
- Droppings (feces) that look like grains of black pepper
- Capsule-shaped egg cases that are brown, dark red, or black and possibly leathery, smooth, or shiny in appearance

Rodents

Rodents are a serious health hazard. They eat and ruin food, damage property, and can spread disease. Most rodents have a simple digestive system. They urinate and defecate as they move around a facility. Their waste can both fall into food and contaminate surfaces. Rats and mice are the most common types of rodent. Rodents hide during the day and search for food at night. Like other pests, they reproduce often.

Typically, they do not move far from their nests. Rats travel only 100 to 150 feet away. Mice travel only 10 to 30 feet. Mice can squeeze through a nickel-sized hole to enter a facility. Rats can slip through holes the size of a half dollar. Rats can also stretch to reach an item as high as 18 inches (46 centimeters), jump three feet (one meter) in the air, and even climb straight up brick walls.

Rats and mice have keen senses of hearing, touch, and smell. Plus, they are smart enough to avoid poison bait and poorly laid traps. Effective control of these rodents requires professional knowledge and experience.

A building can be infested with both rats and mice at the same time. Look for the following signs.

Gnawing   Rats and mice gnaw to reach food and to wear down their teeth, which are always growing. Rats' teeth can gnaw through pipes, concrete, and wood.

Droppings and urine stains   Fresh droppings are shiny and black, as shown in the photo at left. Older droppings are gray. Rodent urine will glow under black (ultraviolet) light.

Tracks   Rodents tend to use the same pathways through your operation. If rodents are a problem, you may see dirt tracks along light-colored walls.

Nesting materials   Rats and mice build their nests with soft materials such as cloth, hair, feathers, grass, and scraps of paper.

Holes   Rats usually nest in holes in quiet places, often near food and water. Their nests may also be found next to buildings.

Technology

Ultrasonic Pest Control: Effective?

Ultrasonic devices, which emit frequencies that the human ear cannot detect but that animals and insects can hear, have long been offered in the marketplace of pest control devices. But the reality is that the effectiveness of these devices is considered unproven.

The intent of the devices is to create an annoying sound to pests, which would drive them away from a specific area. A number of scientific studies have been done since the 1990s, with none showing that any pest is fully repelled by ultrasonic noise. Many were able to adjust to the noise or were not bothered by it at all (ants, spiders, cockroaches).

In 2001, the Federal Trade Commission (FTC) warned manufacturers of ultrasonic pest control devices to avoid making claims about their effectiveness unless they could scientifically prove their claims. The requirement is still in effect.

More information about the studies conducted can be found in the *Journal of Economic Entomology.*

Integrated Pest Management (IPM) Programs	Identifying Pests	Working with a Pest Control Operator (PCO)	Treatment	Using and Storing Pesticides
— Deny Pests Access to the Operation — Deny Food and Shelter	— Flies — Cockroaches — Rodents	— How to Choose a PCO	— Control Measures	

WORKING WITH A PEST CONTROL OPERATOR (PCO)

Few pest problems are solved simply by spraying pesticides—chemical agents used to destroy pests. While you can help reduce the risk of infestation, most pest control should be carried out by professionals. Employ a licensed PCO. Together, you and the PCO can prevent or eliminate pests and keep them from coming back.

You can rely on your PCO to do the following:

- Develop an integrated approach to pest management. This may include a combination of chemical and nonchemical treatments to solve and prevent problems.

- Stay current on new equipment and products.

- Provide prompt service to address problems as they occur. Contracts should include regular visits as well as immediate service when pests are spotted.

- Keep records of all steps taken to prevent and control pests.

How to Choose a PCO

Check references when hiring a PCO and make sure they are licensed (if required by your state). Always require a written service contract that outlines the work to be performed. It clarifies what is expected from both you and the PCO. Here are some things included in a service contract:

- Description of services to be provided, including an initial inspection, regular monitoring visits, follow-up visits, and emergency service

- Period of service

- Your duties, including preventive measures and facility preparation before and after treatment

- Records to be kept by the PCO including:

  - Pests sighted and trapped; species, location, and actions taken

  - Building and maintenance problems noted and fixed

  - Facility maps or photos showing locations of traps, bait, and problem spots

  - Schedule for checking and cleaning traps, replacing bait, and reapplying chemicals

  - Regular written summary reports from the PCO

Key Point

When choosing a PCO, make sure he or she is licensed, if required by your state.

Integrated Pest Management (IPM) Programs	Identifying Pests	Working with a Pest Control Operator (PCO)	Treatment	Using and Storing Pesticides
— Deny Pests Access to the Operation — Deny Food and Shelter	— Flies — Cockroaches — Rodents	— How to Choose a PCO	— Control Measures	

TREATMENT

Effective treatment starts with a thorough inspection of your facility and grounds, as shown in the photo at left. Give the PCO complete access to the building. The PCO will get a clearer picture of the situation if you help in the following ways:

- Prepare staff to answer the PCO's questions.
- Provide building plans and equipment layouts.
- Point out possible trouble spots.

After the initial inspection, your PCO should provide a treatment plan in writing. In addition to price, the plan should address the following:

- Exactly what treatment(s) will be used for each area or problem and the potential risks involved
- Dates and times of each treatment (the federal government requires a PCO to provide enough notice to prepare the facility correctly; staff should not be on-site during the treatment)
- Steps you can take to control pests
- Any building defects that may be a barrier to prevention and control measures
- Timing of follow-up visits, including plans for the PCO to assess the treatment and suggest alternate treatments if pests reappear

Control Measures

PCOs use pest-control methods that are environmentally sound and safe for operations. They also know which techniques will work best to control the types of pests in your area. New technologies are always being developed. Work with your PCO to determine which pest-control methods are best for your operation. In the photo at left, a PCO has determined that a trap is good for controlling mice in an operation.

Integrated Pest Management (IPM) Programs	Identifying Pests	Working with a Pest Control Operator (PCO)	Treatment	Using and Storing Pesticides
— Deny Pests Access to the Operation — Deny Food and Shelter	— Flies — Cockroaches — Rodents	— How to Choose a PCO	— Control Measures	

USING AND STORING PESTICIDES

Sometimes, purchasing and applying pesticides on your own might seem more cost effective. However, there are many reasons not to do so:

- Applied incorrectly, they may be ineffective or harmful.

- Pests can develop resistance and immunity to pesticides.

- Each region has its own pest-control problems. Control measures may vary.

- Pesticides are regulated by federal, state, and local laws. Some are not approved for use in restaurants or foodservice operations.

Rely on your PCO to decide whether pesticides should be used in your operation. They are trained to determine the best pesticide for each pest as well as how and where to apply it, as shown in the photo at left.

Here are some other considerations when pesticides will be used.

Timing   To minimize the hazard to people, have your PCO use pesticides only when you are closed for business and staff are not on-site.

Preparation   When pesticides will be applied, prepare the area to be sprayed by removing all food and movable food-contact surfaces. Cover equipment and food-contact surfaces that cannot be moved, as shown in the photo at left.

Post application   Wash, rinse, and sanitize food-contact surfaces after the area has been sprayed.

MSDS   Pesticides are hazardous materials. You should have a corresponding MSDS any time one will be used or stored on the premises.

Storage   All pesticides used in your facility should also be stored by your PCO. If they are stored on the premises, follow these guidelines:

- Keep pesticides in their original containers.

- Store pesticides in a secure location away from where food, utensils, and food equipment are stored.

Disposal   Pesticides should be disposed of by the PCO. Check regulatory requirements before disposing of pesticides yourself. Many are considered hazardous waste. Dispose of empty containers according to manufacturers' directions and your regulatory requirements.

SUMMARY

- Pests can carry and spread many diseases. Once they have infested a facility, eliminating them can be difficult. Developing and implementing an integrated pest management program is the key.

- An IPM program uses prevention measures to keep pests from entering the operation and control measures to eliminate any pests that do get inside. To be successful, deny pests access to the operation, as well as food and shelter. Also work with a licensed PCO to eliminate pests that do enter.

- Pests can be brought into the operation with deliveries. They can also enter through openings in the building itself. To prevent them from getting inside, check deliveries before they enter your facility. Refuse any shipment in which you find pests or signs of infestation. Screen all windows and vents. Install self-closing doors and air curtains. Keep exterior openings closed when not in use. Fill or cover holes around pipes, and seal cracks in floors and walls.

- A clean and safe operation offers pests little food and shelter. Stick to your master cleaning schedule. Dispose of garbage quickly, and keep all containers clean and tightly covered. Store recyclables as far from your building as allowed. Keep food and supplies away from walls and at least six inches (15 centimeters) off the floor. Rotate food items so pests do not have time to settle into them and breed.

- Roaches live and breed in dark, warm, and moist places. Check for a strong oily odor, droppings that look like grains of black pepper, and egg cases.

- Rodents are a serious health hazard as well. Look for droppings, tracks, holes, nesting materials, and signs of gnawing.

- Rely on your PCO to decide whether pesticides should be used in your operation. PCOs are trained to determine the best pesticide for each pest and how and where to apply it.

- Your PCO should store and dispose of all pesticides used in your facility. If they are stored on the premises, they should be kept in a secure location away from where food, utensils, and equipment are stored.

Apply Your Knowledge

Use these questions to review the concepts presented in this chapter.

DISCUSSION QUESTIONS

1. What is the purpose of an integrated pest management program?

2. How can you prevent pests from entering your operation?

3. How can you tell if your operation has been infested with cockroaches or rodents?

4. What are the storage requirements for pesticides?

5. What precautions must be taken both before and after pesticides are applied in your operation?

For answers, please turn to the Answer Key.

Apply Your Knowledge

The Best Intentions

CASE IN POINT

Now We're Cooking is an operation located in a 90-year-old building. The building is in a shopping area that includes several other restaurants. Fred, the manager, recently remodeled the operation. He chose materials that were easy to clean. All of the new foodservice equipment was designed for ease of cleaning as well. The cleaning procedures listed on Fred's master cleaning schedule were written out in detail and completed by the staff as scheduled with frequent self-inspections. FIFO was followed, and food was stored on metal racks away from walls and six inches (15 centimeters) off the floor.

During a self-inspection two weeks after he finished remodeling, Fred found live cockroaches behind the sinks, in the vegetable-storage area, in the public restrooms, and near the garbage-storage area.

1. What prevention measures might Fred have overlooked in his recent remodeling that could have led to this infestation?

2. What should Fred do to eliminate the roaches?

For answers, please turn to the Answer Key.

Circle the best answer to each question.

① Who should apply pesticides?

A   Shift manager

B   Person in charge

C   Pest control operator

D   Designated pest staff member

② In what type of places are cockroaches typically found?

A   Cold, dry, and light

B   Warm, dry, and light

C   Cold, moist, and dark

D   Warm, moist, and dark

③ What smell may be a sign that cockroaches are present?

A   Strong, oily

B   Warm, spicy

C   Sharp, musty

D   Mild, seaweed

④ The three basic rules of an integrated pest management program are: work with a PCO; deny pests access; and

A   deny pests food, water, and a nesting or hiding place.

B   document all infestations with the local regulatory authority.

C   prepare a chemical application schedule and post it publicly.

D   notify the EPA that pesticides are being used in the operation.

⑤ What should be done with food-contact surfaces after pesticides have been applied?

A   Used only after a 20-minute wait

B   Checked with a sanitizer test kit

C   Washed, rinsed, and sanitized

D   Replaced with new equipment

⑥ If pesticides are stored in the operation, where should they be kept?

A   In a secure location, away from food and equipment

B   In a glass container, in a walk-in cooler

C   In dry storage, on a shelf below the food

D   In a plastic container, in any location

For answers, please turn to the Answer Key.

Notes

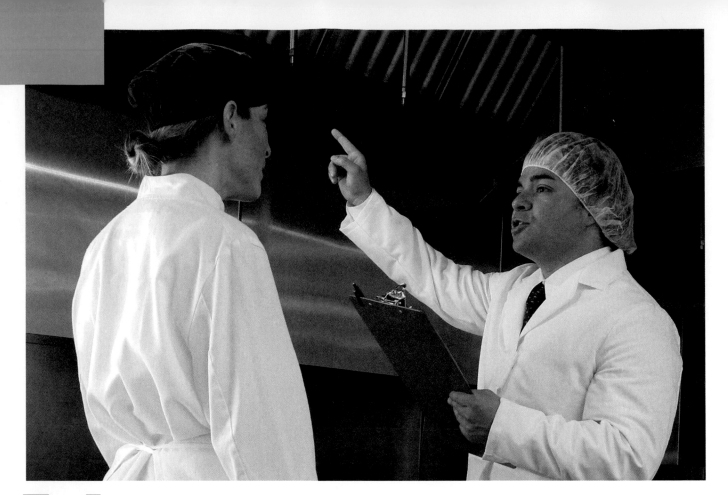

14 Food Safety Regulation and Standards

INSIDE THIS CHAPTER

- Government Agencies Responsible for Preventing Foodborne Illness
- The Inspection Process
- Self-Inspections
- Voluntary Controls within the Industry

OBJECTIVES

After completing this chapter, you should be able to identify the following:

- Government agencies that regulate food operations
- The importance of regulatory inspections and self-inspections
- The key components of an inspection
- Corrective actions to take when found to be in violation of a regulation

KEY TERMS

- Food and Drug Administration (FDA)
- U.S. Department of Agriculture (USDA)
- *FDA Food Code*
- Centers for Disease Control and Prevention (CDC)
- Public Health Service (PHS)
- Food codes
- Health inspectors

Government Agencies Responsible for Preventing Foodborne Illness
– The Role of the FDA
– Other Agencies

The Inspection Process
– Inspection Frequency
– Steps in the Inspection Process
– Closure

Self-Inspections

Voluntary Controls within the Industry

GOVERNMENT AGENCIES RESPONSIBLE FOR PREVENTING FOODBORNE ILLNESS

Several government agencies take leading roles in the prevention of foodborne illness in the United States. The Food and Drug Administration (FDA) and the U.S. Department of Agriculture (USDA) inspect food and perform other critical duties. State and local regulatory authorities create regulations and inspect operations. Agencies such as the Centers for Disease Control and Prevention (CDC) and the U.S. Public Health Service (PHS) help as well.

The Role of the FDA

The FDA inspects all food except meat, poultry, and eggs. It also regulates food transported across state lines. In addition, the agency issues the *FDA Food Code*. This science-based code provides recommendations for food safety regulations. It was created for city, county, state, and tribal agencies. These agencies regulate foodservice for the following groups:

- Restaurants and retail food stores
- Vending operations
- Schools and day-care centers
- Hospitals and nursing homes

Although the FDA recommends that states adopt the *FDA Food Code*, it cannot require it. The FDA also provides technical support and training. This is available for industry and regulatory agencies.

Other Agencies

Several other agencies have an important role in food safety and the prevention of foodborne illness.

USDA   The U.S. Department of Agriculture regulates and inspects meat, poultry, and eggs. The USDA also regulates food that crosses state boundaries or involves more than one state.

CDC The Centers for Disease Control and Prevention (CDC) are agencies of the U.S. Department of Health and Human Services. They assist the FDA, USDA, and state and local regulatory authorities by providing the following services:

- Investigate outbreaks of foodborne illness
- Study the causes and control of disease
- Publish statistical data and case studies in the *Morbidity and Mortality Weekly Report (MMWR)*
- Provide educational services in the field of sanitation
- Conduct the Vessel Sanitation Program—an inspection program for cruise ships

PHS Like the CDC, the Public Health Service (PHS) also assists the FDA, USDA, and state and local regulatory authorities. They conduct research into the causes of foodborne-illness outbreaks. They also assist in investigating outbreaks.

State and local regulatory authorities Regulatory authorities have many responsibilities. Here are some of the responsibilities related to food safety:

- Inspecting operations
- Enforcing regulations
- Investigating complaints and illnesses
- Issuing licenses and permits
- Approving construction
- Reviewing and approving HACCP plans

Regulatory authorities write or adopt food codes that regulate retail and foodservice operations. Food codes may differ from the *FDA Food Code,* because these agencies are not required to adopt it. In fact, food codes differ widely from one state or locality to another. For example, some regulatory authorities require hot-holding food temperatures to be 140°F (60°C) or higher, while others require 135°F (57°C) or higher. This can frustrate efforts by the industry to establish uniform food safety standards. Foodservice managers therefore need to consult with their regulatory authorities to find out which regulations apply to their operations.

In a large city, the local regulatory authority will probably be responsible for enforcing regulatory requirements. In smaller cities or in rural areas, a county or state regulatory authority may be responsible for enforcement. In any case, the manager needs to be familiar with the authorities and their enforcement system. State and local health inspectors (also called sanitarians, health officials, or environmental health specialists) conduct restaurant and foodservice inspections in most states, as shown in the photo at left. Most are trained in food safety, sanitation, and public-health principles.

Government Agencies Responsible for Preventing Foodborne Illness	The Inspection Process	Self-Inspections	Voluntary Controls within the Industry
— The Role of the FDA — Other Agencies	— Inspection Frequency — Steps in the Inspection Process — Closure		

THE INSPECTION PROCESS

Having a foodservice inspection program is important for several reasons. The most important reasons, however, are that failing to ensure food safety can risk your customers' health and cost you your business.

All operations that serve food to the public are subject to inspection. An inspection measures whether an operation is meeting minimum food safety standards. It also produces a written report that notes deficiencies. This report helps an operation comply with safe food practices. Keep in mind that you are ultimately responsible for food safety in your operation.

Regulatory requirements guide the inspection. So keep a current copy of your local or state regulations. Be familiar with them. Compare them often to your operation's procedures.

Regulatory authorities have begun using a more risk-based approach when conducting inspections. They often use the five risk factors for foodborne illness and the FDA's public health interventions as guides.

The FDA recommends that regulatory authorities use the following three risk designations when evaluating operations:

- Priority items
- Priority foundation items
- Core items

Priority items are the most critical. These are actions and procedures that prevent, eliminate, or reduce hazards associated with foodborne illness to an acceptable level. Correct handwashing would be considered a priority item.

Priority foundation items are those that support a priority item. Having soap at a handwashing sink is an example.

Core items relate to general sanitation, the facility, equipment design, and general maintenance. Keeping equipment in good repair is an example.

Regulatory

The CDC's *Morbidity and Mortality Weekly Report*

Known as the *MMWR*, the Centers for Disease Control and Prevention's (CDC) *Morbidity and Mortality Weekly Report* is the CDC's main communication vehicle for public health information. Published weekly, much of the data is provided by state public health departments. Food safety is one topic that is addressed; others include nutrition, disease, and related healthcare concerns.

Electronic subscriptions are free. Visit cdc.gov/mmwr for more information.

Inspection Frequency

State and local regulatory authorities differ in the frequency of their inspections. Some require inspections for operations at least every six months. Others schedule inspections more, or less, often.

The frequency will vary depending on the area, type of operation, or food served. Many authorities use a risk-based approach to decide how often they will inspect. Determining factors can include the following:

Size and complexity Larger operations offering many TCS food items might be inspected more frequently.

Inspection history Operations with a history of low sanitation scores or consecutive violations might be inspected more often.

At-risk populations Nursing homes, schools, day-care centers, and hospitals might receive more inspections.

Resources The regulatory authority's workload and number of available inspectors may determine how often it inspects operations.

Steps in the Inspection Process

In most cases, inspectors will arrive without warning. They will usually ask for the person in charge. Make sure your staff know who is in charge of food safety in your absence. Also be aware of your company's policies for handling an inspection.

The following guidelines can help you get the most out of food safety inspections.

Identification Always ask for it, as the manager in the photo at left has done. Also prohibit entry through the back of the operation without the correct ID. Inspectors will volunteer their credentials. Make sure you know the reason for the inspection as well. It could be a routine visit or the result of a customer complaint.

Do not refuse entry to an inspector. Inspectors have authority to gain access to the operation. They also have authority to revoke the operation's permit for refusing entry.

Cooperation Answer all of the inspector's questions as well as you can. Tell your staff to do the same. You should go with the inspector during the inspection. You will be able to answer any questions and possibly correct problems right away. Tell the inspector when something can be fixed if it cannot be fixed immediately. Open communication helps build a good working relationship with the inspector. You will also learn from the inspector's comments and get good food safety advice.

Notes As you walk with the inspector, make note of any problems pointed out. This will help you remember exactly what was said. Make it clear that you are willing to fix any problems. If you believe the inspector is incorrect about something, ask for clarification and note what was mentioned. Then contact the regulatory authority if you are still unsure about something.

Professionalism   Be polite and friendly, and treat inspectors with respect. Be careful about offering food, drink, or anything else that could be perceived as trying to influence the report.

Records   Be prepared to provide the following records an inspector might request:

- Purchasing records to make sure that food has been received from an approved source
- PCO treatment plan
- Proof of food safety knowledge, such as a food protection manager certificate, as shown in the photo at left
- HACCP records, in some cases

You can ask the inspector why these records are needed. If a request seems inappropriate, check with the inspector's supervisor. You can also check with your lawyer about limits on confidential information. Remember that any records you provide will become part of the public record.

Correction   After the inspection, the inspector will explain the results and the score, if one is given. Study the inspection report. Discuss any violations and time frames for correction with the inspector. You need to understand the exact nature of a violation. You should also know how a violation affects food safety, how to correct it, and whether or not the inspector will follow up.

You will be asked to sign the inspection report. Signing it acknowledges you have received it. Follow your company's policy regarding this issue.

A copy of the report will then be given to you or the person in charge at the time of the inspection. Keep copies of all reports on file in the operation. You can refer to them when planning improvements and assessing operation goals. Copies of reports are also kept on file at the regulatory authority. They are public documents that may be available to anyone upon request.

Action   Act on any deficiencies noted in the inspection report. The manager and chef in the photo at left are discussing deficiencies in an inspection report. You will need to act on deficiencies within the time given by the inspector. Violations of priority items usually must be corrected within 72 hours. Violations of priority foundation items typically must be corrected within 10 calendar days.

Determine their cause by reviewing standard operating procedures. Also review the master cleaning schedule, staff training, and food handling practices. Revise current procedures or set up new ones to resolve any problems. Inform staff of the deficiencies and retrain them if needed.

Closure

After careful review, an inspector might determine an operation poses an imminent health hazard to the public. In some states, he or she may ask for a voluntary closure or issue an immediate suspension of the permit to operate. Examples of hazards calling for closure include the following:

- Significant lack of refrigeration

- Backup of sewage into the operation or its water supply

- Emergency, such as a building fire or flood

- Significant infestation of insects or rodents

- Long interruption of electrical or water service

- Clear evidence of a foodborne-illness outbreak related to the operation

If an operation receives a suspension, it must cease operations right away. However, the owner can request a hearing if he or she believes the suspension was unjustified. Such a request often has a time limit (usually within five to ten days of the inspection). Check your regulations for these limits.

The suspension order may be posted at a public entrance to the operation, as shown in the photo at left. This is not required if the operation closes voluntarily. Regulations vary among different authorities. To reinstate a permit to operate, the operation must eliminate the hazards causing the suspension. Then it needs to pass a reinspection and receive written approval to reopen.

Regulatory

Public Health Inspectors

Public health inspectors, also known as sanitarians or environmentalists, evaluate a variety of foodservice facilities in all segments of the restaurant and foodservice industry. Most inspectors have degrees in a science, and they often must become registered sanitarians in their state. This means that the state recognizes the individual's expertise and ability to take action to protect the public's health.

In addition to restaurant inspections, public health inspectors often participate in investigating foodborne-illness reports, evaluating private and public water supplies, and inspecting private sewage disposal and landfills. Inspectors can be found at all levels of government, and many also work in private industry as quality assurance and compliance experts. A number of former health inspectors can be found as consultants helping companies to design and perform self-audits.

Government Agencies Responsible for Preventing Foodborne Illness — The Role of the FDA — Other Agencies	The Inspection Process — Inspection Frequency — Steps in the Inspection Process — Closure	Self-Inspections	Voluntary Controls within the Industry

Key Point

Consider regulatory inspections a supplement to your ongoing self-inspection programs.

SELF-INSPECTIONS

Well-managed operations perform frequent self-inspections to keep food safe. These are done in addition to—and more often than—regulatory inspections. They can be conducted in-house or by a third-party organization.

A good self-inspection program provides the following benefits:

- Safer food
- Improved food quality
- Cleaner environment for staff and customers
- Higher inspection scores

Strive to exceed the standards of your regulatory authority. This will help you do well on inspections. Your customers will also recognize your commitment to food safety.

Consider these guidelines when conducting a self-inspection:

- Use the same type of checklist that the regulatory authority uses.
- Identify all risks to food safety.
- After the inspection, meet with staff to review any problems.

VOLUNTARY CONTROLS WITHIN THE INDUSTRY

Few professions have devoted as much effort to self-regulation as the restaurant and foodservice and food-processing industries. Scientific and trade associations, manufacturing firms, and foodservice corporations have made voluntary efforts to raise industry standards through research, education, and cooperation with government.

These organizations have recommended legislative policy, sponsored uniform enforcement procedures, and provided educational opportunities. The results for food safety have included the following:

- Increased understanding of foodborne illness and its prevention
- Improvements in the safe design of equipment and facilities
- Industry-wide initiatives to maintain safe food during processing, shipment, storage, and service
- Efforts to make foodservice laws more practical, uniform, and science based

SUMMARY

- Government control regarding food safety in the United States is exercised at three levels: federal, state, and local.

- Recommendations for restaurant and foodservice regulations are issued at the federal level by the FDA in the form of the *FDA Food Code*. Regulations are written and enforced at the state and local level.

- All operations need to follow practices critical to the safety of the food they serve. The inspection process lets the operation know that it is meeting the minimum standards.

- During the inspection, cooperate with the health inspector and keep the relationship professional. Accompany him or her during the inspection. If the inspector points out a problem, take notes. If a deficiency can be corrected right away, do so. Be prepared to provide records that are requested. Discuss any violations and time frames for correction, and then follow up.

- Well-managed operations will inspect themselves often to keep food safe. These inspections are in addition to those by the regulatory authority. Operations with high food safety standards consider regulatory inspections only a supplement to their own self-inspection programs.

Apply Your **Knowledge**	Use these questions to review the concepts presented in this chapter.
DISCUSSION QUESTIONS	① What are some hazards that require the closure of an operation?
	② What are the roles of federal, state, and local agencies regarding the regulation of food safety in operations?
	③ What should a manager do during and after an inspection?
	④ What are some factors that determine the frequency of health inspections in an operation?
	For answers, please turn to the Answer Key.

Apply Your Knowledge

Inspect Thy Self

Brianna was a veteran manager and had been with the company for several years when she got promoted to the company's flagship operation. That operation was where they worked on all new menu concepts and developed all the new recipes that would be used throughout the 42-unit company. Brianna was very proud to have been given a chance to manage this particular operation.

One of the reasons Brianna was promoted was that she had the reputation of always running the cleanest operations in the company, and she always seemed to receive the highest scores on her health inspections.

Brianna had a secret weapon and was determined to use it at her new place. It was a self-inspection system that she had created. It had always kept her one step ahead on inspections and ensured that her staff was keeping food safe.

1 What are the benefits that a self-inspection program provides?

2 What are some guidelines for conducting a self-inspection?

For answers, please turn to the Answer Key.

Study Questions

1. A backup of raw sewage and significant lack of refrigeration can result in

   A a delay of an inspection until the situation is corrected.

   B closure of the operation by the regulatory authority.

   C improved inspection scores.

   D being issued a permit to operate.

2. A person arrives at a restaurant claiming to be a health inspector. What should the manager ask for?

   A Inspection warrant

   B Inspector's identification

   C Hearing to determine if the inspection is necessary

   D One-day postponement to prepare for the inspection

3. Which agency enforces food safety in a restaurant?

   A Centers for Disease Control and Prevention

   B Food and Drug Administration

   C State or local regulatory authority

   D U.S. Department of Agriculture

4. Who is responsible for keeping food safe in an operation?

   A Food and Drug Administration

   B Health inspectors

   C Manager/operator

   D State health department

For answers, please turn to the Answer Key.

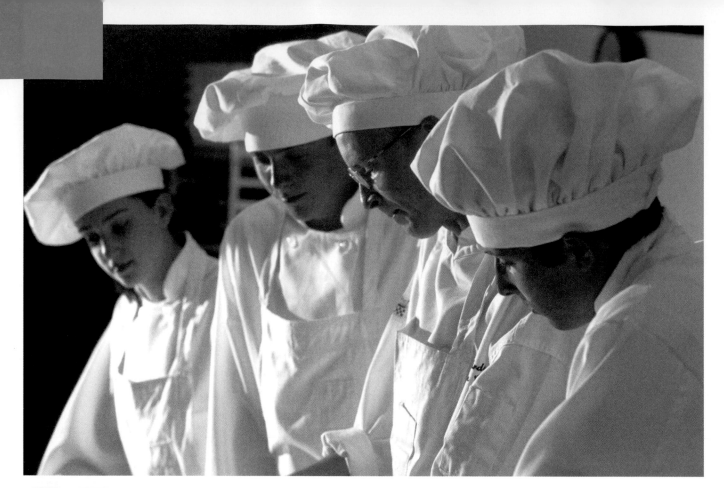

15 Staff Food Safety Training

Training Staff	Ways of Training
– Critical Food Safety Knowledge	– On-the-Job Training
– Retraining	– Classroom Training
– Record Keeping	– Technology-Based Training

INSIDE THIS CHAPTER

- Training Staff
- Ways of Training

OBJECTIVES

After completing this chapter, you should be able to identify the following:

- Staff duties and specific training needs for each duty
- Ways of training specific to staff and their duties
- How to maintain food safety training records
- How to ensure all staff are trained upon and after being hired

KEY TERMS

- Training need

Training Staff	Ways of Training
— Critical Food Safety Knowledge — Retraining — Record Keeping	— On-the-Job Training — Classroom Training — Technology-Based Training

TRAINING STAFF

You do not know how long staff members will be working at your operation. Whether they have been on the job for one day or five years, they need to understand that food safety is important. To make sure you are serving safe food, train your staff when they are first hired and then continue training them.

To ensure staff can handle food correctly, first identify each training need within your operation. A training need is a gap between what staff should know to do their jobs and what they actually know.

For new hires, the need might be obvious. For experienced staff, the need is not always as clear.

Identifying food safety training needs will require some effort. You can achieve this in several ways:

- Observe performance on the job
- Test food safety knowledge
- Identify areas of weakness

All staff need general food safety knowledge. Other knowledge will be specific to tasks. For example, everyone should know how to wash their hands correctly. However, only receiving staff need to know how to inspect produce during receiving, as shown in the photo at left.

Critical Food Safety Knowledge

You cannot assume new hires will understand your operation's food safety procedures without training. They should begin learning about the importance of food safety on their first day. They should also receive training in the critical areas listed on page 15-3. Once staff are trained, monitor them to make sure they are folllowing procedures.

Retraining

Staff need to be periodically retrained in food safety. You can do this by scheduling short training sessions, planning meetings to update them on new procedures, or holding motivational sessions that reinforce food safety practices.

Record Keeping

Keep records of all food safety training at your operation. For legal reasons, be sure to document this training when a staff member completes it.

Critical Food Safety Knowledge for Staff

Good Personal Hygiene

- How and when to wash hands
- Where to wash hands
- Other hand-care guidelines including fingernail length, nail polish, covering wounds
- Proper work attire
- Reporting illness

Controlling Time and Temperature

- TCS food
- How to measure the temperature of food
- Holding and storing TCS food
- How to label food for storage
- Temperature requirements when thawing, cooking, cooling, and reheating food

Preventing Cross-Contamination

- Preventing cross-contamination of food during storage, preparation, and service
- Preventing cross-contamination when storing utensils and equipment
- What to do if cross-contamination happens
- What to do for people who have food allergies

Cleaning and Sanitizing

- How and when to clean and sanitize
- The correct way to wash dishes in a three-compartment sink and in a dishwasher
- How to handle cleaning tools and supplies
- Handling garbage
- Spotting pests

Training Staff	Ways of Training
— Critical Food Safety Knowledge — Retraining — Record Keeping	— On-the-Job Training — Classroom Training — Technology-Based Training

WAYS OF TRAINING

You have several ways to teach staff how to keep food safe. When choosing training, think about what would work best in your operation. Some operations use a traditional approach such as on-the-job training. Others may use a technology-based approach. No one type of training works best, as not everyone learns the same way. Use different methods to achieve the best results.

On-the-Job Training (OJT)

Many operations assign experienced staff to train learners while on the job. Learners perform tasks while the trainers tell them how they are doing.

OJT teaches skills that require thinking and doing. It is good for training staff members one at a time. It can also work for small groups. It is equally effective for teaching skills that require watching someone perform the task correctly.

Success depends on the skill of the person doing the training. Choose the trainer carefully. Before using OJT, also recognize that it takes experienced staff away from their jobs. Plus, it is not as useful for training large groups.

Classroom Training

Today's workforce expects training that will both entertain and teach them. This can be challenging, but it is not impossible. Using an activity-based approach to training can be very effective. People learn by doing rather than by just being told what to do. Your training should include activities that require staff to do something.

Staff should also take part in learning activities. Encourage them to ask questions and allow them to make mistakes. Make them responsible for their own learning as well.

You can use a range of activity-based training to teach food safety to your staff:

- Information search
- Guided discussion
- Role-play
- Games
- Demonstrations
- Jigsaw design
- Training videos and DVDs

Business

Training Dollars

Managers and company leaders must determine how much to spend on training, an area that is sometimes vulnerable when budget dollars are tight elsewhere. Part of the challenge is understanding what the "return on investment," or ROI, is for spending those training dollars. How can you show that training has benefited the worker and the company?

One well-known restaurant group has more than 170 locations and 27,000 employees. On average, the company spends $2,000 on training per hourly worker each year. Training includes everyone in the organization.

For example, servers get two weeks of on-the-job training, and they must get server certificates before working shifts. In fact, all front-of-the-house and kitchen managers are trained in HACCP. This company emphasizes food safety from the beginning, in every aspect of its training program. Its turnover rates are lower than the average in the industry (one potential way to show ROI; another might be to compare inspection results pre- and post-training).

By comparison, a 2011 report by Bersin & Associates estimates that the average American worker (any industry) receives just over $1,200 in training each year.

Information Search

Some people are curious and like to explore things on their own. Make use of their interest by having them discover food safety information for themselves. Here is how:

❶ Put staff in small groups.

❷ Give them questions to answer within a set time.

❸ Give them the following types of tools to answer the questions:

- Operations manuals
- Job aids
- Posters, as shown in the photo at left
- Staff guides

❹ Bring the groups together and have them share what they learned.

Guided Discussion

Ask staff questions that draw on their knowledge and experience. Encourage them to think and then discuss their thoughts. Each time learners answer a question, follow with another question.

Through this approach, a training session on calibrating thermometers might go something like this:

Instructor: How can you find out if a cooked chicken breast has reached the correct temperature?

Learner: Use a thermometer.

Instructor: How can you make sure a thermometer's reading is correct?

Learner: Calibrate it.

Instructor: How do you calibrate a thermometer?

Learner: By using the ice-point method or the boiling-point method.

Games

A game can help make difficult or boring information seem more exciting. You can also use games to practice information that has already been taught. To be effective, games should be the following:

- Easy to play
- Fun
- Suitable for all time frames
- Easy to bring to the training site
- Easy to change for the audience and content

Role-Play

Many trainers use role-play to teach concepts. However, some learners do not like role-playing because it puts them on the spot. Role-play can work if you handle it the correct way. Here is how:

❶ Prepare a script in advance that shows the correct or incorrect way to perform a skill.

❷ Find two volunteers and give them time to rehearse the script. Do this early in the training session. As an alternative, you can play one of the parts in the role-play.

❸ Have the volunteers act out the script.

❹ Ask the rest of the group to decide what the role-players did correctly and incorrectly.

Demonstrations

You will often teach specific food safety tasks by showing them to a person or group. Demonstrations are most effective when you follow the Tell/Show/Practice model as shown below.

Demonstrating a Task Using the Tell/Show/Practice Model

Tell

Tell the learner how to do the task. Explain what you are doing and why.

Show

Show the learner how to do the task.

Practice

Let the learner do the task. As extra practice, have the learner explain how to do the task before showing how to do it. Tell the learner how he or she is doing throughout the practice.

Resources

The FDA Oral Culture Learner Project

The restaurant and foodservice industry workforce is a diverse group. Many cultures can be represented in a single unit, and some workers speak English as a second language. Training, therefore, can be challenging. In response to this challenge, the Food and Drug Administration (FDA) began its Oral Culture Learner Project. The goal of the project is to provide food safety training materials in a way that works for individuals from cultures who learn best through verbalization of topics and stories.

Topics include personal hygiene, employee health, and safe food handling. The materials are available for free at fda. gov. Many of the topics can be found in Hindi, Korean, Russian, Simplified Chinese, Traditional Chinese, Spanish, and English.

Jigsaw Design

There is an old saying that goes, "You have learned something when you can teach someone else how to do it." The jigsaw method follows this principle. Here is how to use it:

1 Put learners in small groups.

2 Assign a specific food safety topic to each group.

3 Tell each group to read about their topic, discuss it, and decide how to teach it to the other groups.

4 Take one person from each group and form new groups.

5 Have each member in the new group teach his or her topic to the other group members.

6 Bring the groups back together for review and questions.

Training Videos and DVDs

Trainers generally believe that learners retain information from their training sessions in the following ways:

- 10 percent of what they read
- 20 percent of what they hear
- 30 percent of what they see
- 50 percent of what they see and hear

Videos and DVDs will help your staff see and hear food safety information. This will make them more likely to remember it. Video is also useful for teaching skills that involve motion, such as calibrating a thermometer.

If your staff are learning food safety on their own by video instruction, supplement their training with print materials.

Technology-Based Training

Many operations use technology-based training, such as online learning, to teach food safety. Technology-based training lets you deliver training when and where your staff needs it. It is most appropriate in the following situations:

- Staff work in different locations and/or need the same training at different times.
- When it is too costly to bring staff to the same place.
- Staff need retraining.
- Staff have different levels of knowledge about a topic.
- Staff have different learning skills.
- Staff need to learn at their own pace.
- You want to collect specific information, such as test scores, time spent on different topics, and/or problem areas.

SUMMARY

- Ensure that staff have the knowledge and skills to handle food safely in your operation.

- First assess your operation's training needs. A training need is a gap between what staff should know to perform their jobs and what they actually know.

- To identify food safety training needs, test your staff's knowledge, observe their performance, or note their areas of weakness.

- All staff need general food safety knowledge. Other knowledge will be specific to tasks. All staff should be retrained periodically.

- Keep records of all food safety training at your operation. For legal reasons, be sure to document this training when a staff member completes it.

- Training can be delivered in various ways. No one type of training works best, as not everyone learns the same way.

- Use different training methods to achieve the best results.

Apply Your **Knowledge**	Use these questions to review the concepts presented in this chapter.
DISCUSSION QUESTIONS	① How can an operation determine its food safety training needs? ② What are some methods that can be used to deliver training? ③ What are some situations where technology-based training would be appropriate? *For answers, please turn to the Answer Key.*

Apply Your Knowledge

Technology Saves the Day

Ryan was a genuine success story. He started with the company when he was 17 years old and worked summers and holidays as he moved up from job to job. He had started washing pots and pans and had been promoted into almost every job there was in the back of the house.

He found himself at age 24, as the director of training for this rapidly growing chain of casual dining restaurants. Ryan was in charge of coordinating food safety training for all company staff. He worked directly with the company's director of food safety to determine the best way to approach the company's goals for food safety training.

One of the problems Ryan faced was that the company employed over 3,000 people in 18 different states. Ryan did not have a clue about how he could ensure that every staff member in the company would be correctly trained in food safety.

Ryan's background had been in the back of the house and his technology skills were extremely limited. Even though Ryan was not comfortable with technology, he realized that it was the answer to making sure all 3,000 staff members were correctly and uniformly trained.

1 Why do you think Ryan was considering a company-wide technology-based training program?

2 List some of the situations where technology-based training is most appropriate?

For answers, please turn to the Answer Key.

15

Circle the best answer to each question.

1 When should staff receive food safety training?

A When hired, and then periodically after that

B When they do not have foodservice experience

C When a new *FDA Food Code* comes out

D Only when they request it

2 New staff must be trained in the critical areas of personal hygiene, cleaning and sanitizing, controlling time and temperature, and

A crisis management.

B equipment handling.

C HACCP plan creation.

D preventing cross-contamination.

3 The manager's responsibility for staff food safety training is to

A test staff's food safety knowledge.

B provide all staff with videos and DVDs for training.

C make sure that staff have the knowledge and skills to keep food safe.

D let staff learn on their own.

4 All new staff should receive training on

A HACCP.

B crisis management.

C general food safety.

D active managerial control.

5 What is the first task in training a large group of servers to prevent contamination of food?

A Assess the training needs of the servers on this topic.

B Make a list of possible information to cover.

C Provide servers with operation manuals on the topic.

D Put the servers into small groups based on service experience.

6 In which training method does a trainer ask a series of questions to draw on the knowledge and experience of the learners?

A Information search

B Guided discussion

C Jigsaw design

D Games

For answers, please turn to the Answer Key.

Notes

Glossary

Note: The number(s) in bold at the end of each entry refers to the chapter in which the term is discussed in detail.

A

Abrasive cleaners. Cleaners containing a scouring agent used to scrub off hard-to-remove dirt. They may scratch some surfaces. **12**

Active managerial control. Food safety management system designed to prevent foodborne illness by addressing the five most common risk factors identified by the Centers for Disease Control and Prevention (CDC). **10**

Air curtains. Devices installed above or alongside doors that blow a steady stream of air across an entryway, creating an air shield around open doors. Insects avoid them. Also called air doors or fly fans. **13**

Air gap. Air space used to separate a water-supply outlet from any potentially contaminated source. The air space between the floor drain and the drainpipe of a sink is an example. An air gap is the only completely reliable method for preventing backflow. **11**

Approved suppliers. Suppliers that have been inspected, are able to provide an inspection report, and that meet applicable local, state, and federal laws. **6**

B

Backflow. Unwanted reverse flow of contaminants through a cross-connection into a drinkable water system. It can be the result of pressure pushing contaminants back into the water supply. It can also happen when high water use in one area of the operation creates a vacuum that sucks contaminants back into the water supply. **11**

Bacteria. Single-celled, living microorganisms that can spoil food and cause foodborne illness. Bacteria present in food can quickly multiply to dangerous levels when food is incorrectly cooked, held, or reheated. Some form spores that can survive freezing and very high temperatures. **2**

Bimetallic stemmed thermometer. The most common and versatile type of thermometer, measuring temperature through a metal probe with a sensor in the end. Most can measure temperatures from 0°F to 220°F (–18°C to 104°C) and are accurate to within ±2°F or ±1°C. They are easily calibrated. **5**

Boiling-point method. Method of calibrating a thermometer based on the boiling point of water. **5**

Booster heater. Water heater attached to hot-water lines leading to dishwashing machines or sinks. Raises water to temperature required for heat sanitizing of tableware and utensils. **11**

C

Calibration. Process of ensuring that a thermometer gives accurate readings by adjusting it to a known standard, such as the freezing point or boiling point of water. **5**

Carriers. People who carry pathogens and infect others, yet never get sick themselves. **4**

Centers for Disease Control and Prevention (CDC). Agencies of the U.S. Department of Health and Human Services that investigate foodborne-illness outbreaks, study the causes and control of disease, publish statistical data, and conduct the Vessel Sanitation Program. **14**

Cleaning. Process of removing food and other types of dirt from a surface, such as a countertop or plate. **12**

Concentration. The amount of sanitizer to water measured in parts per million (ppm). The concentration of sanitizer affects the effectiveness of the sanitizer solution. **12**

Contamination. Presence of harmful substances in food. Some food safety hazards occur naturally, while others are introduced by humans or the environment. **1**

Coving. Curved, sealed edge placed between the floor and wall to eliminate sharp corners or gaps that would be impossible to clean. Coving also eliminates hiding places for pests and prevents moisture from deteriorating walls. **11**

Critical control points (CCPs). In a HACCP system, the points in the process where you can intervene to prevent, eliminate, or reduce identified hazards to safe levels. **10**

Cross-connection. Physical link through which contaminants from drains, sewers, or other wastewater sources can enter a drinkable water supply. A hose connected to a faucet and submerged in a mop bucket is an example. **11**

Cross-contact. The transfer of an allergen from a food containing an allergen to a food that does not contain the allergen. **3**

Cross-contamination. Occurs when microorganisms are transferred from one food or surface to another. **1**

D

Date marking. A date on ready-to-eat TCS food held for more than 24 hours indicating by when the food must be sold, eaten, or thrown out. **7**

Degreasers. Alkaline detergents, often called degreasers, that contain a grease-dissolving agent. **12**

Delimers. Used on mineral deposits and other soils that alkaline cleaners cannot remove, such as scale, rust, and tarnish. **12**

Detergents. Cleaners designed to penetrate and soften dirt to help remove it from a surface. **12**

F

FAT TOM. Acronym for the conditions needed by foodborne bacteria to grow: food, acidity, temperature, time, oxygen, moisture. **2**

FDA Model Food Code. Science-based reference for retail food operations on how to prevent foodborne illness. These recommendations are issued by the FDA to assist state health departments in developing regulations for a foodservice inspection program. **14**

Finger cots. Protective coverings used to cover a correctly bandaged cut or wound on the finger. **4**

First-in, first-out (FIFO). Method of stock rotation in which products are shelved based on their use-by or expiration dates, so oldest products are used first. **7**

Flow of food. Path food takes through an operation, from purchasing and receiving through storing, preparing, cooking, holding, cooling, reheating, and serving. **5**

Food allergen. A naturally-occurring protein in food or in an ingredient that some people are sensitive to. When enough of an allergen is eaten, the immune system mistakenly considers it harmful and attacks the food protein. This can result in an allergic reaction. **3**

Food and Drug Administration (FDA). Federal agency that issues the *FDA Model Food Code*, working jointly with the U.S. Department of Agriculture (USDA) and the Centers for Disease Control and Prevention (CDC). The FDA also inspects foodservice operations that cross state borders—interstate operations such as food manufacturers and processors, and planes and trains—because they overlap the jurisdictions of two or more states. **14**

Food codes. State level food safety regulations that are written and adopted. **14**

Food defense. Program developed and implemented by an operation to prevent deliberate contamination of its food. **3**

Food safety management system. Group of programs, procedures, and measures designed to prevent foodborne illness by actively controlling risks and hazards throughout the flow of food. **10**

Foodborne illness. Illness carried or transmitted to people by food. **1**

Foodborne-illness outbreak. An incident in which two or more people experience the same illness symptoms after eating the same food. An investigation is conducted by the state and local regulatory authorities, and the outbreak is confirmed by a laboratory analysis. **1**

Fungi. Ranging in size from microscopic, single-celled organisms to very large, multicellular organisms. Fungi most often cause food to spoil. Molds, yeasts, and mushrooms are examples. **2**

H

HACCP. Food safety management system based on the idea that if significant biological, chemical, or physical hazards are identified at specific points within a product's flow through the operation, they can be prevented, eliminated, or reduced to safe levels. **10**

HACCP plan. Written document based on HACCP principles describing procedures a particular operation will follow to ensure the safety of food served. See HACCP. **10**

Hair restraint. Device used to keep a food handler's hair away from food and to keep the individual from touching it. **4**

Hand antiseptics. Liquids or gels used to lower the number of microorganisms on the skin's surface. Hand antiseptics should only be used after correct handwashing, not in place of it. Only those hand antiseptics that are compliant with the Food and Drug Administration (FDA) should be used. **4**

Health inspectors. City, county, or state staff members who conduct foodservice inspections. Health inspectors are also known as sanitarians, health officials, and environmental health specialists. They are generally trained in food safety, sanitation, and public health principles. **14**

High-risk populations. People susceptible to foodborne illness due to the effects of age or health on their immune systems, including preschool-age children, elderly people, and people with compromised immune systems, such as people with cancer or on chemotherapy, people with HIV/AIDS, transplant recipients, and people taking certain medications. **1**

I

Ice-point method. Method of calibrating thermometers based on the freezing point of water. **5**

Imminent health hazard. A significant threat or danger to health that requires immediate correction or closure to prevent injury. **10**

Immune system. The body's defense system against illness. People with compromised immune systems are more susceptible to foodborne illness. **1**

Infestation. Situation that exists when pests overrun or inhabit an operation in large numbers. **13**

Inspection stamp. A stamp indicating carcasses and packages of meat have been inspected by the USDA or a state department of agriculture. **6**

Integrated pest management (IPM). Program using prevention measures to keep pests from entering an operation and control measures to eliminate any pests that do get inside. **13**

K

Key drop delivery. The receipt of food by a foodservice operation after-hours while closed for business. **6**

M

Material Safety Data Sheet (MSDS). Sheets supplied by the chemical manufacturer listing the chemical and its common names, its potential physical and health hazards, information about using and handling it safely, and other important information. OSHA requires employers to store these sheets so they are accessible to staff. **12**

Microorganisms. Small, living organisms that can be seen only with the aid of a microscope. There are four types of microorganisms that can contaminate food and cause foodborne illness: bacteria, viruses, parasites, and fungi. **2**

Minimum internal temperature. The required minimum temperature the internal portion of food must reach to sufficiently reduce the number of microorganisms that might be present. This temperature is specific to the type of food being cooked. Food must reach and hold its required internal temperature for a specified amount of time. **8**

Mobile units. Portable foodservice operations, ranging from concession vans to full field kitchens, capable of preparing and cooking elaborate meals. **9**

Mold. Type of fungus that causes food spoilage. Some molds produce toxins that can cause foodborne illness. **2**

N

NSF. Organization that develops and publishes standards for sanitary equipment design. It also assesses and certifies that equipment has met these standards. Restaurant and foodservice managers should look for an NSF International Mark (or UL EPH product mark) on commercial foodservice equipment. **11**

O

Off-site service. Service of food to someplace other than where it is prepared or cooked, including catering and vending. **9**

P

Parasite. Organism that needs to live in a host organism to survive. Parasites can be found in water and inside many animals, such as cows, chickens, pigs, and fish. Correct cooking and freezing will kill parasites. Avoiding cross-contamination and practicing correct handwashing can also prevent illness. **2**

Pathogens. Illness-causing microorganisms. **2**

Pest control operator (PCO). Licensed professional who uses safe, current methods to prevent and control pests. **13**

Pesticides. Chemicals used to control pests, usually insects. **13**

Porosity. Extent to which water and other liquids are absorbed by a substance. Term usually used in relation to flooring material. **11**

Public Health Service (PHS). A federal agency that conducts research into the causes of foodborne illness and assists with the investigation of outbreaks. **14**

R

Ready-to-eat food. Any food that is edible without further preparation, washing, or cooking. It includes washed fruit and vegetables, both whole and cut; deli meats; and bakery items. Sugars, spices, seasonings, and correctly cooked food items are also considered ready to eat. **1**

Reduced-oxygen packaged (ROP). Packaging method that reduces the amount of oxygen available in order to slow microbial growth. ROP methods include *sous vide*, MAP, and vacuum packaging. **7**

Resiliency. Ability of a surface to react to a shock without breaking or cracking, usually used in relation to a flooring material. **11**

S

Sanitizing. Process of reducing the number of microorganisms on a clean surface to safe levels. **12**

Shellstock identification tags. Each container of live, molluscan shellfish received must have an ID tag that must remain attached to the container until all the shellfish have been used. Tags are to be kept on file for 90 days from the date recorded on the tag. **6**

Slacking. Process of gradually thawing frozen food in preparation for deep-frying. **8**

Sneeze guards. Food shields placed over self-service displays and food bars that extend seven inches beyond the food and fourteen inches above the food counter. **9**

Spore. Form that some bacteria can take to protect themselves when nutrients are not available. Spores are commonly found in dirt and can contaminate food grown there. A spore can resist heat, allowing it to survive cooking temperatures. Spores can also revert back to a form capable of growth. This can occur when food is not held at the correct temperature or cooled or reheated correctly. **2**

T

TCS food. Food that contains moisture and protein and has a neutral or slightly acidic pH. Such food requires time-temperature control to prevent the growth of microorganisms and the production of toxins. **1**

Temperature danger zone. The temperature range between 41°F and 135°F (5°C to 57°C), within which most foodborne microorganisms rapidly grow. **2**

Temporary units. Operations operating in one location for no more than 14 consecutive days in conjunction with a special event or celebration. Usually serve prepackaged food or food requiring only limited preparation. **9**

Thermistors. Thermometers that check food temperature through a sensor on the tip of a metal probe. **5**

Thermocouples. Thermometers that check food temperature through a sensor on the tip of a metal probe. **5**

Time-temperature abuse.
Food has been time-temperature abused any time it has been allowed to remain too long at a temperature favorable to the growth of foodborne microorganisms. **1**

Time-temperature indicator (TTI).
Time and temperature monitoring device attached to a food shipment to determine if the product's temperature has exceeded safe limits during shipment or subsequent storage. **5**

Toxins. Poisons produced by pathogens, plants, or animals. Some occur in animals as a result of their diet. **2**

Training need. Gap between what staff are required to know to do their jobs and what they actually know. There are several ways to identify food safety training needs, including observing job performance, testing food safety knowledge, and surveying staff to identify areas of weakness. **15**

U

U.S. Department of Agriculture (USDA). Federal agency responsible for the inspection and quality grading of meat, meat products, poultry, dairy products, eggs and egg products, and fruit and vegetables shipped across state lines. **14**

V

Variance. Document issued by a regulatory agency that allows a requirement to be waived or modified. **10**

Virus. Smallest of the microbial food contaminants. Viruses rely on a living host to reproduce. They usually contaminate food through a food handler's incorrect personal hygiene. Some survive freezing and cooking temperatures. **2**

W

Water activity (a_w). Amount of moisture available in food for microorganisms to grow. It is measured in a scale from 0.0 to 1.0, with water having a water activity (a_w) of 1.0. TCS food typically has a water-activity value of 0.85 or higher. **2**

Water hardness. The amount of minerals in water. Water hardness affects how well a sanitizer works. **12**

Y

Yeast. Type of fungus that causes food spoilage. **2**

Answer Key

1   KEEPING FOOD SAFE

Page	Activity

1-1   Case in Point: Baked Potato Outbreak

① Baked potatoes are a TCS food and pathogens can grow well in them. They need time and temperature control to limit this growth. The baked potatoes at the café were time-temperature abused. They were not cooled correctly after baking, and they were stored at room temperature for a long period of time. This provided the perfect conditions for pathogens on the potatoes to grow, which caused the outbreak. To prevent this, the potatoes should have been removed from the foil after baking, and then correctly cooled. Then they should have been stored in a cooler.

1-10   Discussion Questions

① The potential costs associated with foodborne-illness outbreaks include the following:

- Loss of customers and sales
- Loss of reputation
- Negative media exposure
- Lawsuits and legal fees
- Increased insurance premiums
- Lowered staff morale
- Staff absenteeism
- Staff retraining
- Closure
- Human costs, such as lost work, medical costs, long-term disability, and death

② As people age, there are changes in their organs. For example, stomach-acid production decreases as people get older. This allows more pathogens that may have been eaten to enter the intestines. A change in the stomach and intestinal tract also allows the body to store food for longer periods. This gives toxins more time to form.

③ The three major types of contaminants are: biological, chemical, and physical. Biological contaminants include bacteria, viruses, parasites, and fungi. Chemical contaminants include foodservice chemicals such as cleaners, sanitizers, and polishes. Physical hazards include foreign objects such as metal shavings, staples, bandages, glass, and dirt. Naturally occurring objects, such as fish bones in fillets, are another example.

1-11 Case in Point: Undercooked Chicken Sends Children to the Hospital

① The chicken that the children ate was time-temperature abused. It was not cooked enough to kill pathogens, which resulted in the outbreak. The manager of the operation should have been monitoring food handlers to ensure that all food was being cooked to required internal temperatures. They must also make sure that food is being checked with calibrated thermometers.

② The reason so many children got sick was because preschool-age children have a higher risk of getting a foodborne illness. That is because they have not had enough time to build up a strong immune system.

1-11 Case in Point: With Power Comes Responsibility

① As the person in charge in his operation, the regulatory authority will hold Russell accountable for making sure the following standards are met:

- Food is not being prepared in a private home or in a room where people are living or sleeping.

- People other than food handlers are restricted from prep, storage, and dishwashing areas. If other people are allowed in these areas, steps are taken to protect food, utensils, and equipment from contamination.

- Maintenance and delivery workers are following food safety practices while in the operation.

- Staff handwashing is monitored in the operation.

- The inspection of deliveries is monitored to ensure that food is received from an approved source; at the correct temperature; and has not been contaminated.

- Food delivered after-hours is monitored to make sure it is received from an approved source; stored in the correct location; protected from contamination; and accurately presented.

- Food handlers are being monitored to make sure TCS food is cooked to required temperatures. Temperatures are being checked using calibrated thermometers.

- Food handlers are monitored to make sure TCS food is being cooled rapidly.

- Consumer advisories are posted notifying customers of the risk of ordering raw or partially cooked food.

- Cleaning and sanitizing procedures are monitored to make sure that sanitizer solutions are at the correct temperature and concentration and remain in contact with items for the correct amount of time.

- Customers are notified that they must use clean tableware when returning to a self-service area.

- Staff is handling ready-to-eat food with utensils or single-use gloves.

- Staff are trained in food safety, including allergy awareness.

- Staff, including conditional staff, are reporting illnesses and symptoms of illness that can be transmitted through food.

- Food safety procedures are written, implemented, and maintained where required by the regulatory authority.

1-12 Study Questions

① A   ② C   ③ D   ④ D   ⑤ D   ⑥ B

2 UNDERSTANDING THE MICROWORLD

Page	Activity

2-1 Case in Point: *Shigella* Outbreak

(1) The outbreak could have been prevented if the cook had reported his illness to management. Most likely the cook suffered from diarrhea. If he had told management, they would have been required to exclude the cook from the operation. This most certainly would have prevented the outbreak. Another thing that may have prevented it was correct handwashing. The cook failed to wash his hands several times throughout the day. This was a critical mistake, especially if he failed to wash his hands after using the restroom.

(2) To prevent an outbreak like this in the future, owners and management should do the following:

- Reinforce the importance of reporting illness with food handlers.

- Exclude food handlers who have diarrhea and have been diagnosed with an illness from *Shigella* spp.

- Remind food handlers of the importance of handwashing. If necessary, retrain them on how, when, and where to wash hands.

- Control flies inside and outside the operation.

2-31 Discussion Questions

(1) The six conditions that support the growth of bacteria are:

- Food: carbohydrates or proteins

- Acidity: food that contains little or no acid

- Temperature: temperatures between 41°F and 135°F (5°C and 57°C)

- Time: the longer food spends at temperatures between 41°F and 135°F (5°C and 57°C), the more opportunity bacteria in the food have to grow to unsafe levels

- Oxygen: some grow with oxygen, others grow without it

- Moisture: food with high levels of available moisture

(2) You can help keep food safe by controlling FAT TOM. In your operation, however, you will most likely be able to control only time and temperature. To control time, limit how long TCS food spends in the temperature danger zone. To control temperature, keep TCS food out of the temperature danger zone.

(3) An outbreak of Norovirus can be prevented by practicing personal hygiene. This is the most important prevention measure and includes the following:

- Excluding staff with diarrhea and vomiting from the operation

- Excluding staff who have been diagnosed with Norovirus from the operation

- Washing hands

- Avoiding bare-hand contact with ready-to-eat food

(4) To prevent a seafood-specific foodborne illness, food must be purchased from an approved, reputable supplier. This is the single most important prevention measure.

⑤ According to the FDA, there are over 40 different kinds of bacteria, viruses, parasites, and molds that can occur in food and cause a foodborne illness. Of these, six have been singled out by the FDA. These have been dubbed the "Big Six" because they are highly infectious. They include the bacteria *Shigella* spp., *Salmonella* Typhi, nontyphoidal *Salmonella,* and shiga toxin-producing *E. coli.* They also include two viruses—hepatitis A and Norovirus. These pathogens are often found in very high numbers in an infected person's feces and can be transferred to food easily. A person does not have to eat much of the pathogen in order to get sick and that illness is often severe. For this reason, food handlers diagnosed with illnesses from these pathogens cannot work in a foodservice operation while they are sick.

2-31 Case in Point: Rice Makes Children Sick

① The illness was caused by the bacteria *Bacillus cereus*. It is commonly linked with cooked rice including fried rice. The outbreak occurred because the pathogen was allowed to grow when the rice was cooled incorrectly and held at the wrong temperature. Once this occurred, the bacteria formed a toxin, which when eaten made the children sick.

2-32 Study Questions

①C	③D	⑤A	⑦A	⑨B
②A	④C	⑥C	⑧B	⑩B

3 CONTAMINATION, FOOD ALLERGENS, AND FOODBORNE ILLNESS

Page   Activity

3-1 Case in Point: Man Hospitalized after Allergic Reaction

① The allergic reaction could have been prevented if there had been good communication in the restaurant between the server and the kitchen staff. Kitchen staff should also have taken the necessary steps to prevent cross-contact between the customer's steak and any shellfish prepped in the kitchen. Putting the steak on a grill used to cook shellfish was careless and led to cross-contact. In the future, separate grills should be used for shellfish and other grilled products. If that is not possible, then this should be communicated to customers with shellfish allergies.

3-8 Discussion Questions

① There are several ways to keep chemicals from contaminating food:

- Make sure chemicals are approved for use in a foodservice operation.
- Purchase chemicals from approved, reputable suppliers.
- Store chemicals away from prep areas, food-storage areas, and service areas.
- Separate chemicals from food and food-contact surfaces by spacing and partitioning.
- Do not store chemicals above food or food-contact surfaces.
- Use chemicals for their intended use and follow manufacturer's directions.
- Only handle food with equipment and utensils approved for foodservice use.
- Make sure the manufacturer's labels on original chemical containers are readable.
- Keep MSDS current, and make sure they are accessible to staff at all times.
- Follow the manufacturer's directions and local regulatory requirements when throwing out chemicals.

② There are several ways to prevent the deliberate contamination of food:

- Make sure that the products you receive are from safe sources.

- Monitor the security of products in the operation.

- Know who is in the operation.

- Keep information related to food defense accessible.

- Identify what you will do and who you will contact if there is suspicious activity or a threat at your operation.

③ There are several measures that can be taken by both service staff and kitchen staff to ensure the safety of customers with food allergies.

Service staff:

- Describe dishes so customers know how they are prepared.

- Tell customers if the food they are allergic to is in the menu item.

- Identify any secret ingredients.

- Suggest menu items that do not contain the food that the customer is allergic to.

- Clearly mark the order for the guest with the identified food allergy.

- Deliver food separately from other food delivered to a table.

Kitchen staff:

- Check recipes and ingredient labels to confirm that the allergen is not present.

- Wash, rinse, and sanitize cookware, utensils, and equipment before prepping food.

- Make sure the allergen does not touch anything for customers with food allergies, including food, beverages, utensils, equipment, and gloves.

- Wash your hands and change gloves before prepping food.

- Use separate fryers and cooking oils when frying food for customers with food allergies.

- Label food packaged on-site for retail sale. Name all major allergens on the label, and follow any additional labeling requirements.

3-8   Case in Point: The 1984 Rajneeshee Bioterror Attack

① Although the attack occurred at a time when national security was not as heightened as it is now, it still may have been possible to prevent the attack. Guests should have been monitored as they used the salad bars. A staff member should have been assigned to monitor guests. Not only would this have helped prevent the accidental contamination of food by guests, but it may have stopped the terrorists from deliberately contaminating it.

3-9   Study Questions

①A   ②B   ③C   ④A   ⑤D

4 THE SAFE FOOD HANDLER

Page	Activity

4-1 Case in Point: Hepatitis A Scare

① If the food handler had symptoms, the situation could have been prevented if he or she had immediately reported them to management. The outbreak might also have been avoided if the food handler practiced correct and frequent handwashing while working, especially after using the restroom. Management must always remind staff of the importance of reporting illnesses.

4-13 Discussion Questions

① Staff must meet the following work attire requirements:

- Wear a clean hat or other hair restraint.

- Wear clean clothing daily.

- Remove aprons when leaving food-preparation areas.

- Remove jewelry from hands and arms before preparing food or when working around prep areas.

② The following personal behaviors can contaminate food:

- Wiping or touching the nose

- Rubbing an ear

- Scratching the scalp

- Touching a pimple or an infected wound

- Running fingers through the hair

③ How an infected wound is covered depends on where it is located:

- Cover wounds on the hand or wrist with an impermeable cover. "Impermeable" means that liquid cannot pass through the cover. Examples include bandages and finger cots—protective coverings. Next, place a single-use glove over the cover.

- Cover wounds on the arm with an impermeable cover, such as a bandage. The wound must be completely covered.

- Cover wounds on other parts of the body with a dry, durable, tight-fitting bandage.

④ Food handlers must follow these procedures when wearing gloves to handle food:

- Wash hands before putting on gloves when starting a new task. Hands do not need to be rewashed each time gloves are changed as long as food handlers are performing the same task and hands have not become contaminated. Never use gloves in place of handwashing.

- Choose the correct glove size.

- Hold gloves by the edge when putting them on. Avoid touching the glove as much as possible.

- Check gloves for rips and tears after they have been put on.

- Never blow into gloves.

- Never roll gloves to make them easier to put on.

- Never wash and reuse gloves.

⑤ These staff health problems pose a possible threat to food safety:

- Sore throat with fever. Restrict the food handler from working with or around food. Exclude the food handler from the operation if you primarily serve a high-risk population.

- Vomiting, diarrhea, or jaundice from an infectious condition. Exclude the food handler from the operation. Food handlers who vomited or had diarrhea cannot return to work unless they have had no symptoms for at least 24 hours, or have a written release from a medical practitioner. Food handlers with jaundice must be reported to the regulatory authority. Food handlers who have had jaundice for seven days or less must be excluded from the operation. They cannot return to work unless they have a written release from a medical practitioner and approval from the regulatory authority.

- A foodborne illness caused by one of these pathogens along with diarrhea or vomiting:
  - Norovirus
  - *Shigella* spp.
  - Nontyphoidal *Salmonella*
  - Shiga toxin-producing *E. coli*

Exclude the food handler from the operation.

- A foodborne illness caused by one of these pathogens:
  - Hepatitis A
  - *Salmonella* Typhi

Exclude the food handler from the operation.

Some food handlers diagnosed with an illness may not experience symptoms, or their symptoms may have ended. Work with the medical practitioner and the local regulatory authority to determine whether these food handlers must be excluded from the operation or restricted from working with or around food. They will also determine when the employee can safely return to the operation and/or carry out their regular food-handling duties.

4-13 Case in Point: More Than They Bargained For

① The food handler did not cover the infected wound on her hand correctly. While she did cover the wound with a waterproof bandage, which was impermeable, she did not put a single-use glove over it. This would have prevented any leakage from the wound from getting on food or a food-contact surface. It also would have prevented the bandage from falling off into the food.

4-14 Case in Point: Randall's Day

① Randall and his manager made the following errors:

- Randall did not take a bath or shower before work.

- Randall wore a dirty uniform to work.

- Randall should have removed his watch and rings (with the exception of a plain band) before prepping and serving food.

- Randall did not wear a hair restraint.

- Randall did not report his illness to the manager before coming to work.

- Randall did not wash his hands before handling the raw chicken.

- Randall did not wash his hands after handling the raw chicken.

- The manager did not ask about Randall's symptoms. If Randall were to report that he had diarrhea, the manager should have sent him home.

- Randall did not wash his hands correctly after taking out the garbage.

- Randall did not wash his hands correctly after using the restroom.

- Randall did not dry his hands correctly after washing them. He got them dirty again when he wiped them on his apron.

- Randall wore his apron into the restroom.

- The manager did not make sure the restroom was stocked with paper towels.

- Randall touched the ready-to-eat chicken with his contaminated hands.

- Randall was eating chicken while prepping food.

4-15 Case in Point: Kurt's Dilemma

① Jackie should not have asked Kurt to come to work. By doing so she was inviting a potential foodborne-illness outbreak. Kurt was vomiting and had diarrhea. These are two symptoms that require a manager to exclude a food handler from an operation.

② Not only should Jackie have told Kurt to stay home, but she should have told him to stay there until he was symptom-free for at least 24 hours. As an alternative, Kurt could have been asked to get a doctor's release to return to work.

4-16 Study Questions

① D	④ A	⑦ A	⑩ A
② D	⑤ B	⑧ C	
③ C	⑥ D	⑨ C	

5   THE FLOW OF FOOD: AN INTRODUCTION

Page	Activity

5-1   Case in Point: University Outbreak

① Here is what could have been done to prevent this situation from occurring:

- The operation should have supplied food handlers with color-coded cutting boards to keep things separate when prepping different types of food. For example, it could have supplied yellow cutting boards for prepping raw chicken, and green cutting boards for prepping produce—like the lettuce. Of course it would be critical to train food handlers on the correct use of each color.

- The food handler should have cleaned and sanitized all work surfaces, equipment, and utensils after each task, including the knife and cutting board.

- The operation could have chosen to purchase prepared lettuce to eliminate the necessity of chopping it for their chicken Caesar salads.

5-9   Discussion Questions

① TCS food is being time-temperature abused whenever it is handled in the following ways:

- Cooked to the wrong minimum internal temperature
- Held at the wrong temperature
- Cooled or reheated incorrectly

② Cross-contamination can be prevented in the operation by:

- Using separate equipment when preparing each type of food
- Cleaning and sanitizing all work surfaces, equipment, and utensils after each task
- Preparing raw meat, fish, and poultry and ready-to-eat food at different times (when using the same prep table)
- Purchasing ingredients that require minimal preparation

③ These are the steps for calibrating a thermometer using the ice-point method:

❶ Fill a large container with crushed ice. Add clean tap water until the container is full. Stir the mixture well.

❷ Put the thermometer stem or probe into the ice water so the sensing area is completely submerged. Wait 30 seconds, or until the indicator stops moving. Do not let the stem or probe touch the sides or bottom of the container. Keep the stem or probe in the ice water.

❸ Hold the calibration nut securely with a wrench or other tool and rotate the head of the thermometer until it reads 32°F (0°C). On some thermocouples or thermistors, you can press a reset button.

5-10   Case in Point: Cross-Contamination Stops Truck in Its Tracks

① The food truck operator should have used separate equipment for preparing different kinds of food. For example, he could have used one set of knives and cutting boards for the raw poultry, another for the raw meat, and a third for the produce. Also, he could have prevented cross-contamination by prepping raw and ready-to-eat food at different times. For example, he could have prepped the ready-to-eat food before prepping the raw food. Finally, the food truck operator should have washed, rinsed, and sanitized his utensils and equipment after each task.

5-10 Case in Point: Tour Cancelled by Outbreak

① The food in the box lunches was time-temperature abused. Because the box lunches were stored in the warm luggage compartment of the bus, pathogens on the food grew and made the food unsafe.

② The box lunches should have been stored in a way that would have kept the food out of the temperature danger zone. The food needed to be held at 41°F (5°C) or lower. This would have kept any pathogens that may have been on the food from growing and making the seniors sick.

5-11 Study Questions

① C   ③ C   ⑤ C   ⑦ A

② D   ④ C   ⑥ B

6   THE FLOW OF FOOD: PURCHASING AND RECEIVING

Page   **Activity**

6-1 Case in Point: More Than They Bargained For

① The chef purchased the fish from an unapproved source. This put her customers at risk for a foodborne illness.

② The chef should have purchased her fish from approved, reputable suppliers. These suppliers have been inspected and can show you an inspection report. They also meet applicable local, state, and federal laws. Barracuda are a predatory tropical reef fish and should be used with caution because they are commonly linked with ciguatera fish poisoning.

6-12 Discussion Questions

① Here are some general guidelines for receiving food safely:

- Have suppliers deliver food when there is time to inspect it.
- Make specific staff responsible for receiving. Train them to follow food-safety procedures including checking items for correct temperatures, expired code dates, signs of thawing and refreezing, and pest damage.
- Make sure there are enough trained staff to receive and inspect food promptly.
- Visually inspect delivery trucks for signs of contamination.
- Inspect each delivery immediately to check for damaged food and look for items that might have been repacked or mishandled. Take sample temperatures of all TCS food.
- Inspect and store each delivery before accepting another one.
- Receive cold TCS food at 41°F (5°C) or lower unless otherwise specified. Receive hot TCS food at 135°F (57°C) or higher
- Make sure packaging is intact and clean and protects food and food-contact surfaces from contamination. Reject items with leaks, dampness, or water stains.
- Reject food that is moldy or has an abnormal color. Food that is moist when it should be dry, such as salami, should also be rejected. Reject frozen food that has large ice crystals on it. This may be evidence of thawing and refreezing.
- Reject meat, fish, or poultry that is slimy, sticky, or dry. Also reject it if it has soft flesh that leaves an imprint when you touch it.
- Reject food with an abnormal or unpleasant odor.

② Here is how to check the temperature of each product:

- Fresh poultry: insert the thermometer stem or probe into the thickest part of the poultry. The center is usually the thickest part. The temperature should be 41°F (5°C) or lower.

- Carton of milk: open the carton and insert the thermometer stem or probe into the milk. Fully immerse the sensing area. The stem or probe must not touch the carton. The temperature should be 45°F (7°C) or lower when receiving the milk. However, it must be cooled to 41°F (5°C) or lower in four hours.

③ A shipment of fresh poultry should be rejected under the following conditions:

- Purple or green discoloration around the neck

- Dark wing tips (red tips are acceptable)

- Stickiness under wings or around joints

- Abnormal, unpleasant odor

- Temperature above 41°F (5°C)

④ Cans must be rejected for the following reasons:

- Bulging or swollen ends

- Rust or dents

- Labels that are not intact

6-12 Case in Point: A Decision to Make

① All food must be purchased from approved, reputable suppliers. The partners could contact other foodservice operations to ask whether a supplier is reputable. Because an approved supplier is one that is inspected, the partners simply must ask the supplier for a copy of a recent inspection report

6-13 Case in Point: Delivery Decision Could Cost Them

① Betty should have asked the delivery driver to come back later. Products must be delivered when staff have enough time to inspect them. Deliveries must be inspected immediately. By putting the deliveries away without inspecting them, Sunnydale missed an important opportunity to identify food that:

- Was not delivered at the correct temperature

- Was damaged or mishandled

- Had been thawed and refrozen

- Had expired code dates

- Showed signs of a pest infestation

6-14 Study Questions

① D   ③ B   ⑤ C   ⑦ A   ⑨ D
② B   ④ B   ⑥ D   ⑧ B   ⑩ A

7 THE FLOW OF FOOD: STORAGE

Page	Activity

7-1 Case in Point: Fatal Outbreak Linked to Incorrect Storage Practices

① The packages of raw ground beef should have been stored separately from the ready-to-eat rolls and cartons of chocolate milk. If that was not possible, then the ground beef should have been stored below these items. This would have prevented the juices from the raw ground beef from dripping onto ready-to-eat food and causing the outbreak.

7-10 Discussion Questions

① The recommended top-to-bottom order for storing the items in the same cooler is:

- Pecan pie
- Raw trout
- Uncooked beef roast
- Raw ground beef
- Raw chicken

② Live shellfish must be stored in its original container at an air temperature of 41°F (5°C) or lower. Shellstock identification tags must be kept on file for 90 days from the date the last shellfish was sold or served from the container.

③ Food packaged in the operation that is being sold to customers for use at home, such as bottled salad dressing, must be labeled. The label must include the following information:

- Common name of the food or a statement that clearly identifies it.
- Quantity of the food.
- List of ingredients and sub-ingredients in descending order by weight. This is necessary if the item contains two or more ingredients.
- List of artificial colors and flavors in the food. Chemical preservatives must also be listed.
- Name and place of business of the manufacturer, packer, or distributor.
- Source of each major food allergen contained in the food. This is not necessary if the source is already part of the common name of the ingredient.

These labeling requirements do not apply to customers' leftover food items placed in carry-out containers.

④ Many operations use the first-in, first-out (FIFO) method to rotate their refrigerated, frozen, and dry food during storage. Here is one way to use the FIFO method:

❶ Identify the food item's use-by or expiration date.

❷ Store items with the earliest use-by or expiration dates in front of items with later dates.

❸ Once shelved, use those items stored in front first.

❹ Throw out food that has passed its manufacturer's use-by or expiration date.

7-11 Case in Point: Storage Problems at Enrico's

① Here are the storage errors that occurred:

- A food handler at the restaurant failed to shut the door to the walk-in freezer. This could have warmed the interior of the freezer and allowed products to thaw.

- Alyce placed the case of sour cream into an already overloaded refrigerator. This could prevent good airflow and make the units work harder to stay cold.

- The stockpot of soup should not have been stored on the floor of the cooler. Food must be stored at least six inches (15 cm) off the floor.

- Alyce should not have stored the fresh salmon above the ready-to-eat soup. The salmon could drip fluids into the soup cross-contaminating it. Ready-to-eat food must always be stored above raw meat, poultry, and seafood.

- Alyce should not have stored the ground beef near the door, which is the warmest part of the unit. Raw meat, poultry, and seafood should be stored in the coldest part of the unit.

- Mary was lining the shelving with aluminum foil. This can restrict airflow in the unit.

7-12 Case in Point: A Second Chance

① Here are some things that Chase and his staff should consider:

- Determine where meat, poultry, and seafood will be stored. Ideally they will want to store it in the warmest part of the unit away from the door.

- Ensure that there is at least one air temperature measuring device in each storage unit. That device must be located in the warmest part of the unit. This might include a hanging thermometer.

- Install cold curtains in walk-in coolers and freezers to help maintain temperatures in the units.

- Purchase open shelving for walk-in coolers and freezers. This will ensure that they have good airflow in the units. The shelving should also be adjustable so that food is stored at least six inches (15 centimeters) from the floor.

- Create procedures which identify the designated storage location for each stored product. That includes both food and nonfood items, such as paper napkins and single-use cups.

- Purchase storage containers intended for food.

- Identify the storage location for dirty linen.

- Establish a procedure for the correct storage order for raw and ready-to-eat food.

7-13 Study Questions

① C   ③ C   ⑤ A

② C   ④ D   ⑥ A

8 The Flow of Food: Preparation

Page	Activity

8-1 Case in Point: Undercooked Meatballs Lead to Fatal Outbreak

① Simply browning the outside of the meatballs was not enough to reduce the *Salmonella* on them to a safe level. The only way to do that was to cook them to a minimum internal temperature of 165°F (74°C) for 15 seconds. To be sure that the meatballs had reached this internal temperature, the chef should have checked them with a thermometer.

8-15 Discussion Questions

① The minimum internal cooking temperatures are:

- Poultry: 165°F (74°C) for 15 seconds
- Fish: 145°F (63°C) for 15 seconds
- Pork: 145°F (63°C) for 15 seconds (roasts for four minutes)
- Ground beef: 155°F (68°C) for 15 seconds

② The four correct methods for thawing food are:

- Thaw it in a refrigerator at a product temperature of 41°F (5°C) or lower.
- Submerge it under running, drinkable water at a temperature of 70°F (21°C) or lower.
- Thaw it in a microwave oven if it will be cooked immediately afterward.
- Thaw it as part of the cooking process as long as the product reaches the required minimum internal cooking temperature.

③ There are a number of methods that can be used to cool food, including:

- Using ice-water baths
- Stirring food with an ice paddle
- Using a blast chiller or tumble chiller
- Adding ice or cold water as an ingredient

④ The rules for correctly cooking food in a microwave include:

- Cover food to prevent the surface from drying out.
- Rotate or stir food halfway through the cooking process to allow heat to reach the food more evenly.
- Let food stand for at least two minutes after cooking to let the food temperature even out.
- Check the temperature in at least two places to make sure the food is cooked through.
- Heat seafood, poultry, and eggs to 165°F (74°C).

8-15   Case in Point: Something's Fishy

① Here is what John did wrong:

- He failed to wash his hands before starting work and between the different prep tasks.

- He failed to thaw the shrimp correctly. When food is thawed under running water, the temperature of the water should be 70°F (21°C) or lower.

- He took out more whole fish from the walk-in cooler than he could prepare in a short period of time, unnecessarily subjecting the fish to time-temperature abuse.

- He failed to clean and sanitize the boning knife, cutting board, and worktable correctly after cleaning and filleting the fish. Pathogens that may have been on the fish could have been transferred to the shrimp that John prepared with the contaminated knife and cutting board.

- He failed to wash his hands and put on gloves before handling the ready-to-eat produce.

8-16   Case in Point: Chicken on the Fly

① Here is what Aiden did wrong:

- He prepared a large batch of batter.

- He added new batter to old batter.

- He overloaded the fryer baskets.

- He did not allow the fryer oil temperature to recover before lowering the next basket of chicken into the fryer.

- He failed to use a thermometer to check the oil and food temperatures.

② Here is what Aiden should have done differently:

- Aiden should have prepped the batter in smaller amounts. This would help prevent time-temperature abuse of both the batter and food being coated during preparation.

- He should have thrown out the unused batter at the end of the shift.

- He should have placed an amount of chicken in the fryer basket that would maximize cooking efficiency while still allowing the fryer oil to maintain the correct temperature.

- He should have allowed the fryer oil temperature to recover between batches.

- He should have used a thermometer to check the fryer oil and food temperatures.

8-17   Study Questions

| ① A | ③ B | ⑤ C | ⑦ D | ⑨ C | ⑪ C |
| ② B | ④ D | ⑥ D | ⑧ C | ⑩ A | ⑫ D |

9 THE FLOW OF FOOD: SERVICE

Page	Activity

9-1 Case in Point: One Hundred Sickened by Norovirus Outbreak

① The food handler should have reported the vomiting and diarrhea to management the week before the outbreak. He also should have been washing his hands correctly, especially after using the restroom. Food handlers carrying pathogens, such as Norovirus, can easily transfer them to food if they do not wash their hands correctly after using the restroom.

9-10 Discussion Questions

① To minimize contamination in self-service areas:

- Protect food on display using sneeze guards, display cases, or packaging to protect it from contamination

- Label food located in self-service areas

- Do not let customers refill dirty plates or use dirty utensils at self-service areas

- Stock food displays with the correct utensils for dispensing food

② Many operations prep food at one location and then deliver it to remote sites. The longer the time between preparation and consumption, the greater the risk that food will be exposed to contamination or time-temperature abuse. To prevent these hazards do the following:

- Pack food in insulated food-grade containers. They should be designed so food cannot mix, leak, or spill.

- Clean the inside of delivery vehicles regularly.

- Practice good personal hygiene when distributing food.

- Check internal food temperatures. If containers or delivery vehicles are not maintaining the correct temperature, reevaluate the length of the delivery route or the efficiency of the equipment being used.

- Label food with a use-by date and time, and reheating and service instructions for staff at offsite locations.

- Store raw meat, poultry, and seafood and ready-to-eat items separately.

③ Ready-to-eat, TCS food can be displayed or held without temperature control (up to six hours for cold food and up to four hours for hot food) under the following conditions:

Cold Food

- It was held at 41°F (5°C) or lower before removing it from refrigeration.

- It does not exceed 70°F (21°C) while it is being served.

- It has a label that specifies both the time it was removed from refrigeration and the time it must be thrown out.

- It is sold, served, or thrown out within six hours.

Hot Food

- It was held at 135°F (57°C) or higher before removing it from temperature control.

- It has a label that specifies when the item must be thrown out.

- It is sold, served, or thrown out within four hours.

④ When serving food off-site, you must protect it from contamination and time-temperature abuse:

- Make sure staff practice good personal hygiene.

- Ensure there is safe water for cooking, dishwashing, and handwashing.

- Check internal food temperatures regularly.

- Label food with use-by dates and times.

- Make sure garbage is stored away from food-prep, storage, and serving areas.

- Store ready-to-eat food separately from raw food.

- Use insulated containers to hold TCS food

9-11 Case in Point: In the Weeds

① Here is what Jill did wrong:

- She packed the deliveries in cardboard boxes.

- She failed to make sure that the internal temperature of the food on the serving line was checked at least every four hours. This would have alerted her to the fact that the steam table was not maintaining the correct temperature and that the casserole was in the temperature danger zone.

② Here is what Jill should have done:

- She should have packed the food in food-grade, insulated containers.

- She should have checked the temperature of the food on the service line at least every four hours. Doing it this way means that any food not at the correct temperature would need to be thrown out. Because the casserole was only 130°F (54°C), she should have thrown it out. As an alternative Jill could have checked the temperature of items on the serving line every two hours. This would have left time for corrective action.

9-12 Case in Point: Megan's Day

① Megan made the following errors:

- She tasted the food on the customer's plate.

- She failed to wash her hands after clearing the dirty dishes from the table.

- She failed to clean the table correctly after busing it. Megan should not have wiped the table with the cloth she kept in her apron.

- She incorrectly scooped ice into glassware. Megan should not have used the glass itself to retrieve ice from the bin. Using a glass this way could cause it to chip or break in the ice.

- She re-served bread and butter that had been previously served to a customer. Uneaten bread or rolls should never be re-served to other customers.

- She failed to wash her hands after scratching a sore. By scratching it and not washing her hands afterward, she could easily have contaminated everything else she touched.

② Here is what Megan should have done:

- She should have washed her hands after clearing the table and before she touched the water glasses.

- When cleaning tables between guest seatings, Megan should have wiped up spills with a disposable, dry cloth. The table should then have been cleaned with a clean cloth stored in a sanitizer solution (see Chapter 11).

- She should have used tongs or an ice scoop to get ice.

- She should have served a fresh basket of bread and butter.

- She should have washed her hands immediately after scratching the sore.

9-13 Study Questions

①D	③C	⑤C	⑦B
②D	④A	⑥B	⑧D

10 FOOD SAFETY MANAGEMENT SYSTEMS

Page   Activity

10-1 Case in Point: Blue Skies Handles It Correctly

① Here is what the owner of the café did correctly:

- She took each complaint seriously and expressed concern to the guests.

- She filled out an incident report after each call.

- She contacted the regulatory authority when she realized that she had received similar complaints.

- She cooperated with the regulatory authority to determine the cause of the outbreak.

10-20 Discussion Questions

① The following programs are a foundation for a food safety management system:

- Personal hygiene program

- Food safety training program

- Supplier selection and specification program

- Quality control and assurance program

- Cleaning and sanitation program

- Standard operating procedures (SOPs)

- Facility design and equipment maintenance program

- Pest control program

② There are many ways to achieve active managerial control in the operation. According to the Food and Drug Administration (FDA), you can use simple tools such as training programs, manager supervision, and the incorporation of SOPs. Active managerial control can also be achieved through more complex solutions, such as a HACCP Program.

Monitoring is critical to the success of active managerial control. Food will be safe if managers monitor critical activities in the operation. Managers must take the necessary corrective action when required. They must also verify that the actions taken to control the risk factors for foodborne illness are actually working.

③ The seven HACCP principles are:

- Principle 1: Conduct a hazard analysis.

- Principle 2: Determine critical control points (CCPs).

- Principle 3: Establish critical limits.

- Principle 4: Establish monitoring procedures.

- Principle 5: Identify corrective actions.

- Principle 6: Verify that the system works.

- Principle 7: Establish procedures for record keeping and documentation.

④ Certain specialized food-prep processes require a variance from the regulatory authority. They include the following:

- Smoking food as a method to preserve it (but not to enhance flavor).

- Using food additives or adding components, such as vinegar, to preserve or alter it so it no longer requires time and temperature control for safety.

- Curing food.

- Custom-processing animals. For example, this may include dressing deer in the operation for personal use.

- Packaging food using reduced-oxygen packaging (ROP) methods. This includes MAP, vacuum-packed, and *sous vide* food. *Clostridium botulinum* and *Listeria monocytogenes* are risks to food packaged in these ways.

- Treating (e.g., pasteurizing) juice on-site, and packaging it for later sale.

- Sprouting seeds or beans.

10-20 Case in Point: Trouble at Nathan's

① Here is what was wrong with the way Nathan handled the crisis:

Nathan forgot that, despite his best efforts, a foodborne illness or other crisis could still occur. He was not prepared for it. One of his most obvious problems was that he had no communication with the media. He also failed to communicate with his key audiences, which included both his staff and his customers.

② Here is what should have been done differently:

In addition to his HACCP program, Nathan needed a crisis management program. He should have started by developing a crisis management team, which would have certainly included his chef and general manager. Nathan definitely could have benefitted from having a crisis communication plan. This would have included a trained spokesperson, as well as a list of media responses that could have been used in the event of an outbreak. He also needed a plan for communicating with his staff and customers. He should not have relied on the media alone to get the word out. The press should not have access to staff. They should be directed by staff to the designated spokesperson.

10-21 Case in Point: Maria's Challenge

① Here is what Maria did wrong:

- She started by identifying CCPs.

- She determined that the critical limit for grilled hamburgers was cooking them to 150°F (66°C) for 15 seconds.

- She determined that critical limits would be monitored by checking for doneness using feel and color.

- She failed to determine how to verify whether the HACCP plan was working as intended.

- She failed to include record keeping in her HACCP plan.

② Here is what Maria should have done differently:

- She should have started creating her HACCP program by conducting a hazard analysis.

- She should have established the correct critical limit for grilled hamburgers. This would include cooking them to 155°F (68°C) for 15 seconds.

- She should have identified a method for determining if her HAACP program was working as intended. This might have included checking records to determine if critical limits were being met and CCPs were actually being controlled.

- She should have identified records that should be kept. These would be important when verifying whether the HACCP program was working as intended.

10-22 Study Questions

| ① B | ③ A | ⑤ C | ⑦ B |
| ② D | ④ A | ⑥ B | ⑧ D |

11   SAFE FACILITIES AND EQUIPMENT

Page	Activity

11-1   Case in Point: Café Owners Stopped From Opening

① Here is what the owners need to fix in order to open for business:

- The floor tiles that are cracked must be replaced. Once installed, flooring must be kept in good condition and be replaced if damaged or worn.

- New adhesive should be applied to the loose coving so it can be adhered to the wall. Coving tile or strip must adhere tightly to the wall. This will help eliminate hiding places for insects.

- The burned out lightbulbs need to be replaced. Once lighting has been installed in each area in the operation, it needs to be monitored. Replace any bulbs that have burned out. Make sure they are the correct size as well.

- A service call should be placed to make sure the ventilation system is working correctly. It will probably also need to be cleaned.

- Any household equipment in the restaurant needs to be replaced with a commercial equivalent. This includes the bread toasters. Only commercial foodservice equipment should be used in operations. Household equipment is not built to withstand heavy use.

- The cutting boards need to be replaced because they have several large cracks.

- The milk dispenser needs to be sealed to the countertop, or mounted on legs with a clearance of four inches (10 centimeters) between the base of the equipment and the tabletop.

- The hot water supply to the handwashing sinks in the restroom will need to be fixed. Restroom handwashing sinks must have hot and cold water available for handwashing.

- The Dumpster lid must be replaced. Outdoor garbage containers must have tight-fitting lids and their drain plugs must be in place except during cleaning.

11-19 Discussion Questions

① One of the most important considerations when selecting flooring for food-preparation areas is the material's porosity, or the extent to which it will absorb liquids. Avoid high porosity flooring. Its absorbency often makes it ideal for pathogen growth. Flooring should also be smooth, durable, and easy to clean. It should resist wear and help prevent slips.

② A backup of raw sewage in an operation is cause for immediate closure of the area, correction of the problem, and thorough cleaning. If the backup is a significant risk to the safety of food, service must be stopped. Then the local regulatory authority must be notified.

③ To prevent backflow in an operation:

- Avoid creating a cross-connection. Do not attach a hose to a faucet unless a backflow prevention device, such as a vacuum breaker, is attached.

- Install air gaps where necessary. This is the only sure way to prevent backflow. An air gap is an air space that separates a water supply outlet from a potentially contaminated source.

④ Sources of approved water include:

- Approved public water mains

- Private water sources regularly maintained and tested

- Closed portable water containers

- Water transport vehicles

If an operation uses a private water supply, such as a well, rather than an approved public source, it should check with the local regulatory authority for information on inspections, testing, and other requirements. Nonpublic water systems should be tested at least annually, and the report kept on file in the operation

⑤ The requirements of a handwashing station include:

- Hot and cold running water that is drinkable, and meets temperature and pressure requirements.

- Soap in liquid, bar, or powder form.

- A way to dry hands. Disposable paper towels or a continuous towel system that supplies the user with a clean towel can be used. Hands can also be dried with a hand dryer using either warm air or room-temperature air delivered at high velocity.

- A garbage container. This is required if disposable paper towels are used.

- A clearly visible sign or poster that tells staff to wash hands before returning to work. The message should be in all languages used by staff in the operation.

Handwashing stations are required in restrooms or directly next to them. Handwashing stations are also required in areas used for food prep, service, and dishwashing. Handwashing sinks must be used only for handwashing and not for any other purpose. Make sure these stations work correctly and are well stocked and maintained. They must also be available at all times. Handwashing stations cannot be blocked by portable equipment or stacked full of dirty kitchenware.

⑥ When installing stationary equipment:

- Put floor-mounted equipment on legs at least six inches (15 centimeters) high. Another option is to seal it to a masonry base.

- Put tabletop equipment on legs at least four inches (10 centimeters) high. Or, seal it to the countertop.

11-20 Case in Point: Go or No-Go

① The manager appeared to handle the sewage backup correctly. First, she evaluated the situation and determined there was no significant risk to food or food-contact surfaces. This allowed her to remain open.

When there is a backup of sewage, the affected area should be closed right away. Then the problem must be corrected and the area thoroughly cleaned. Again, the manager followed the correct procedures. She closed the prep area and contacted building management to get a plumber. She also assigned a staff member to clean up the backup.

11-20 Case in Point: Where There's Smoke

1. The ventilation system is not working correctly. When this happens, grease and condensation will build up on walls and ceilings.

2. The regional manager should ask the store manager to schedule maintenance on the ventilation system. It is also likely that the ventilation and ductwork needs to be cleaned. This should be performed periodically by a professional.

11-21 Study Questions

1) D	4) C	7) A	10) C
2) D	5) A	8) B	11) B
3) B	6) A	9) A	

12 CLEANING AND SANITIZING

Page	Activity

12-1 Case in Point: Slicer Tied to Outbreak

1. The outbreak could have been prevented if the slicer had been cleaned and sanitized correctly. In general, stationary equipment, such as slicers, should be cleaned and sanitized following these steps:

- Unplug the equipment.
- Take the removable parts off the equipment. Wash, rinse, and sanitize them by hand. You can also run the parts through a dishwasher if allowed.
- Scrape or remove food from the equipment surfaces.
- Wash the equipment surfaces. Use a cleaning solution prepared with an approved detergent. Wash the equipment with the correct cleaning tool such as a nylon brush or pad, or a cloth towel.
- Rinse the equipment surfaces with clean water. Use a cloth towel or other correct tool.
- Sanitize the equipment surfaces. Make sure the sanitizer comes in contact with each surface. The concentration of the sanitizer must meet requirements.
- Allow all surfaces to air-dry. Put the unit back together.

12-18 Discussion Questions

1. Food-contact surfaces must be cleaned and sanitized at the following times:

- After they are used
- Before food handlers start working with a different type of food
- Any time food handlers are interrupted during a task and the items being used may have been contaminated
- After four hours if items are in constant use

② Cleaning is the process of removing food and other types of dirt from a surface, while sanitizing is the process of reducing the number of pathogens on that surface to safe levels.

③ These are the steps that must be taken when cleaning and sanitizing items in a three-compartment sink:

❶ Rinse, scrape, or soak items before washing them. If items are being soaked in the first sink, change the solution when food bits start to build up or the suds are gone.

❷ Wash items in the first sink. Use a brush, cloth towel, or nylon scrub pad to loosen dirt. Change the water and detergent when the suds are gone or the water is dirty.

❸ Rinse items in the second sink. Spray the items with water or dip them in it. Make sure to remove all traces of food and detergent from the items being rinsed. If dipping the items, change the rinse water when it becomes dirty or full of suds.

❹ Sanitize items in the third sink. Change the sanitizing solution when the temperature of the water or the sanitizer concentration falls below requirements. Never rinse items after sanitizing them. This could contaminate their surfaces. The only exception to this rule is when you are washing items in a dishwasher that can safely rinse items after they have been sanitized.

❺ Air-dry items on a clean and sanitized surface. Place items upside down so they will drain.

④ Clean and sanitized tableware, utensils, and equipment should be stored in the following way:

- Store tableware and utensils at least six inches (15 centimeters) off the floor. Protect them from dirt and moisture.

- Clean and sanitize drawers and shelves before storing clean items.

- Store glasses and cups upside down on a clean and sanitized shelf or rack. Store flatware and utensils with handles up so staff can then pick them up without touching food-contact surfaces.

- Clean and sanitize trays and carts used to carry clean tableware and utensils. Check them daily, and clean as often as needed.

- Keep the food-contact surfaces of stationary equipment covered until ready for use.

⑤ Several factors affect the efficiency of a sanitizer. The most critical include concentration, water temperature, contact time, water hardness, and pH.

12-18 Case in Point: Another Way

① The tableware can be washed, rinsed, and sanitized in a three-compartment sink until the machine has been repaired. Before cleaning and sanitizing the items, clean and sanitize each compartment and all work surfaces. Then follow these steps:

❶ Rinse, scrape, or soak the items before washing them.

❷ Wash the items in the first sink.

❸ Rinse the items in the second sink

❹ Sanitize the items in the third sink.

❺ Air-dry the items on a clean and sanitized surface.

12-19 Case in Point: Keep It Separate

① This situation could have been avoided if the operation had designated specific tools for cleaning the restroom. These should have been color-coded to prevent using the tools to clean food-contact surfaces. One of the most important things that could have prevented the situation was training. Staff must be trained in the correct use of cleaning tools and the correct procedure for cleaning them.

12-20 Study Questions

①C ③A ⑤C ⑦A
②D ④A ⑥C ⑧A

13 INTEGRATED PEST MANAGEMENT

Page **Activity**

13-1 Case in Point: Rats!

① Methods that can be used to keep the rats out include:

- Installing self-closing doors and door sweeps
- Repairing gaps and cracks in door frames and thresholds
- Keeping all exterior openings tightly closed
- Filling holes around pipes
- Covering floor drains with hinged grates
- Sealing cracks in floors and walls

Most importantly the restaurateurs need to work with their PCO to keep the rats out.

13-11 Discussion Questions

① The purpose of an integrated pest management program is to prevent pests from entering the operation and eliminate any pests that do get inside.

② To prevent pests from entering your operation:

- Use approved, reputable suppliers. Check all deliveries before they enter your operation. Refuse shipments that have pests or signs of pests, such as egg cases and body parts.
- Screen all windows and vents with at least 16 mesh per square inch screening.
- Install self-closing devices and door sweeps on all doors.
- Repair gaps and cracks in door frames and thresholds. Use weather stripping on doors with no thresholds.
- Install air curtains above or alongside doors.
- Keep all exterior openings closed tightly.
- Use concrete to fill holes or sheet metal to cover openings around pipes.
- Install screens over ventilation pipes and ducts on the roof.
- Cover floor drains with hinged grates.
- Seal all cracks in floors and walls.

③ Signs of a cockroach infestation include:

- Strong oily odor

- Droppings (feces) that look like grains of black pepper

- Capsule-shaped egg cases that are brown, dark red, or black and possibly leathery, smooth, or shiny in appearance

Signs of a rodent infestation include:

- Signs of gnawing

- Urine stains revealed by black (ultraviolet) light

- Droppings that are shiny and black (fresh) or gray (older)

- Tracks

- Nesting materials, such as scraps of paper, cloth, hair, and other soft materials

- Holes in quiet places, near food and water, and next to buildings

④ All pesticides used in your operation should also be stored by your PCO. If they are stored on the premises, follow these guidelines:

- Keep pesticides in their original containers.

- Store pesticides in a secure location away from where food, utensils, and food equipment are stored.

⑤ To minimize the hazard to people, have your PCO use pesticides only when you are closed for business, and staff are not on-site. When pesticides will be applied, prepare the area to be sprayed by removing all food and movable food-contact surfaces. Cover equipment and food-contact surfaces that cannot be moved. Wash, rinse, and sanitize food-contact surfaces after the area has been sprayed. Anytime pesticides are used or stored on the premises, you should have a corresponding Material Safety Data Sheets (MSDS), because they are hazardous materials.

13-11 Case in Point: The Best Intentions

① Fred may have overlooked several measures for preventing pests. First, he may not be inspecting deliveries before they enter his operation. This is important since pests can enter an operation with deliveries. Perhaps Fred is not keeping exterior openings tightly closed when not in use. He may also have failed to seal openings around pipes, or sealed cracks in floors and walls. Maybe Fred did not think about installing door sweeps on his doors, or there are cracks in his door frames or thresholds.

② Fred needs to contact a pest control operator to help him eliminate the roaches. The PCO will also be able to help him determine how the roaches are getting into the operation and decide the best way to fix the problem.

13-12 Study Questions

① C	③ A	⑤ C
② D	④ A	⑥ A

14 FOOD SAFETY REGULATION AND STANDARDS

Page	Activity

14-1 Case in Point: Off on the Wrong Foot

① Here is what Brian did wrong:

- He failed to ask the inspector for identification.
- He refused the inspector entry to the operation.
- He was not cooperative.
- He failed to walk with the inspector during the inspection, or take notes.
- He failed to provide the records asked for by the inspector.
- He was not polite or friendly, nor did he treat the inspector with respect.
- He failed to discuss any violations or time frames for correction with the inspector.

14-9 Discussion Questions

① The following hazards require the closure of an operation:

- Significant lack of refrigeration
- Backup of sewage into the operation or its water supply
- Emergency, such as a building fire or flood
- Significant infestation of insects or rodents
- Long interruption of electrical or water service
- Clear evidence of a foodborne-illness outbreak related to the operation

② The FDA and USDA inspect food and regulate food transported across state lines. The FDA also issues the *FDA Model Food Code*, which is the government's recommendations for food safety regulations. The CDC and the PHS assist the FDA and the USDA by conducting research into the causes of foodborne-illness outbreaks. State and local regulatory authorities write or adopt food codes that regulate retail and foodservice operations. These codes differ widely from one state or locality to another. State and local regulatory authorities enforce these food codes. In addition, they investigate complaints and illnesses, issue licenses and permits, and approve construction.

③ During an inspection, a manager should do the following:

- Ask for identification.
- Cooperate.
- Take notes.
- Keep the relationship professional.
- Be prepared to provide records requested by the inspector.

After the inspection, the manager should do the following:

- Discuss violations and time frames for correction with the inspector.
- Act on all deficiencies noted in the report by determining why each problem occurred, and then establish new procedures or revise existing ones. It may also be necessary to retrain staff.

④ Factors that determine the frequency of a health inspection include:

- Size and complexity of the operation. Larger operations offering a large number of TCS food items might be inspected more frequently.

- Inspection history of the operation. Operations with a history of low sanitation scores or consecutive violations might be inspected more frequently.

- Clientele's susceptibility to foodborne illness. Nursing homes, schools, day-care centers, and hospitals might receive more frequent inspections.

- Workload of the local health department and the number of inspectors available.

14-10 Case in Point: Inspect Thy Self

① A self-inspection program provides the following benefits:

- Safer food

- Improved food quality

- Cleaner environment for staff and customers

- Higher inspection scores

② Consider these guidelines when conducting a self-inspection:

- Use the same type of checklist that the regulatory authority uses.

- Identify all risks to food safety.

- After the inspection, meet with staff to review any problems.

14-11 Study Questions

①B   ③C

②B   ④C

15   STAFF FOOD SAFETY TRAINING

Page	Activity

15-1 Case in Point: What Do You Know?

① A training need is a gap between what staff needs to know to perform their jobs and what they actually know. Katherine most likely identified her staff's food safety training needs by:

- Observing performance on the job.

- Testing their food safety knowledge.

- Identifying areas of weakness.

15-8 Discussion Questions

① An operation can determine its food safety training needs by doing the following:

- Testing staff members' food safety knowledge

- Observing staff job performance

- Questioning or surveying staff members to identify areas of weakness

② Methods that can be used to deliver training include:

- On-the-job training
- Classroom training
- Information search
- Guided discussion
- Games
- Role-play
- Demonstrations
- Jigsaw design
- Training videos and DVDs
- Technology-based training

③ Technology-based training is most appropriate in the following situations:

- Staff work in different locations and/or need the same training at different times.
- It is costly to bring staff to the same place.
- Staff need retraining.
- Staff have different levels of knowledge about a topic.
- Staff have different learning skills.
- Staff need to learn at their own pace.
- You want to collect specific information, such as time spent on different topics, test scores, number of tries until the training was finished, and/or problem areas.

15-9 Case in Point: Technology Saves the Day

① Technology-based training would allow Ryan to deliver food safety training when and where staff members needed it. It also could ensure that all staff received the same information.

② Technology based training is most appropriate when:

- Staff work in different locations and/or need the same training at different times.
- It is costly to bring staff to the same place.
- Staff need retraining.
- Staff have different levels of knowledge about a topic.
- Staff have different learning skills.
- Staff need to learn at their own pace.
- You want to collect specific information, such as time spent on different topics, test scores, number of tries until the training was finished, and/or problem areas.

15-10 Study Questions

① A	③ C	⑤ A
② D	④ C	⑥ B

Index

A

acidity **2-4 to 2-5**

Acquired Immune Deficiency Syndrome (AIDS) **1-7, 4-3**

active managerial control **10-3 to 10-4**

additive (*see* food additive)

air curtain **13-3**

air gap (*see* plumbing)

allergen (*see* food allergy)

allergy (*see* food allergy)

Americans with Disabilities Act (*see* government regulations and regulatory agencies)

amnesic shellfish poisoning (ASP) (*see* foodborne illness: specific illnesses)

anisakiasis (*see* foodborne illness: specific illnesses)

Anisakis simplex (*see* parasite)

antiseptic (*see* hygiene: hands)

apron (*see* hygiene: attire)

aseptically packaged food **7-9**

    storing **7-9**

Aspergillus flavus (*see* fungi)

Aspergillus parasiticus (*see* fungi)

attire (*see* hygiene)

B

Bacillus cereus (*see* bacteria)

backflow (*see* plumbing)

backsiphonage (*see* plumbing)

bacteria **2-8 to 2-15, 8-5, 8-6**

    Bacillus cereus **2-10**

    bacterial illness **2-8 to 2-15**

    bacterial growth **2-5, 2-6 to 2-7**

    Campylobacter jejuni **2-11**

    characteristics **2-4, 2-9,**

        growth **2-6 to 2-7**

        temperature **2-5**

        toxin production **2-4**

    Clostridium botulinum **2-12, 7-8**

    Clostridium perfringens **2-12**

    death phase **2-6 to 2-7**

lag phase **2-6 to 2-7**

Listeria monocytogenes **2-10**

log phase **2-6 to 2-7**

Nontyphoidal *Salmonella* **2-7, 2-13**

Salmonella Enteritidis **8-5**

Salmonella Typhi **2-3, 4-11**

shiga toxin-producing *Escherichia coli (E. coli)* **2-3, 2-11, 4-11**

Shigella spp. **2-3, 2-18, 4-11**

spores **2-7**

Staphylococcus aureus **2-14**

stationary phase **2-6**

Vibrio parahaemolyticus **2-15**

Vibrio vulnificus **2-15**

bandage (*see* hygiene)

bare-hand contact **4-4, 4-7, 9-4, 9-5, 10-4**

batter and breading **8-5**

beef **1-6, 8-4, 8-8 to 8-9, 8-11, 8-13**

   cooking requirements **8-8 to 8-9**

   receiving criteria **6-9**

   storing **7-5**

blast chiller **8-13, 11-12**

botulism (*see* foodborne illness: specific illnesses)

bread **9-5**

bulk food **6-5, 9-6**

   labeling **9-6**

C

canned food **7-9, 10-17**

   storage requirements **7-9**

carrier (*see* hygiene)

Centers for Disease Control and Prevention (CDC) (*see* government regulations and regulatory agencies)

cheese **2-24, 6-10**

   receiving criteria **6-10**

chemicals **1-4, 3-3, 3-4, 7-2, 7-5, 12-2, 12-4, 12-11, 12-13 to 12-14, 12-16, 13-7**

handling **3-3, 4-6**

   storage **3-3, 3-4, 7-5,**

chewing tobacco (*see* hygiene)

cleaners **1-4, 3-3, 12-2 to 12-3, 12-16**

   abrasive cleaner **12-3**

   degreaser **12-3**

   delimer **12-3**

   detergent **12-3, 12-4 to 12-5**

      general-purpose cleaner **12-3**

      heavy-duty cleaner **12-3**

      surfactant **12-3**

cleaning **1-5, 1-7, 1-8, 5-2, 7-5, 11-15, 12-2 to 12-3, 12-11 to 12-16, 13-4, 15-3**

   cleaning program **12-15 to 12-16**

      development **12-15 to 12-16**

      implementation **12-16**

      master cleaning schedule **12-15**

      monitoring **12-16**

      training **12-16**

   critical knowledge **15-3**

   tools **12-13 to 12-14, 12-16 to 12-14, 12-22, 13-5**

      storage **12-13**

   wood surfaces **12-10**

Clostridium botulinum (*see* bacteria)

clothing (*see* hygiene: attire)

Code of Federal Regulations (CFR) (*see* government regulations and regulatory agencies)

color-coding **5-2, 12-13**

communicable disease (*see* hygiene; foodborne illness)

condensation **11-7, 11-11, 11-16, 11-17**

condiments **9-5**

confidentiality **4-3**

construction (*see* facility)

consumer advisory **1-8, 8-10 to 8-11, 10-4**

contaminants **1-4, 3-2 to 3-3**

   biological **1-4**

   chemical **1-4, 3-3**

      sources **3-3**

      symptoms **3-3**

      prevention **3-3**

   physical **1-4, 3-2**

      sources **3-2**

      symptoms **3-2**

      prevention **3-2**

contamination **1-4, 2-2 to 2-29, 3-2 to 3-7, 4-2 to 4-3, 6-3, 6-4, 6-6, 9-5, 9-6, 9-7 to 9-9, 10-4, 11-2, 11-3, 11-7, 11-9, 11-11, 11-14 to 11-17, 12-11, 12-13**

   biological **2-2 to 2-29**

   chemical **3-3**

   deliberate **3-4**

   physical **3-2**

cooking **3-6, 8-3, 8-5, 8-8 to 8-11**

cooking requirements **8-5, 8-8 to 8-11**

   beef **8-8, 8-9**

   shell eggs **8-8, 8-9**

   fish **8-99**

   game **8-9**

   ground meat **8-8**

   ground seafood **8-8**

   injected meat **8-8**

   lamb **8-9**

   legumes **8-9**

   mechanically tenderized meat **8-8**

   microwave **8-10**

   pork **8-9**

   poultry **8-8**

   produce **8-9**

   ratites **8-8**

   shellfish **8-9**

   stuffing **8-88**

   TCS food **8-8, 8-10, 8-13**

   tea **8-9**

   veal **8-9**

cooler 5-5, 7-4, 7-5, 7-6, 7-7, 7-8, 7-9, 8-2, 8-3, 8-4, 10-15, 11-3, 11-11 to 11-12

    reach-in 11-11 to 11-12

    walk-in 11-11 to 11-12

cooling 8-12 to 8-13

    methods 8-12 to 8-13

copper (see toxic metals)

crisis-management program 10-11 to 10-19

    assessment 10-15

    communication plan 10-12

    contact list 10-12

    crisis kit 10-12

    crisis-management team 10-11

    crisis response 10-13 to 10-14

    imminent health hazards 10-15 to 10-19

        response 10-15 to 10-19

            fire 10-18

            flood 10-18 to 10-19

            foodborne-illness outbreak 10-14

            power outage 10-16

            water service interruption 10-17

    media relations 10-13

    press conference 10-13

    plan 10-11 to 10-19

    preparation 10-13

    recovery and assessment 10-15

    spokesperson 10-12

critical control point (CCP) (see Hazard Analysis Critical Control Point food safety system)

critical limits 10-4, 10-6, 10-7

cross-connection (see plumbing)

cross-contamination 1-4, 1-5, 1-7, 4-8, 5-2, 5-6, 5-8, 7-4 to 7-5, 8-2, 8-4, 8-5, 8-13, 15-3

    critical knowledge 15-3

crustaceans 1-6, 6-9, 8-9

    receiving criteria 6-9

minimum internal temperature 8-9

cryptosporidiosis (see foodborne illness: specific illnesses)

Cryptosporidium parvum (see parasite)

custom-processed animals 8-7, 10-10

customer 1-3, 1-8, 3-5 to 3-7, 4-2, 4-4, 4-8, 7-2, 8-2, 8-10 to 8-11, 9-5, 9-6, 9-8, 10-4, 10-13, 10-14, 10-15, 12-12

    complaints 10-14

    sick customers 12-12

cutting board 5-2, 8-2, 11-12, 12-6

    cleaning 12-6

    synthetic 11-12

    wooden 11-12

D

dairy 1-6, 6-5, 6-10, 7-4, 9-8

    receiving criteria 6-5, 6-10

    storage requirements 7-4

date marking 7-3

deep-frying 8-3, 8-5

deliveries 1-8, 3-4, 6-3 to 6-4, 13-2

    delivery truck 6-3

    key drop deliveries 6-3

    inspecting 6-5 to 6-10

    reconditioning 6-4

    rejecting 6-4, 6-5 to 6-10

dishes 9-4, 12-8, 13-4, 15-3

dishwashing machine 11-10 to 11-11, 12-8 to 12-9

    batch-type, dump machine 11-10

    chemical-sanitizing machine 12-8

    circular conveyor (carousel) machine 11-10

    conveyor machine 11-10

    flight-type machine 11-10

    high-temperature machine 12-8

    manifold 12-8

operation of 12-9

    recirculating, door-type, nondump machine 11-10

    single tank 11-10

dishwashing, manual 12-9 to 12-10

    three-compartment sink 12-9 to 12-10

drain (see plumbing)

dressing room 11-4, 11-9

dry food 7-3, 7-9

    storage requirements 7-9

E

E. coli (see bacteria: shiga toxin-producing *E. coli*)

eating and drinking (see hygiene)

eggs 1-6, 2-5, 3-5, 6-5, 6-7, 6-10, 7-7, 8-5, 8-8, 8-9, 8-10 to 8-11, 14-2

    cooking requirements 8-8, 8-9, 8-10 to 8-11

    pooled eggs 8-5

    preparation 8-5

    receiving criteria 6-5, 6-10

    shell eggs 1-6, 6-5, 6-10, 7-7, 8-5, 8-15

    storage requirements 7-7

employee (see staff)

equipment 1-4, 1-5, 1-8, 3-3, 3-7, 5-2, 5-3, 5-6, 5-8, 8-2, 8-5, 8-10, 10-3, 10-8, 10-16 to 10-19, 11-3, 11-8, 11-10 to 11-13, 12-7, 12-11

    cleaning 12-7

    NSF mark 4-7, 11-10

    portable equipment 11-8

    sanitation standards 11-12

    stationary equipment 11-13

    storage 12-11

Escherichia coli (*E. coli*) (see bacteria: shiga toxin-producing *E. coli*)

    exclusion (see hygiene)

    expiration date 6-6, 7-3, 7-8, 9-9

F

facility **11-2 to 11-17**

  cleaning and sanitizing **11-11, 12-12**

  construction **11-2 to 11-6**

    finishes **11-6**

      ceramic tile **11-6**

      stainless steel **11-6**

      vinyl **11-6**

    flooring **11-4 to 11-6**

    materials **11-3 to 11-6**

    screens **11-7, 13-3**

    walls **11-6**

  design

    interior construction **11-2 to 11-6**

    layout **11-3**

    plan review **11-2**

    workflow **11-3**

  dressing room **11-4, 11-9**

  outdoor dining area **13-4**

  restroom **11-9**

  sanitary conditions **11-2 to 11-17**

  sealant **11-13**

FAT TOM **2-4 to 2-6**

FDA (*see* government regulations and regulatory agencies)

FDA Food Code (*see* government regulations and regulatory agencies)

feces **2-2, 2-3, 2-16**

finger cot (*see* hygiene: hands)

fingernails (*see* hygiene: hands)

first-in, first-out method (FIFO) (*see* product rotation)

fish **1-6, 2-7, 2-20, 2-25, 3-5, 5-2, 6-5, 6-6, 6-8, 7-5, 7-6, 8-4, 8-8**

  cooking requirements **8-9**

  preparation **8-4**

  receiving criteria **6-6, 6-7, 6-8**

  storage requirements **7-6**

flooring **11-4 to 11-6**

  carpeting **11-5**

  hard-surface flooring **11-5**

  nonporous, resilient flooring **11-4**

  porosity **11-4**

  resiliency **11-4**

  special flooring needs **11-6**

    coving **11-6**

    nonslip surface **11-6**

    rubber mat **11-6**

flow of food **5-2 to 5-8, 6-2 to 6-10, 7-2 to 7-9, 8-2 to 8-13, 9-2 to 9-9**

food additive **8-2, 8-7, 10-10**

food allergy **3-5 to 3-7, 13-9**

  allergen **3-5 to 3-6**

    common **3-5**

  allergic reaction **3-6 to 3-7**

    prevention **3-6 to 3-7**

  cross-contact **3-6, 3-7**

    prevention **3-7**

  customers and **3-5 to 3-7**

  sensitivity **3-6**

  symptoms **3-5**

Food and Drug Administration (FDA) (*see* government regulations and regulatory agencies)

food-contact surface **1-5, 3-3, 4-7, 5-8, 6-6, 9-4, 9-5, 12-4 to 12-7**

  cleaning and sanitizing **12-4 to 12-7**

food defense **3-4**

  A.L.E.R.T. **3-5**

food handler **4-2 to 4-11**

food preparation (*see* preparation)

food safety **1-2 to 1-9, 2-2 to 2-29, 3-2 to 3-7, 4-2 to 4-11, 5-2 to 5-8, 6-2 to 6-10, 7-2 to 7-9, 8-2 to 8-13, 9-2 to 9-9, 10-2 to 10-19, 14-2 to 14-8, 15-2 to 15-7**

  active managerial control **10-3 to 10-4**

  challenges **1-2**

  crisis management **10-11 to 10-19**

  critical knowledge **15-3**

  food safety knowledge **10-3 to 10-4**

  foodservice inspection program **14-4 to 14-8**

  HACCP system **10-4 to 10-10**

  management system **10-2 to 10-19**

  marketing of **1-9**

  monitoring **10-7**

  potential hazards **1-7**

    biological **1-7**

    chemical **1-7**

    physical **1-7**

  regulations and standards **14-2 to 14-8**

  risk factors **1-4, 10-3, 10-4**

  self-inspection **14-8**

Food Safety and Inspection Service (FSIS) (*see* government regulations and regulatory agencies)

food security **3-4**

food sensitivity (*see* food allergy)

food shield (*see* sneeze guard)

food tasting **4-10**

foodborne illness **1-2 to 1-9, 2-2 to 2-29, 3-2 to 3-7, 4-3, 4-4, 4-11, 8-4, 8-6, 8-7, 8-11, 10-3, 10-4, 10-10, 10-11 to 10-15**

  costs of **1-3**

  prevention measures **2-4, 2-8, 2-16, 2-17, 2-20, 2-24**

  specific illnesses

    amnesic shellfish poisoning (ASP) **2-29**

    anisakiasis **2-22**

    botulism **2-12, 7-8**

    ciguatera fish poisoning **2-27**

    cryptosporidiosis **2-22, 8-6**

    cyclosporiasis **2-23**

    gastroenteritis

      Bacillus cereus **2-10**

      Clostridium perfringens **2-12**

      Norovirus **2-3, 2-16, 2-17, 2-19, 11-15**

Staphylococcal
(*Staphylococcus aureus*) 2-14, 4-2

Vibrio vulnificus 2-15

giardiasis 2-23

hemorrhagic colitis
(*E. coli*) 2-11

hepatitis A 2-3, 2-17, 2-19,
4-2, 4-11, 8-6, 11-15

listeriosis 2-10

neurotoxic shellfish poisoning
(NSP) 2-28

paralytic shellfish poisoning
(PSP) 2-28

primary septicemia 2-15

salmonellosis 2-13

scombroid poisoning
(histamine poisoning) 2-27

shigellosis 2-14

foodborne-illness outbreak 1-2, 4-3,
8-4, 10-13, 10-11 to 10-15

incident report form 10-13
to 10-14

responses to 10-14

food handling 4-2 to 4-10

foodservice chemicals 3-3

storage 3-3

freezer 7-4 to 7-5, 10-16

freezing 6-3, 6-5, 6-6, 6-7, 8-3

refreezing 6-3, 6-6, 6-7

frozen food 6-5, 6-7, 7-4, 7-5, 7-6
to 7-8, 8-3, 9-9

receiving criteria 6-5, 6-7

storing 7-4, 7-6 to 7-8

fryer oil 3-6

fungi 2-24, 13-5

mold 2-24, 7-8

yeast 2-24

G

game 8-9

cooking requirements 8-9

garbage 9-8, 11-17, 12-6, 13-4

container 9-8, 11-17

disposal of 11-17

gastroenteritis (*see* foodborne
illness: specific illnesses)

glassware 9-4, 12-11

storage 12-11

gloves 1-8, 3-7, 4-6, 4-7 to 4-8

Good Agricultural Practices (GAP)
(*see* government regulations and
regulatory agencies)

Good Manufacturing Practices
(GMP) (*see* government regulations
and regulatory agencies)

government regulations and
regulatory agencies 1-8, 3-4, 4-3,
4-6, 4-7, 6-2, 6-4, 6-6, 6-7, 10-4,
12-4, 14-2 to 14-7

Americans with Disabilities
Act 4-3

Centers for Disease Control and
Prevention (CDC) 14-3

*Morbidity and Mortality
Weekly Report (MMWR)* 14-3

Vessel Sanitation
Program 14-3

Code of Federal Regulations
(CFR) 4-6

Environmental Protection
Agency (EPA) 12-4

Food and Drug Administration
(FDA) 1-8, 2-3, 2-24, 3-4, 4-6,
6-2, 6-4, 6-6, 14-2, 14-3, 14-4

A.L.E.R.T. 3-4

Good Agricultural Practices
(GAP) 6-2

Good Manufacturing Practices
(GMP) 6-2

FDA Model Food Code 10-4,
14-2 to 14-3

National Advisory Committee on
Microbiological Criteria for
Foods 10-4

Occupational Safety and Health
Administration (OSHA) 12-14

U.S. Department of Agriculture
(USDA) 6-2, 6-4, 6-7, 14-2, 14-3

grading stamp 6-7

inspection stamp 6-7

U.S. Department of Health and
Human Services 14-3

U.S. Public Health Service 14-3

grease 11-16, 11-17

grease condensation 11-16

grease extractor 11-17

grease trap 11-16

ground meat (*see* meat)

gum (*see* hygiene)

H

hair restraint (*see* hygiene: attire)

hand antiseptic (*see* hygiene: hands)

hand maintenance (*see* hygiene)

handwashing (*see* hygiene)

handwashing station 11-8

continuous cloth towel
system 11-8

paper towels 11-8

soap 11-8

warm-air dryer 11-8

waste container 11-8

water 11-8

Hazard Analysis Critical Control
Point (HACCP) 6-2, 8-6, 8-7, 10-4
to 10-11, 10-14, 14-3

corrective action 10-7, 10-8,
10-9

critical control point (CCP) 10-4,
10-6, 10-9

critical limit 10-6, 10-9

evaluation 10-7 to 10-8

HACCP principles 10-4 to 10-9

hazard analysis 10-5, 10-9

Manager Daily HACCP Check
Sheet 10-9

monitoring 10-7, 10-9

record keeping and
documentation 10-8, 10-9

special processing
methods 10-10

hazardous materials **12-13 to 12-14, 13-9**

    disposal of **12-13**

    labeling **12-13**

    Material Safety Data Sheet (MSDS) **3-3, 12-13, 13-9**

    storing **12-13**

health department **14-3**

health inspection **14-3, 14-4 to 14-8**

    closure **14-7**

        suspension **14-7**

        voluntary **14-7**

    correction **14-6**

    frequency **14-5**

    hearing **14-7**

    inspection report **6-2, 14-6**

    process **14-45 to 14-6**

    risk-based approach **14-4, 14-5**

    self-inspection **14-8**

    violation **14-5, 14-6**

health inspector **14-3 to 14-7**

    identification **14-5**

hemorrhagic colitis (*see* foodborne illness: specific illnesses)

hepatitis A (*see* foodborne illness: specific illnesses; virus)

hepatitis B and C **4-3**

high-risk populations **1-2, 1-7, 4-7, 8-5, 8-6, 8-11, 14-5**

    children **1-7**

    elderly people **1-7**

    immune-compromised people **1-7**

histamine (*see* pathogen: toxin)

histamine poisoning (*see* foodborne illness: specific illnesses: scombroid poisoning)

holding food **8-13, 9-2 to 9-3**

    cold food **9-3**

    hot food **8-13, 9-3**

    without temperature control **9-3**

    hot-holding equipment **9-2**

Human Immunodeficiency Virus (HIV) **4-3**

humidity **7-7, 7-8**

hygiene **1-4 to 1-5, 1-7, 1-9, 2-8, 2-16, 2-17, 4-2 to 4-11, 9-6, 9-11, 10-3, 15-3**

    attire **4-9**

        apron **4-9**

        clothing **4-9**

        hair restraint **4-9**

        jewelry **4-9**

    bandage **4-7**

    carrier **4-2**

    chewing tobacco **4-6**

    communicable disease **4-3**

    critical knowledge **15-4**

    drinking **4-6, 4-10**

    eating **4-6, 4-10**

    exclusion **4-10 to 4-11**

    finger cot **4-7**

    gum **4-6, 4-10**

    hands **4-4 to 4-7**

        antiseptic **4-6**

        fingernails **4-6 to 4-7**

        nail polish **4-7**

    handwashing **2-7, 3-7, 4-4 to 4-6, 4-8, 8-4, 9-6, 10-20, 11-10, 11-11**

        handwashing station **11-10, 11-11**

    program **4-4 to 4-11**

    restriction **4-10 to 4-11**

    saliva **4-10**

    smoking **4-6, 4-10**

    wounds **4-2, 4-7**

I

ice **7-6, 7-8, 8-4, 8-7, 8-13, 9-4, 10-17**

    preparation **8-7**

ice paddle **8-13**

ice scoop **8-7**

ice-water bath **8-13**

immune system **1-7**

incident report form (*see* foodborne illness: foodborne-illness outbreak)

infestation (*see* integrated pest management program; pests)

injected meat **8-8**

    cooking requirements **8-8**

inspection (*see* health inspection)

insulated container **9-8**

integrated pest management program (IPM) (*see also* pest) **13-2 to 13-9**

    control measures **13-8**

    denying access **13-2 to 13-3**

        deliveries **13-2**

        doors, windows, vents **13-3**

        floors and walls **13-3**

        pipes **13-3**

    denying food and shelter **13-4**

    identifying pests **13-5 to 13-6**

    infestation **13-2, 13-5, 13-7**

    treatment **13-8**

internal temperature (*see* temperature)

invoice **6-4**

J

jewelry (*see* hygiene)

juice **8-6, 8-7, 10-10**

    preparation **8-6**

K

kitchen **11-2 to 11-6, 11-13**

    equipment maintenance **11-13**

    installation of equipment **11-13**

kitchen layout **11-2 to 11-3**

    contamination **11-3**

    equipment accessibility **11-3**

    work flow **11-3**

kitchen staff (*see* staff)

L

labeling 7-2 to 7-3, 7-8, 9-6

lawsuit 1-3

lead (*see* toxic metals)

leftovers 8-4, 9-8

lighting 11-16 to 11-17

    foot-candle 11-16

Listeria monocytogenes (*see* bacteria)

listeriosis (*see* foodborne illness: specific illnesses)

locker 11-9

M

manager 1-8 to 1-9, 4-2, 4-3, 4-9, 4-10, 14-3, 15-2 to 15-7

master cleaning schedule 12-15 to 12-16

Material Safety Data Sheet (MSDS) (*see* hazardous materials)

meat 1-6, 5-2, 6-5, 6-6, 6-7, 6-9, 7-4, 7-5, 7-6, 8-4, 8-8 to 8-9, 8-10, 8-11, 9-7, 9-8

    cooking requirements 8-8 to 8-9, 8-10

    grading 6-7

    ground meat 8-8

    preparation 8-4

    receiving criteria 6-5, 6-6, 6-9

    storage requirements 7-4, 7-6, 9-7

medical bracelet 4-9

menu 3-6, 8-10 to 8-11, 10-4, 10-5

menu item 3-5 to 3-6, 9-5, 9-7, 10-4

microorganism (*see* pathogen)

microwave 8-3, 8-10, 8-13

milk 1-6, 3-5, 6-5, 6-10, 7-7, 9-8

    receiving requirements 6-5, 6-10

    storing 7-7

modified atmosphere packaging (MAP) 7-8

moisture 2-4 to 2-6

mold (*see* fungi)

mushrooms 2-29

N

National Advisory Committee on Microbiological Criteria for Foods (*see* government regulations and regulatory agencies)

National Restaurant Association 1-3

neurotoxic shellfish poisoning (NSP) (*see* foodborne illness: specific illnesses)

Nontyphoidal *Salmonella* (*see* pathogen: bacteria)

Norovirus (*see* foodborne illness: specific illnesses: gastroenteritis; virus)

NSF 4-7, 11-10

    mark 4-7, 11-10

O

Occupational Safety and Health Administration (OSHA) (*see* government regulations and regulatory agencies)

off-site service 9-7 to 9-9

    catering 9-8

    delivery 9-7

    mobile unit 9-9

    temporary unit 9-8

    vending machine 9-9

on-the-job training (*see* training: methods)

open shelving (*see* storage)

OSHA (*see* government regulations and regulatory agencies)

outdoor dining area 13-4

oxygen 2-4 to 2-6

P

paralytic shellfish poisoning (PSP) (*see* foodborne illness: specific illnesses)

parasite 2-2, 2-3, 2-20 to 2-23

    Anisakis simplex 2-22

    characteristics 2-20

        location 2-20

        prevention measure 2-20

        sources 2-20

    Cryptosporidium parvum 2-22, 8-6

    Cyclospora cayetanensis 2-23

    Giardia duodenalis 2-23

pasteurized food 7-9, 8-5

pathogen 1-2, 1-4 to 1-6, 1-7, 2-2 to 2-29, 4-2, 4-4, 4-6, 4-9, 4-10, 5-2, 5-3, 6-7, 7-3, 7-4, 7-5, 8-2 to 8-6, 8-8, 8-12, 10-4, 10-15, 11-2, 11-4, 11-7, 11-16, 12-4, 12-5, 13-5

    controlling growth of 2-5 to 2-6

    growth of 2-4 to 2-7

        controlling 2-6

        FAT TOM 2-4 to 2-6

personal hygiene (*see* hygiene)

personal protective equipment (PPE) 12-14

pest control operator (PCO) 13-2 to 13-9

    license 13-7

    service contract 13-7

pest management (*see* also integrated pest management program) 13-2 to 13-9

    control 13-8

    prevention 13-2 to 13-4

pesticide 13-9

pests (*see* also integrated pest management program) 6-6, 6-7, 7-9

    cockroaches 13-5

    flies 13-5

    identification 13-5 to 13-6

    infestation 13-2, 13-10, 13-12, 13-13 to 13-17

    rodents 13-6

pH 2-5, 2-6, 12-4, 12-5

plumbing 11-11, 11-15 to 11-16

    air gap 11-15

    backflow 11-15

prevention **11-15**

backsiphonage **11-15**

cross-connection **11-15**

drain **11-9, 11-11, 11-15 to 11-16**

leaks **11-7, 11-16**

sewage **11-16**

backup **11-16**

vacuum breaker **11-15**

wastewater **11-15 to 11-16**

pork **1-6, 6-9, 7-5, 7-6, 8-8, 8-9**

cooking requirements **8-8, 8-9**

receiving criteria **6-9**

poultry **1-6, 2-2, 2-5, 2-7, 6-5, 6-7, 6-9, 7-4, 7-5, 7-6, 8-4, 8-8, 8-10, 8-11, 8-13**

cooking requirements **8-8, 8-10**

grading **6-7**

preparation **8-4**

receiving criteria **6-5, 6-7, 6-9**

storage requirements **7-4, 7-6, 8-13**

premises (*see* facility)

preparation **8-2 to 8-13**

thawing **8-3**

primary septicemia (*see* foodborne illness: specific illnesses)

produce **1-2, 6-3, 6-10, 7-8, 8-2, 8-6, 15-2**

preparation **8-6**

receiving criteria **6-3, 6-10**

storage requirements **7-8**

product rotation **6-6, 7-3**

first-in, first-out method (FIFO) **7-3**

puffer fish (*see* toxin: seafood toxin)

purchasing **1-4, 2-8, 2-20, 2-26, 6-2**

Q

quaternary ammonium compounds (quats) (*see* sanitizing: chemical sanitizing)

R

ratites **8-8**

cooking requirements **8-8**

raw food **7-5**

ready-to-eat food **1-5, 1-7, 1-8, 4-4, 4-7, 5-2, 7-3, 7-5, 8-2, 8-13, 9-4, 9-6, 9-8**

bare-hand contact **4-7, 9-4**

cooking requirements **8-10**

date marking **7-3**

recalls **6-5**

receiving **6-3 to 6-10**

key drop deliveries **6-3**

inspecting food **6-3 to 6-10**

recalls **6-5**

rejecting shipments **6-4**

record keeping **10-8, 10-9, 15-2**

recyclables **13-4**

reduced-oxygen packaged food (ROP) **6-5, 6-6, 7-8, 8-7, 10-10**

receiving criteria **6-5**

storage requirements **7-8**

refrigeration **7-3, 8-4, 9-3, 10-15 to 10-16, 14-7**

refrigerator (*see* cooler)

regulatory agency (*see* government regulations and regulatory agencies or health department)

reheating **8-13, 9-2**

restroom (*see* facility)

S

salad **8-4**

preparation **8-4**

saliva (*see* hygiene)

Salmonella (*see* pathogen: bacteria)

Salmonella Typhi (*see* pathogen: bacteria)

salmonellosis (*see* foodborne illness: specific illnesses)

sanitizing **1-5, 1-7, 1-8, 5-2, 5-8, 6-2, 8-4, 8-5, 12-4 to 12-10**

chemical sanitizing **12-4 to 12-5**

chlorine **12-4**

concentration **12-4**

contact time **12-5**

effectiveness **12-4 to 12-5**

iodine **12-4 to 12-5**

quaternary ammonium compounds (quats) **12-4**

temperature **12-5**

critical knowledge **15-4**

heat sanitizing **12-4**

wood surfaces **12-10**

saxitoxin (*see* pathogen: toxins)

scombroid poisoning (histamine poisoning) (*see* foodborne illness: specific illnesses)

screen (*see* facility: construction)

sealant **11-13**

self-regulation **14-8**

server **9-4**

serving **9-2 to 9-9**

off-site **9-7 to 9-9**

re-serving **9-5**

self-service **9-6**

sewage (*see* facility: plumbing)

shelf life **7-9, 9-9**

shellfish **1-6, 2-25, 3-5, 6-5, 6-6, 6-8, 7-7, 8-7, 8-9, 9-6**

receiving criteria **6-5, 6-6, 6-8**

storage requirements **7-7**

shellstock identification tag **6-6, 7-7**

shiga toxin-producing *E. coli* (*see* bacteria: shiga toxin-producing *E. coli*)

Shigella spp. (*see* pathogen: bacteria)

shigellosis (*see* foodborne illness: specific illnesses)

single-use item **6-4, 6-6, 7-4, 9-8, 10-16**

sink **11-8, 11-9, 11-11, 11-14, 12-9 to 12-10, 12-13**

three-compartment sink **11-11, 12-9 to 12-10**

slacking **8-3**

smoked food **8-7, 10-10**

smoking (*see* hygiene)

sneeze guard **9-2, 9-6**

sous vide **7-8, 8-7, 10-10**

spore (*see* pathogen: bacteria)

sprouting seeds **1-6, 8-6, 8-7, 8-11, 10-10**

staff **1-2 to 1-3, 1-9, 3-3, 3-4, 4-2 to 4-11, 9-4 to 9-5, 10-3, 10-12 to 10-13, 12-8, 12-11, 12-15 to 12-16, 15-2 to 15-7**

  kitchen staff **9-4**

  service staff **9-4**

  staff health control **10-3**

  staff illness and injury **4-10 to 4-11**

  training **10-13, 12-8, 12-11, 12-15 to 12-16, 15-2 to 15-7**

storage **7-2 to 7-9, 12-11, 12-13, 13-4, 13-9**

  cleaning tools and supplies **12-13**

  dry storage **7-5, 7-7, 7-8, 7-9, 11-9**

  frozen storage **7-4, 7-6 to 7-7**

  open shelving **7-4**

  pesticides **13-9**

  tableware **12-11**

stuffing **8-8**

  cooking requirements **8-8**

supplier **1-2, 1-7, 3-2, 3-3, 3-4, 2-8, 2-20, 2-26, 2-29, 6-2, 6-3, 6-7, 7-8, 10-2, 12-2 to 12-5, 12-14**

  choosing **6-2**

T

tableware **9-5, 12-4, 12-8, 12-11**

  storage **12-11**

TCS food **1-6, 1-8, 2-5 to 2-6, 5-3, 6-3, 6-5, 7-3, 7-4, 7-8, 8-3 to 8-6, 8-8, 8-10, 8-12 to 8-13, 9-2, 9-8, 9-9, 10-5, 10-15 to 10-16**

  cooking requirements **8-8, 8-10**

  cooling **8-12**

  receiving criteria **6-5**

  reheating **8-13**

  storing **7-4**

tea **8-9**

  cooking requirements **8-9**

temperature **2-5 to 2-7, 2-8, 5-3 to 5-8, 6-3, 6-5, 7-4, 7-5 to 7-9, 8-3 to 8-13, 9-2 to 9-3, 9-9, 10-4, 12-4 to 12-5, 12-8, 12-9, 14-3**

  internal temperature **7-5 to 7-9**

  minimum internal cooking temperature **7-5, 8-8 to 8-10**

  receiving temperature **6-5**

temperature danger zone **2-5, 5-3, 5-4, 8-3, 8-12, 8-13, 9-2, 10-4, 10-16**

temperature recording device **5-6**

thawing **8-3**

  methods **8-3**

thermometer **1-8, 5-4 to 5-8, 6-3, 6-5, 7-4, 8-3, 8-5, 8-10, 9-2, 12-8, 12-9**

  bimetallic stemmed **5-4, 5-8**

  calibration **5-6 to 5-7, 5-8**

    boiling-point method **5-7**

    ice-point method **5-7**

  general guidelines **5-8**

  glass **5-8**

  infrared **5-6**

  probe **5-5, 5-7, 5-8, 6-5**

    air probe **5-5**

    immersion probe **5-5**

    penetration probe **5-5**

    surface probe **5-5**

  thermistor **5-4, 5-5, 5-7**

  thermocouple **5-4, 5-5, 5-7**

time-temperature abuse **1-4 to 1-5, 5-3 to 5-4, 5-6, 6-6, 6-7, 7-6, 8-2, 8-5, 9-6 to 9-9**

time-temperature control **5-3 to 5-8**

  corrective action **5-4**

  monitoring **5-3 to 5-8**

  recording **5-8**

time-temperature indicator **5-6**

towels **12-13**

toxins **2-2, 2-4, 2-10, 2-14, 2-24, 2-25 to 2-29**

  aflatoxin **2-24**

  brevetoxin **2-28**

  ciguatoxin **2-27**

  domoic acid **2-29**

  histamine **2-27**

  mushroom toxins **2-29**

  plant toxins **2-29**

  saxitoxin **2-28**

  seafood toxin **2-25**

    fish toxin **2-25**

      puffer fish **2-25**

    shellfish toxin **2-25**

    systemic toxin **2-25**

  shiga toxin (*see* bacteria: shiga toxin-producing *E. coli*)

training **12-16, 15-2 to 15-7**

  methods **15-4 to 15-7**

  activity-based **15-6 to 15-10**

  classroom training **15-4 to 15-7**

  demonstration **15-6**

    "tell/show/practice" **15-6**

  DVD **15-7**

  games **15-5**

  guided discussion **15-5**

  information search **15-5**

  jigsaw design **15-7**

  on-the-job training (OJT) **15-4**

  role-playing **15-6**

  technology-based **15-7**

  video **15-7**

  record keeping **15-3**

retraining **15-2**

training needs **15-2 to 15-3**

    identification of **15-2 to 15-3**

tuberculosis **4-3**

tumble chiller **8-13, 11-12**

typhoid fever **2-13**

U

ultra-high temperature (UHT) food **7-9**

    storage requirements **7-9**

U.S. Department of Agriculture (USDA) (*see* government regulations and regulatory agencies)

U.S. Public Health Service (*see* government regulations and regulatory agencies)

utensils **1-5, 1-8, 3-3, 3-7, 4-10, 5-2, 6-6, 8-2, 9-4 to 9-5, 9-6, 12-3, 12-4, 12-8, 12-11**

    storage **9-5, 12-11**

utilities **11-14 to 11-17**

    garbage **11-17**

    lighting **11-16 to 11-17**

    plumbing **11-15 to 11-16**

    sewage **11-16**

    ventilation **11-17**

    water supply **11-14 to 11-16**

V

vacuum breaker **11-15**

vacuum-packed food **6-6, 6-9, 7-8, 8-7, 10-10**

variance **7-7, 8-7, 10-10**

vending machine **9-9**

ventilation **11-17**

ventilation **11-17**

    grease extractor **11-17**

    hood filter **11-17**

Vibrio vulnificus (*see* bacteria)

virus **2-2, 2-3, 2-16 to 2-19, 13-5**

    characteristics **2-16, 2-17**

        location **2-16**

        sources **2-16**

        transfer **2-16**

    hepatitis A **2-3, 2-17, 2-19, 4-2, 4-11, 8-6, 11-15**

    Norovirus **2-3, 2-16, 2-17, 2-19, 11-15**

    prevention measures **2-16**

W

wastewater **11-15 to 11-16**

water **2-5, 5-6 to 5-7, 6-6, 7-7, 7-8, 8-3, 8-6, 8-7, 9-5, 9-8, 10-15 to 10-19, 11-7 to 11-9, 11-14 to 11-16, 12-4, 12-7**

    bottled **10-18**

    hardness **12-2**

water activity (a_w) **2-5 to 2-6, 2-24**

water heater **11-14**

    booster heater **11-14**

water supply **11-14 to 11-16**

    hot water **11-14**

    nonpublic water systems **11-14**

wounds (*see* hygiene)

Y

yeast **2-24**

Z

zinc (*see* toxic metals)

Notes